THE LIVING LANDSCAPE OF BRITAIN

THE LIVING LANDSCAPE OF BRITAIN

by

WALTER SHEPHERD

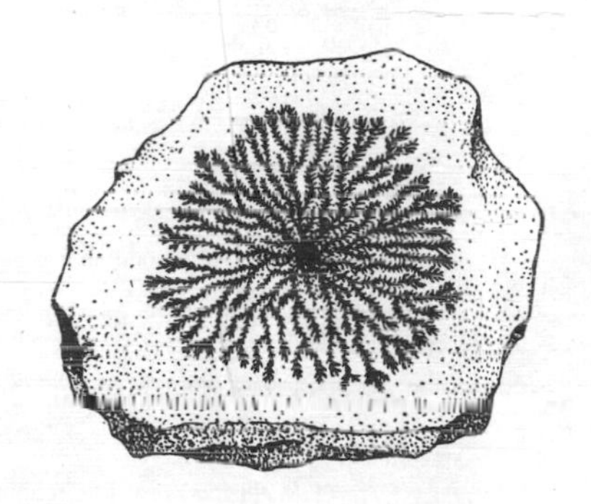

FABER AND FABER LIMITED
24 Russell Square
London

First published in mcmlii
by Faber and Faber Limited
24 Russell Square London W.C.1
First published in this edition mcmlxiii
Printed in Great Britain by
Latimer Trend & Co Ltd Whitstable

Contents

*

Contents

Illustrations

*

PLATES

after page 96

SCENIC PROFILES

[illegible]

Acknowledgments

*

Acknowledgments are made to the following for permission to reproduce photographs. Messrs G. P. Abraham, Ltd.: Pls. I B; III A, B; IV A; VIII B; XVI A, B. Mr R. M. Adam: Pl. II B. Messrs Aerofilms, Ltd.: Pls. VI A; XIII A; XXIV B. Messrs Aero Pictorial, Ltd.: Pls. XIV A; XV C. Air Ministry: Pl. XI B. Ashmolean Museum: Pls. XXIII A; XXIV A; XXVI A. Miss Elizabeth Barrett: Pl. XXVI C. Professor S. H. Beaver: Pl. VII A. Mr G. Douglas Bolton: Pl. XXIII D. Central Office of Information: Pls. II A; VIII A; X B; XIII B; XXV B; XXVI B. Messrs Flatters and Garnett, Ltd.: Pl. XVIII A. Messrs Fox Photos, Ltd.: Pls. XXI C; XXV C, D; XXVIII B, C. H.M. Geological Survey Museum: Pls. I A; V B, C; VI B; VII B, C, D; VIII C, D; IX A, B, C, D; X A, C, D; XI A; XII A, B, C; XVI B; XV A, B, D; XVII A, B, C; XVIII B, C; XIX C; XX B; XXI A; XXII A, B; XXVIII A. Messrs A. Horner and Sons, Ltd.: Pl. VI C. Messrs Judges', Ltd.: Pl. XIX B.

Acknowledgements

Preface

About Nature consult nature herself.—BACON.

No better advice than this of Bacon's was ever given, yet far more people read books about nature at home than attempt direct observation of her 'in the field'. The books on their library shelves represent many lifetimes of patient study, and reading seems to them to be the shortest route to knowledge. But there is a sense in which the knowledge thus acquired is not knowledge of nature at all, but only knowledge of other people's knowledge. These 'armchair naturalists' do not know nature any more than they knew Bernard Shaw, though they may have read all his plays and have his life-story at their finger-tips.

There is all the difference in the world between knowing a person by meeting him and knowing all about him without meeting him, and in this respect nature is much like a person. It is surely true that a brief experience of vital contact is worth more to ordinary folk than any amount of second-hand information, and this in spite of the fact that the second-hand information may be far more accurate, factually, than the direct impression.

Now, this may be considered dangerous talk. It is dangerous to personify nature in the first place, and it is dangerous to base an impression of nature on anything but ascertained fact. Yet who dare say that a true acquaintance with nature is available only to those who have made themselves book-masters of the subject? In point of fact, there is at least one way in which we can acquire real, factual knowledge of nature with very little in the way of written introduction.

This 'short path' is the appreciation of scenery, and it is to be recommended above all others to the casual rambler. Unlike any other branch of nature-study, the study of landscape requires a knowledge of general principles only. This book attempts to present these principles so that they will appeal to the reader as simple formulations of common-sense. Moreover, in the study of landscape there is none of the labour and disappointment involved in hunting elusive objects, as there is in the study of wild life, for here nature meets the rambler—not half-way, but almost on his own door-step. The moment he can see *ground* instead of house or pavement, in that moment he may begin his studies.

It might be urged that collecting and naming wild flowers, and similar pursuits, are just as instructive as appreciating scenery, but this is not so. To know the name of a wild flower is to know nothing new about the flower, but only of the activities of a gentleman named Linnaeus, long since deceased. To watch the flower grow, day by day, or observe its fertilization by an insect, is highly valuable, but there is little that may be done in this line on a Saturday afternoon walk. Without special knowledge you cannot tell the story of a flower by simply looking at it, but that is exactly the way in which you *do* tell the story of a landscape. Let those who seek an introduction to the study of nature begin, therefore, by contemplating the form of the world around them. And should any desire to collect tangible evidence of their experiences, let them take a camera and collect photographs.

The rambler's brief guide to landscape need contain no special scientific terms, or only such as have passed into common speech or save the labour of repeating familiar descriptions. Much geological knowledge may be acquired without the use of words like 'Jurassic' and 'Pleistocene,' or 'geosyncline' and 'inlier'. In this book the chief emphasis is laid on the visible *forms* of things, not on their structure, though there are occasional excursions into structural geology which the reader is at liberty to skip. It is true that the accident of a form may mean nothing—or any one of a number of things—to a geologist, but to a rambler it is the chief object of interest. He is concerned entirely with those facts which are *observably related to form*, whether geologically significant or not. He needs only to guard against making hasty inferences which he cannot test by further ready observation.

Though this book does not go deeply into technicalities it covers a very wide field. It attempts to explain every common type of landscape feature which is open to instant recognition. It also covers, in two chapters, a subject unaccountably missing from most books on the open air—the queer stones and common fossils frequently picked up by ramblers, but only to be cast aside for lack of a clue to their nature. Since these generally contribute to the story of the landscape in which they are found, they have been deemed proper objects for inclusion on the same general terms as the rest of the matter.

For this is not a book of particulars but of generalities, not of quantities but of qualities. Here is hardly any reference to particular mountains or beauty-spots, and only occasional distinction between east and west or north and south. Mountains and moors, hills and plains, are dealt with at length, but in such general terms that the reader may be anywhere he pleases upon them. If he is able to account for some of the outstanding features of the scenery, and to recognize an odd stone or two which he has found, that will be all he has time for on the afternoon picnic or the week-end walk.

'About Nature consult nature herself.' The question of *consultation* has not been forgotten. It takes two to make a consultation, and the proper relation between nature and the understanding observer is vital to the full appreciation of landscape. This book does not exhort the rambler to examine landscapes with the critical detachment proper to geologists, but rather to locate himself in the world of nature to which he belongs. His personal reactions are therefore of the utmost importance. It is one thing to look at a piece of limestone and say casually, 'Oh yes, that's just a consolidated deep-sea ooze,' and quite another to picture that ancient sea—here, at our very feet—and watch in imagination the slow transformation of its oozy bed into the hard rock on which we stand.

This is where imagination, if it is not to play us false, must be soundly informed, but it needs to be informed only in a *general* sense, for the rambler's appreciation of nature is essentially a qualitative one. The significance of this rock, to the rambler, is that it was once a coral reef. It is not of the least importance to him whether it was formed in mesozoic or palaeozoic times. He may have a rough idea that the older rocks of Britain lie in the west, but such phrases as 'millions of years ago' will represent the only sort of dating he is likely to require.

Nevertheless, some attempt has been made to help him to appreciate the time-scales involved in the production of scenery, particularly in reference to more recent features. The rambler is at least to know when the word 'million' is really justifiable, and to guard against too glib a use of it. But it is surely a mistake to instruct a rambler as if he intended becoming a geologist. He needs only to be able to understand the sort of world he lives in by looking at it himself, and I shall be satisfied if this book helps him to that end. For the reader desiring to follow this introduction to landscape by more detailed or technical knowledge I give at the end of the volume a short bibliography of readily available books for further study.

I have nowhere referred to unique, anomalous, or rare phenomena. It has been a main part of my creed that it is the familiar which is most in need of explanation and understanding. For many people the old familiar places are all that they have a chance of seeing, and it is the 'dull familiar' which I should feel most gratified to have illuminated. I hope at least that it will no longer seem dull.

Grateful acknowledgments are due to Miss Elizabeth Barrett, for the loan of her negative of a Sussex dew-pond, to Professor S. H. Beaver for the negative of Salisbury Crags, to Mr C. P. Chatwin for information on the folk-names and horizons of several fossils, and to Dr J. F. Kirkaldy for confirmation of the geological structure illustrated in Fig. 78. I owe a debt also to my wife, for much useful criticism and for reading the proofs, and another to Mr Donald Munro, at whose suggestion this book was planned and written.

W. S.

CHAPTER I

The Framework of Scenery

There is a magnificent view from the top of the hill, well worth a morning's hard climb. Behind us the mountains rise in a great wall of sombre grey, while at our feet the broad, flat valley lies chequered with fields and threaded with silver streams. Beyond this are rolling moors, purple now with heather, and through a narrow gap we catch the glint of sunlight on the sea.

We are entranced. Time stands still. We gaze abroad for what seems like half an hour, but is really four minutes. Then we sit on the grass, unpack the sandwiches, and talk cricket and politics. We have seen the view, and what more can you do with a view than see it?

Well, if that is all, we are missing nearly everything. We have gained a fine advantage at some cost, and now we propose to throw it away. We are like people who buy handsome volumes for their library shelves and then neglect to read them. The landscape before us is just a closed book with a pretty cover, but there is really no reason why it should remain so. It tells a story which he who runs may *not* read, but which may yet be plain enough to anybody who will pause to observe its main features with a little care.

The tract of country in view may have no obvious structure, but its form is not therefore a matter of chance. In point of fact, *every* landscape is a highly developed mechanical system, the forms and curves of which are obedient to strict mathematical laws. The buttresses of the hills, the levels at their feet, the corrugations of the valleys—all these have, with the passage of time, assumed forms perfectly adapted to their internal structure and materials. The rambler is not in the least concerned with the mathematics of physical processes, but he is with their results, and every detail he observes yields up its story to him. For him, 'the hills, rock-ribbed, and ancient as the sun,' are no haphazard heaps of earth and stone, but the very framework of scenery.[1] Their individual forms give life and meaning to the landscape as a whole, and it is the landscape as a whole which it is the rambler's art to perceive.

It would be misleading to suggest that every landscape is easily brought to life by mere inspection, but it is true to say that all the broad, common types of landscape may be recognized and appreciated without the least difficulty. And once the rambler is familiar with these, he will find that many strange formations which formerly puzzled him now become full of meaning, and their stories may be as enthralling as they are surprising.

The very first thing to strike the viewer of a new landscape is the type of surface it presents. It is flat or rolling, inclined or escalading, craggy or mountainous. Its chief feature may be a plain, a lake, a tor, a valley, a terrace, or a cliff, and such features we propose to call 'elements of scenery'. Now, elements of the same character are generally due to similar causes, and the list of such elements and their causes is surprisingly small. The immense variety of landscape, like the distinctive character of men's handwriting, is not due to the basic forms but to superficial accident.

For the sake of simplicity we present the principal elements of scenery to the reader in the form of 'profiles'. A profile is simply a section across the landscape, and an anticipatory glance at Figs. 2 and 4 should make this definition clear. The diagrams are necessarily idealized, but it is seldom difficult mentally to ignore the small irregularities which may break the outline of an actual hillside or valley and assign it to its proper profile. This sort of generalization is, in fact, what everybody does automatically when he remarks on the shape of a hill, and it yields the first piece of positive information to be gained by *looking at* a landscape instead of merely seeing it.

We begin our story with the profiles of valleys,[2] for those of the hills and mountains are largely dependent upon them. That most valleys have been cut by rivers is common knowledge, yet few people realize the enormous amount

[1] 'Rock-ribbed.' The traditional use of anatomical metaphor in descriptive geography is noteworthy, for it is not paralleled in any other science except—in a very small degree—in botany.

Such general terms as *shoulder*, *arm*, *elbow*, *limb*, *foot*, *talus* (*ankle*), *flank*, *head*, *ness* (*nose*), *jaws*, *col* (*neck*), *throat*, *gorge*, *gully* (*gullet*), *mouth*, and so on, are common words in geographical literature, and refer to scenic *forms*.

Many terms describing scenic movement and disposition are similarly anthropomorphic in origin, and include *swallow*, *reach*, *stretch*, *creep*, and *dormant*, while a few—such as *bill*, *roche moutonnée*, *greywether*, *hog-back*, *leg-of-mutton*, *saddle*, and *chine*—have bird or animal associations. Particular localities with anatomical names are legion, and anything may be found from *Bowerman's Nose* to the *Blind Cow* (which is not an inn, but a rock off the Dorset coast).

[2] It should be emphasized that the profiles we employ are *scenic* forms, and their geological significance comes second to our consideration. Thus, while valleys are hardly to be considered 'basic' forms in geology, they *are* among the basic forms of scenery.

of rock-material which even a small river removes in carving out its valley. When the reader next surveys a small valley from some vantage point, he is recommended to exercise his imagination by refilling it in his mind's eye. A glance at Fig. 1 is not likely to lessen his astonishment, and he may, at first, find it quite incredible that such a little stream can have done so much work.

The tools the river uses for its excavating are the rocks and stones split off from the mountains by alternate frost and sunshine, and in Plate XV(B) an efficient-looking collection of them is shown in a river-bed which has temporarily run dry. But the river is assisted by the rain also, which washes in the sides of the valley as it grows deeper, and adds tributary streams to the flood. Again, if the sides are steep frequent landslips may occur, and the river will quickly carry away the debris in readiness for the next consignment of rock-rubbish. The process goes on continuously, night and day, and time is no object. It may take many thousands of years to carve out even a small valley.

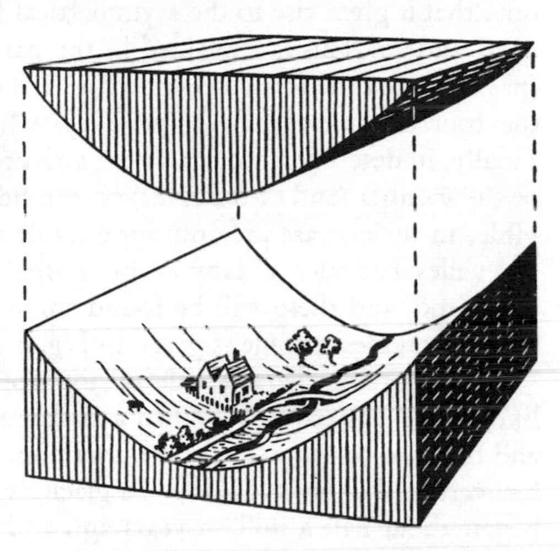

FIG. 1. Block-diagram showing the immense amount of rock-material removed by a river in cutting its valley.

The typical profiles of valleys are given in Fig. 2, and the small valley illustrated in Fig. 1 is intermediate between profiles B and C. The removal of the immense amount of rock and soil which has now become so conspicuous by its absence raises an obvious question. What has happened to it all? It has been carried along by the river to its lower reaches, where the river is wider and slower, and here it has been deposited as 'alluvium' and probably now forms water-meadows. The large pebbles will have settled first, then the sand, and finally the mud. Some of the mud may even have been carried out to sea.

There are generally these two agencies at work in carving out a valley—the river itself, cutting vertically downwards, and the weather (aided by gravity) washing in the sides. If the gradient is steep and the river swift, the vertical cutting will go on faster than the side-washing, and the valley will have steep sides as at A and B, and as pictured in Plate I, A. But as the river keeps removing land from its upper reaches and depositing it in its lower ones, it gradually reduces its gradient and flows more and more slowly. The downward cutting now eases off but the side-washing continues as before, and so the valley begins to widen out, as at C.

The widening of a valley is also accomplished by the meandering to which slow streams are prone, but this process need not trouble us here except to note that it gives rise to the asymmetrical forms shown at Fig. 2 E and in Figs. 55 A and 57. This is explained in the paragraphs on meanders in Chapter IV (page 73), but the form shown in Fig. 2 E occurs also where a river flows along the foot of an escarpment (page 13) whether meanders are present or not. Finally, in desert regions, or where a river traverses very hard rocks, the action of the weather (and of the river) on the sides of the valley may be almost negligible, in which case the only appreciable work done is the vertical cutting and the valley becomes a 'canyon' or 'gorge'. Gorges may be produced in other ways, too, and these will be found summarized at the foot of page 82, while the general ideal profile is given in Fig. 2 at D.

An important characteristic of any normal river valley is that it is shaped like a wide or narrow V. When a U-shaped valley (Fig. 2, F) is encountered—and they are common in the mountainous parts of Britain—the rambler may feel certain that he is looking at a glacier valley dating from the Ice Age, which began about half a million years ago and ended about twenty thousand years ago. These two types of valley are shown together, for comparison, in Plate I.

A stream, small or large, is usually found flowing along the bed of a glacier valley, but it should not be taken to be the carver of the valley. It is merely using the existing valley as a ready-made drainage channel, though it may have started to cut its own V-shaped trench in the valley-floor. Ice alone is able to round the sides and bottom of a valley to produce the characteristic U-shape.

Another mark of the glacier valley is its straight, or almost straight, course. Rivers, by contrast, seldom flow in perfectly straight courses even where they are swift, and among the mountains they are joined at frequent intervals by tributary torrents. The valleys of these tributaries cut the walls of the main valley into 'spurs' (or 'shoulders'), and the winding course of the river causes the spurs to dove-tail together or overlap.

Now, when a glacier invades such a valley (as happened everywhere at the onset of the Ice Age) it drives a straight passage through it slicing off all the spurs as it goes. In many U-shaped valleys the truncated spurs form prominent features, and the reader may pick out three or four in the illustration of the Pass of Llanberis (Plate I). The shortened tributary valleys probably held little tributary glaciers, but these would not be able to cut downward as fast as the main glacier, so that their channels remain at a much higher level. Such valleys are called 'hanging valleys', and now that the ice has all disappeared their mouths may often be seen high up on the sides of the main valley, as shown in Fig. 3. Small streams will generally be found to occupy them, and to

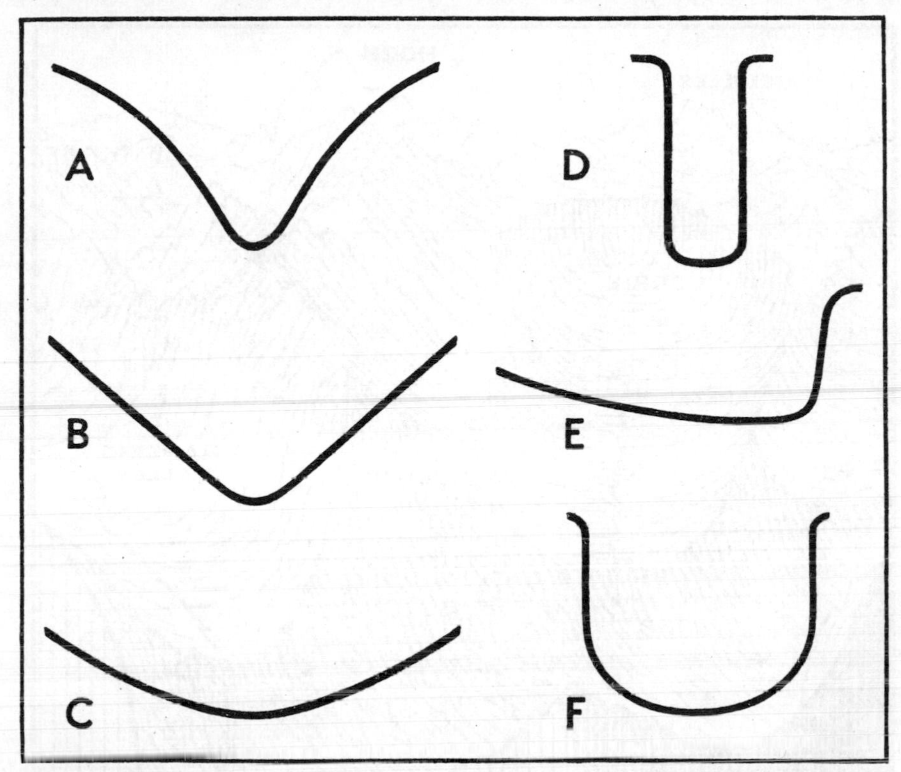

FIG. 2. Profiles, or cross-sections, of typical valley-forms. A, B, young river valleys; C, middle-aged valley; D, gorge or canyon; E, asymmetrical valley (see page 75); F, glacier valley.

tumble into the main valley as waterfalls.

You cannot have valleys of any sort without hills, or adjacent hills without valleys. High land without rivers (or glaciers) is generally featureless, and when once you are on top there is nothing to distinguish it from low land. Many a rambler to the Grampian Mountains of Scotland has been disappointed when first he reached the centre[1] of this plateau, for in large areas there is nothing to

[1] The principal area referred to lies to the west of Kingussie, where there are some two hundred square miles of level plateau at a height of 2,000 feet, from which scarcely a single hill rises more than 600 feet. We do not wish to belittle the magnificent mountain scenery to be found in other parts of the Grampian Mountains.

suggest that the low hills with which it is hummocked are really mountains three or four thousand feet high. Then he comes across a deep-cut river valley, and at once the great height of the top is plain.

It is the river valleys which make a featureless plateau into a group of

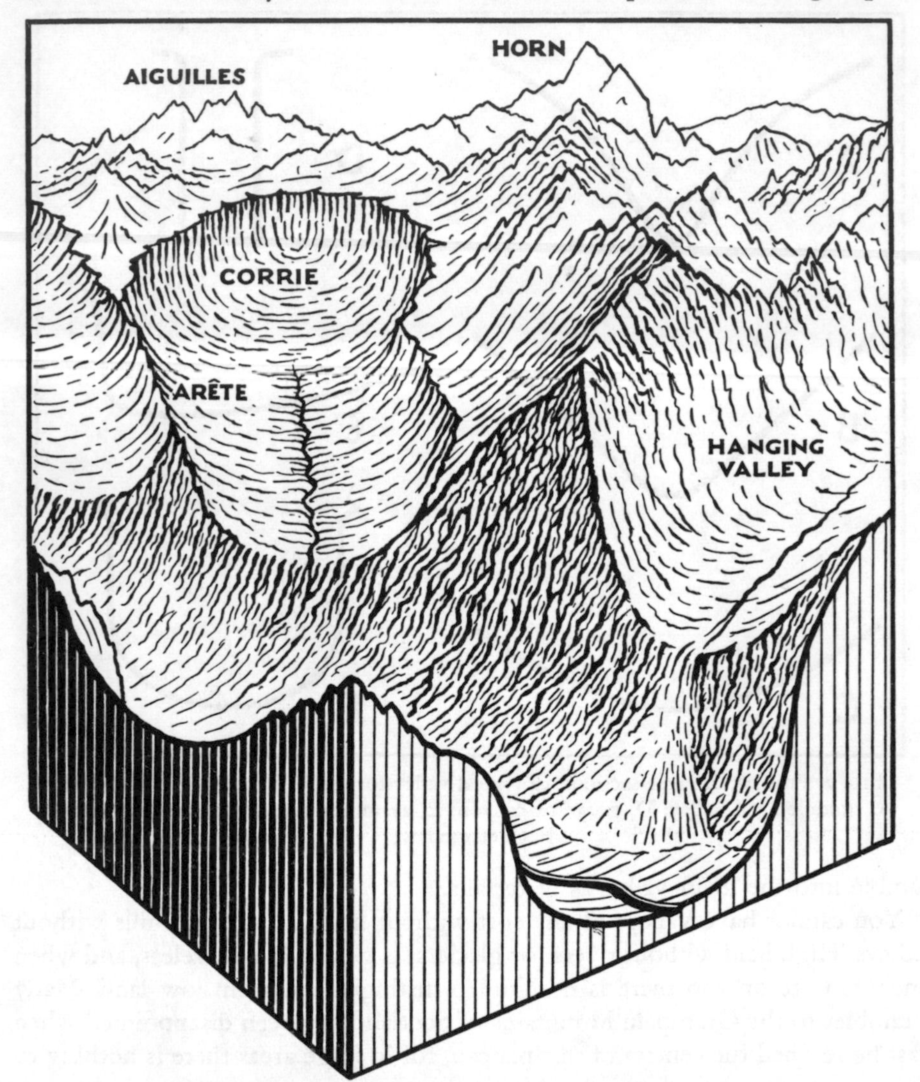

FIG. 3. Mountains and valley-forms typical of glaciated regions. Such forms are common in North Wales and in the northern counties of Britain, and owe their existence to the glaciers of the Great Ice Age.

mountains, as may be seen in the block-diagram in Fig. 104 at B. The formal relation between mountains and rivers is well illustrated in the silhouette view of Rhinog Fach and Rhinog Fawr in Plate XXI. Fill in the V-shaped valleys,

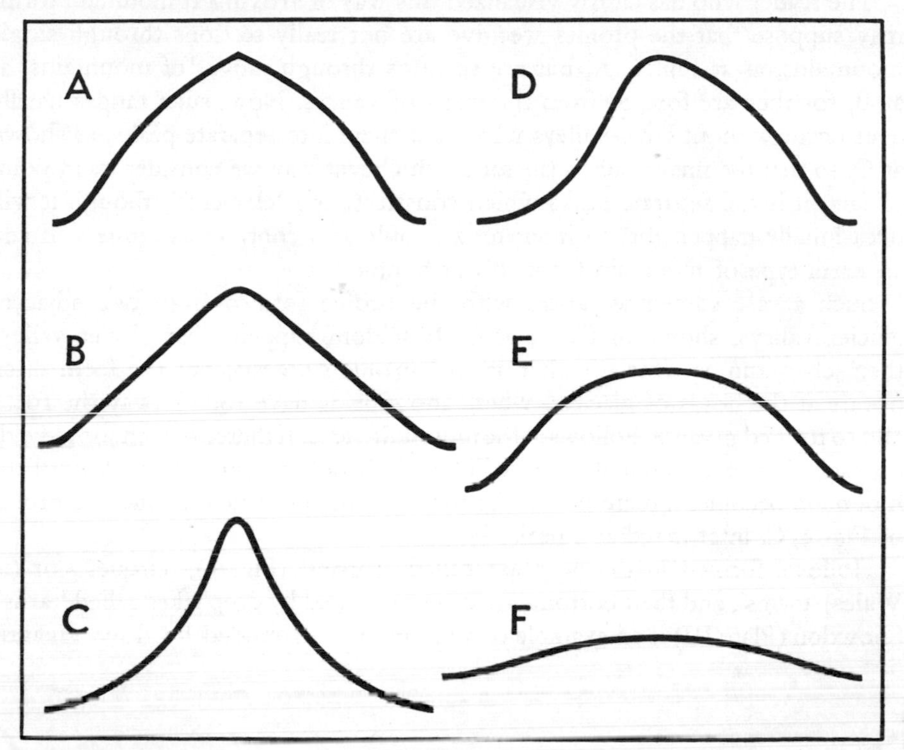

Fig. 4. Profiles of mountains which owe their forms primarily to the action of rivers and the weather. Examples of such mountains will be found in Plates II, III and IV.

and the individual mountains vanish. It is also clear that the *shapes* of these mountains are determined by the forms of the valleys. The rambler will therefore not be surprised to find that many common mountain profiles can be arrived at by setting together in various combinations the profiles shown in Fig. 2 at A, B and F.

Of the six possible combinations of these, the four most useful to the rambler are those shown in Fig. 4 at A, B, C and D, and the reader may find mountains of these forms illustrated (in order) in Plates II, III and IV. In each of the diagrams in Fig. 4 the valleys are presumed completed on each side of the mountain, though they may occur at different levels. Sometimes a valley has been partly filled in by sediments which mark the position of an old lake (see Plate XVI), or by wide sheets of alluvium (see page 75), but it is usually quite easy to recognize when this sort of thing has happened.

The reader who has clearly visualized this way of arriving at mountain forms may suppose that the profiles we give are not really sections through single mountains, as at Fig. 6, A, but are sections through ranges of mountains, as at B, for they are formed from the walls of valleys. Now, such ranges hardly ever occur without cross-valleys which cut them into separate peaks, as shown at C, so that the final result is the same whichever way we consider it. In point of fact, it is the separate peaks which constitute our 'elements', though it will occasionally happen that to interpret a profile as a continuous range will add an extra type of mountain form to our simple list.

Such a case sometimes arises with the profile formed from two adjacent glacier valleys, shown in Fig. 4 at C. It seldom happens that glacier valleys themselves run as close together as this profile suggests, but the form often occurs at the heads of glaciers, where snow-fields have rotted away the rocks and so formed gigantic hollows in the mountain sides. If there are such snow-fields on each side of a mountain, they will cut their hollows steadily back until the mountain becomes a mere relic of its former self, and it now shows the profile of Fig. 4, C, interpreted as a peak.

Hollows formed in this way are called 'corries' (Fig. 3), 'cirques', or (in Wales) 'cwms', and their bottoms are often occupied by deep lakes called 'tarns'. Snowdon (Plate III) is an example of a mountain surrounded by three gigantic

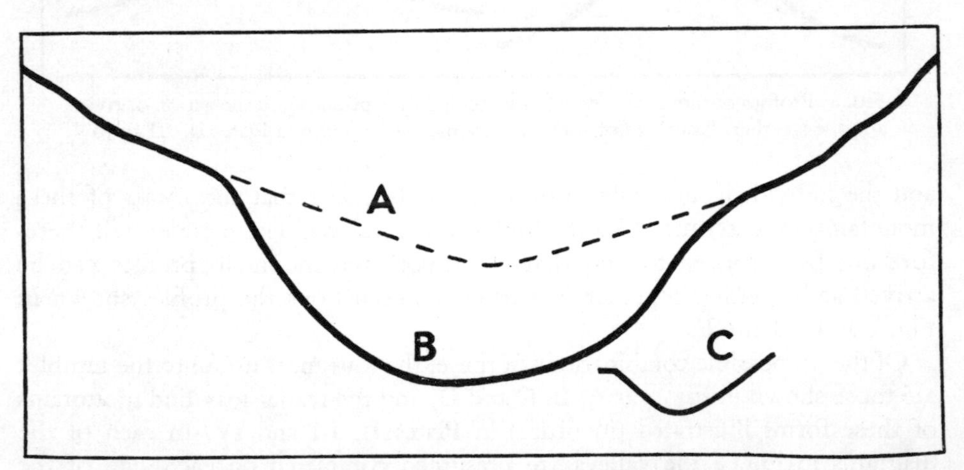

FIG. 5. Explanation of the photograph of the Pass of Llanberis in Plate I. A, the original river valley. B, the glacier valley. C, the young valley of the modern stream.

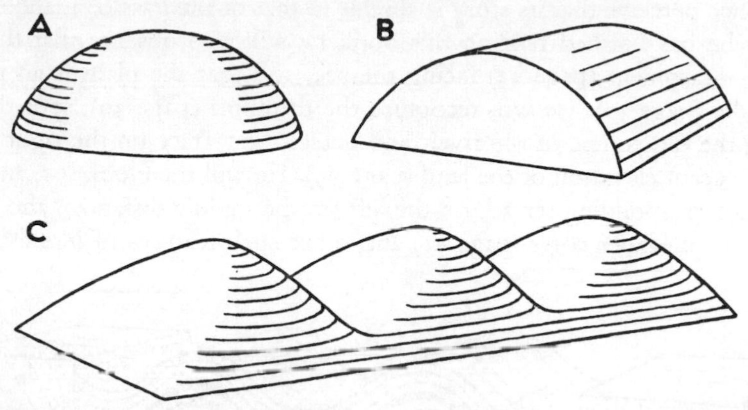

FIG. 6. A and B show two idealized mountain-forms which would yield the same cross-section. C shows how the form at B develops into a 'range' of A's by the cutting of transverse valleys.

cwms, the largest having perpendicular cliffs 1,500 feet high, and a lake nearly 200 feet deep at its foot.[1]

A mountain peak, which is usually pyramidal (see Fig. 19), is often situated at the heads of the corries, but where the *sides* of these encroach on one another the result is not a peak but a sharp ridge, called an 'arête' (Fig. 3). Striding Edge, Helvellyn (Plate III), affords a fine example, and shows the profile in Fig. 4, C, interpreted as a 'range'.

It sometimes happens that a mountain or valley fails to approximate to any of the ideal shapes given in our profiles, even when ruthlessly stripped of its irregularities. Such features will usually be found to represent simple combinations of profiles, and may be illustrated by the mountains flanking the Pass of Llanberis (Plate I). It is clear from the explanatory diagram in Fig. 5 that these mountains were carved in two stages, for their upper slopes reflect the V-shaped valley of an old river (A), and their lower slopes the U-shaped valley of the glacier which subsequently invaded and 'overdeepened' it (B). A second V-shaped valley is now being cut by a modern stream at C.

The rambler is to be encouraged to use his imagination freely in this way, and once he has grasped the general principles which govern the shaping of mountains, he may do so with reasonable confidence.

Should he now view the imaginary landscape at the head of this chapter, he

[1] *Cwms*, pronounced as it is spelt in Southern England—*coombes*. The origin of the coombes which occur in the South Downs and elsewhere in regions which did not suffer glaciation during the Ice Age is unknown, but it is generally associated with the action of deep snow. The various 'Devil's Dykes' and 'Devil's Punchbowls' are believed to be similar phenomena. A 'Devil's Punchbowl' is illustrated in Fig. 78, and a smaller coombe in Plate XIX.

will at once perceive that its story is similar to that of the Pass of Llanberis. By the time he has finished reading this book he will also observe that the hills form an escarpment (page 13) facing the sea, and that the plain is an infilled glacial lake (page 30). He will recognize the drumlins (page 30), spot the cliff marking the old course of the river, and detect the terrace on the right which tells of a recent elevation of the land (page 79). He will then look for, and duly note, the corresponding terrace on the left (in the middle distance), and search for signs of meander cores (page 80) and other such features of interest.

FIG. 7. The folding of strata illustrated by squeezing a pile of cloth patterns.

In short, the landscape will now *mean* something to him, and he will have graduated in the art of bringing landscapes to life. Henceforth it will be seldom indeed that he does not discover at least one tell-tale feature in every view to which he turns, and his interest in general scenery will be multiplied ten-fold. The inevitable presence of features which are *not* easily interpreted need not discourage him. There are many problems about which even the experts are not agreed, and the rambler can well afford to pass them by.

What we have so far said about valleys and mountains requires a corollary. Hard rocks are naturally more durable than soft ones, so that 'young' profiles may be found to persist in old mountains when these have proved sufficiently resistant to the weather. The Malvern Hills, for instance (Plate II), are very old indeed, even by geological standards. Moreover, the convexity of their slopes has become accentuated by prolonged weathering of their peaks, and by soil-creep (page 35)—an effect which should always be looked for when rivers are no longer present or actively down-cutting.

It also occasionally happens that an irregular mountain of very hard rock will refuse to conform to any recognizable profile or combination of profiles, but stands, bare and defiant, as a monstrous misfit in the surrounding landscape.

It is plainly a case for the expert. On the other hand, mountains of very soft rocks may wear away rapidly while they are still (geologically) young, and be reduced to little more than large mounds (Plate II, C), with the profile shown in Fig. 4 at F. Thus, while the shape of a mountain may tell its story, it does not, by itself, tell how long the story was a-writing.

The worn mountain of soft rock (Fig. 4, E) is usually circular or elliptical in shape, and is in fact a low dome, but the same profile would be yielded by a portion of a cylinder (see Fig. 6, B). When this is the case, there may be an explanation of quite a different kind. Before we can give an account of this it will be necessary to describe briefly the chief ways in which familiar rocks are liable to occur.

Sandstones, limestones, shales and clays, no matter how hard or how soft, all began their existence as sediments deposited in water.[1] They frequently occur in visible layers or beds (Plates IV B, X D and XI A, and Figs. 33 and 80), and in all cases these layers must originally have been flat and horizontal. But sooner or later deep volcanic forces raised them high above sea-level, and during this process they almost always became bent and broken. The forces which raised them seldom operated vertically, like a lift, but were squeezing forces, working horizontally, and they were probably due to strong currents in the molten rock at very great depths in the earth's crust.

The *modus operandi* may be illustrated by placing a pile of cloth patterns between two blocks of wood, as shown in Fig. 7. The patterns represent the layers—or 'strata'—of sedimentary rocks, and the blocks represent the massive granite cores of the continents, which reach right down to the molten rock beneath the earth's crust. Now move the two blocks slowly toward each other, so as to cause the patterns to buckle up into 'mountains' (or *anticlines*) and 'valleys' (or *synclines*).

This is what has happened on a grand scale in nature, but the mountains usually emerge so slowly that the weather gets to work on them as fast as they rise, and the mountains finally presented to the rambler's inspection are due almost entirely to the action of weather, water and ice, as we have already described.

Sometimes, however, a simple fold-mountain will persist in the form shown in Fig. 8, and illustrated in Plate IV, B, and this gives our second case of the profile in Fig. 4, E. A series of folds of this type might be expected to produce 'rolling' scenery of the kind typified in Fig. 9 at A, but the rambler is warned that it does so only in favoured localities. The 'fold' interpretation of such forms should be reserved for small examples in which at least a part of the

[1] In a few cases, in deserts. The reader is referred to Chapter V for a more detailed account of rocks.

folding can actually be seen (say in a cliff-face). On a big scale the folds usually do little more than modify the forms carved on the surface by the agents of erosion.

These modifications are not always what we should expect. It is true that rivers often tend to carve their valleys along the directions of the folds, but these are very seldom complete. It is never safe to identify the valleys with the bottoms of the folds and the mountains with their tops, for if the tops are of soft rocks they will be worn away as fast as they come up, and they will be the first to suffer from the action of running water. The adjacent hollows of

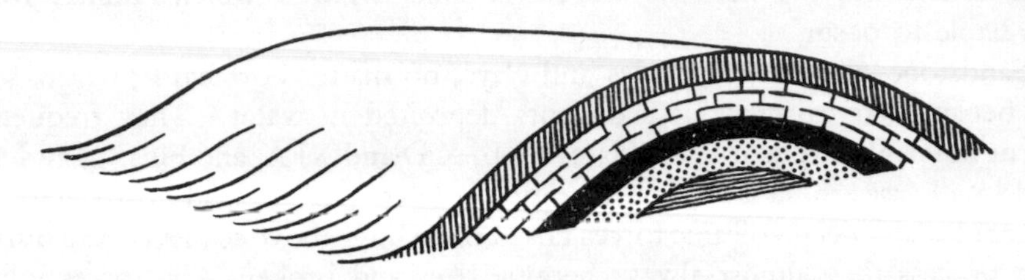

FIG. 8. A simple fold (anticline). An example of such a fold at Plynlimmon is shown in Plate IV.

the folds may contain much harder rock, and if so it is these which will eventually stand out as mountains. Thus, the tops of the folds may become deep valleys, and the mountains between them may consist of the enduring *bottoms*, as shown in Fig. 10; Snowdon (Plate III) is a mountain of this kind.

Quite often a river system is found to be independent even of the directions of the folds over which it flows, yet the folds may still have power to influence the final forms produced. There is no hard and fast rule, but mountains whose tops happen to coincide with the tops of folds tend to have convex sides and flattened summits, as at Fig. 4, E, while those whose summits coincide with the bottoms of folds tend to have straight or concave sides and a well-marked peak.[1]

Most of the mountain profiles we have considered are virtually independent of their geological structure, which does little more than modify their slopes. However, a whole crop of new profiles is liable to arise when the rivers have been at work long enough to cut down to the very cores of the folds.

When a large fold of the kind illustrated in Fig. 8 suffers wholesale denuda-

[1] The disposition of the strata is usually hidden, and has to be deduced by painstaking study of occasional exposures in cliff and quarry. This is the work of geological experts, and the rambler is therefore not advised to theorize too freely about the effects of folding where it is invisible. He must be content to think in 'probabilities'. The work of surface agencies generally suffices to explain the main forms of scenery as we have so far described them.

tion, its exposed summit weathers most rapidly and the successive layers of rock become uncovered in turn as the top disappears. These are usually of different degrees of hardness, and while the softer layers are quickly removed

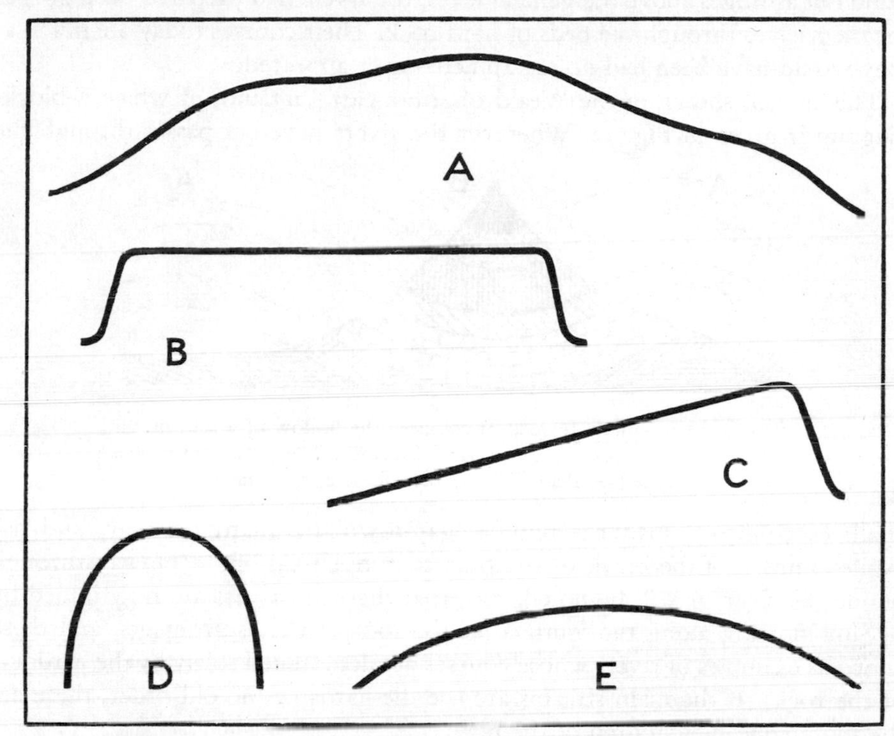

FIG. 9. Profiles of mountains which owe their forms primarily to their structure. Examples of such mountains will be found in Plates V, VI and VII.

the hard bands may persist for a surprising time as a set of ridges. These are called 'escarpments'.

It is common to find such a formation in the state shown in Fig. 11, in which the top of the original fold has completely vanished. Relics of the harder layers of rock now exist as reclining sheets on its flanks, and produce mountains with the profile shown in Fig. 9, C. Photographs of such escarpments are given in Plate V.

The river system of a region with this sort of structure often dates right back to the time when the fold was complete, and the streams naturally flowed straight down from summit to base. Now, rivers as a class are a conservative lot, and are not often deflected from their old ways by new developments. The barriers of escarpments which now lie athwart their paths prove to have been no barriers to *them*. They carved their valleys much faster than the general land-surface was wearing away, and even before the escarpments began to stand out as ridges above the general level, the rivers had prepared deep gorges for themselves through the beds of hard rock. Their courses today are much as they would have been had no escarpments ever appeared.

This is well shown in the Weald of south-east England, of which a block-diagram is given in Fig. 12. Wherever the rivers have cut passes through the

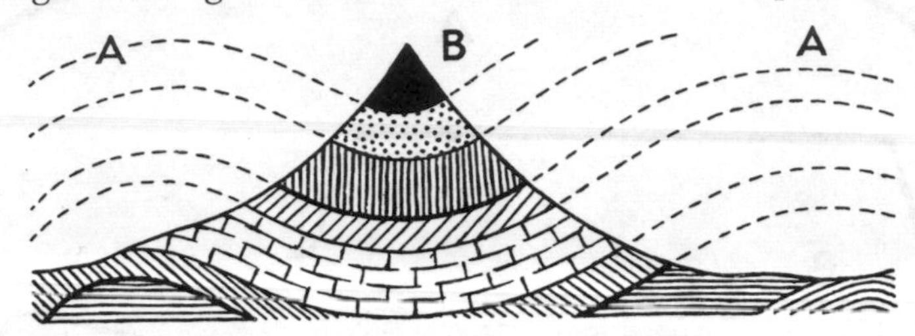

FIG. 10. A mountain formed of rocks in the hollow of a fold by the removal of the rocks on either side. Snowdon is a mountain of this type (see Plate III). A, anticlines; B, syncline.

chalk escarpments, man has built a 'gap-town' to guard the way, and has availed himself of the break in the hills to run a road and a railway through beside the river. It will be noted, too, that the main rivers are now joined by streams flowing along the 'gutters' at the foot of the escarpments, and these afford us examples of rivers whose courses are determined solely by the hardness of the rocks. If the main streams are the die-hards of the old order, these are the more educable children of the new.

The folding of the rocks is often very much more violent than has occurred in the Weald. Cases of fairly intense folding are shown in Plate VII, C, and in Fig. 28, and the rambler along the coasts of Britain will find many other such examples clearly exposed to view in the cliffs. The beds of rock are not uncommonly doubled right over, so that they now lie upside-down, but the most marked effects on the surface scenery occur when they are vertical.

A bed of hard rock, set vertically, will often stand out as a ridge or 'hog-back', the famous Hog's Back in Surrey affording an example caused by nearly vertical beds of chalk. The Purbeck Hills (Plate VI) are a similar formation, as may be seen by comparing the photograph with its explanation in Fig. 13.

An idealized section through a typical hog-back is given in Fig. 14, A, and it is clear that we may regard this as an extreme case of escarpment (B), the other extreme occurring when the hard bed is horizontal, as at C. The profile produced by A is usually one of those shown in Fig. 4 at B or D, but interpreted as a ridge instead of a peak, while that produced by Fig. 14, C, is shown in Fig. 9 at B. It remains to explain how horizontal strata may come to be elevated in this way.

In many cases a large area of land has been raised vertically till the strata, still horizontal, reach a great height. Rivers and the weather then carve it up into blocks. These blocks grow smaller and finally disappear, save for a few exceptionally robust 'mesas' or 'tabular hills'. The rocks at the foot of a mesa are generally different in character, and always different in age, from those

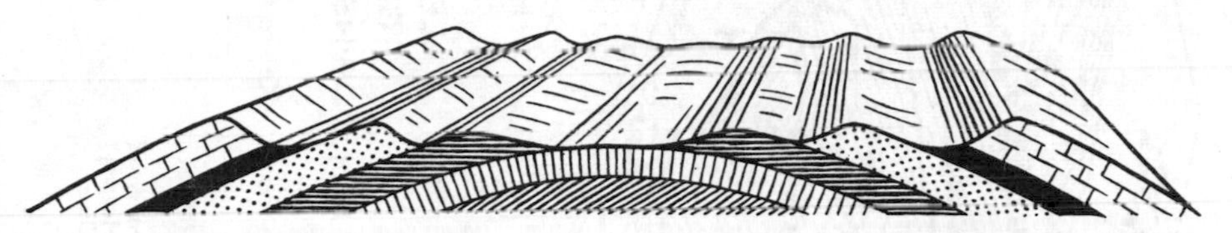

FIG. 11. The formation of a series of escarpments by the removal of top of an anticline.

which cap it, the example illustrated in Plate VI, B, showing a protective cap of hard sandstone on a base of shales.

The raising and folding of massive rock formations imposes prodigious stresses on the beds. Though the motions are imperceptibly slow, no rock will stand unlimited bending, stretching or compression. When the strain becomes too great the strata give way and slip out of alignment, as shown in Fig. 15 A. Such a slip is called a 'fault', and most earthquakes are caused by sudden slips of this kind.[1]

However, faulting more often proceeds in minute stages, without catastrophe, and the final result may be a displacement of anything from a fraction of an inch to a mile or more. If the displacement is greater than a foot or so, and especially if the fault is 'reversed' (Fig. 15 B), a fault may become a visible feature in a landscape. It appears as an otherwise inexplicable ledge, ridge or trough, but the alternative explanations of such slight forms (see Fig. 25) are usually to be preferred in the absence of expert opinion.

A really large fault may produce a line of cliffs—called a 'fault-scarp'—as illustrated in Plate VI, C, while two parallel series of faults may produce a gorge, the 'steps' shown in Fig. 26 B, or either of the features shown in Fig. 15 at C and D. As an example of a large rift-valley (C) we may cite the entire

[1] In Britain, more than a thousand earthquakes ('subterranean thunder') have been recorded since the tenth century. Faulting in the London Clay caused two severe shocks in 1750, when Westminster Abbey was damaged, and again in 1884, when 1,212 buildings were damaged or thrown down, chiefly at Colchester.

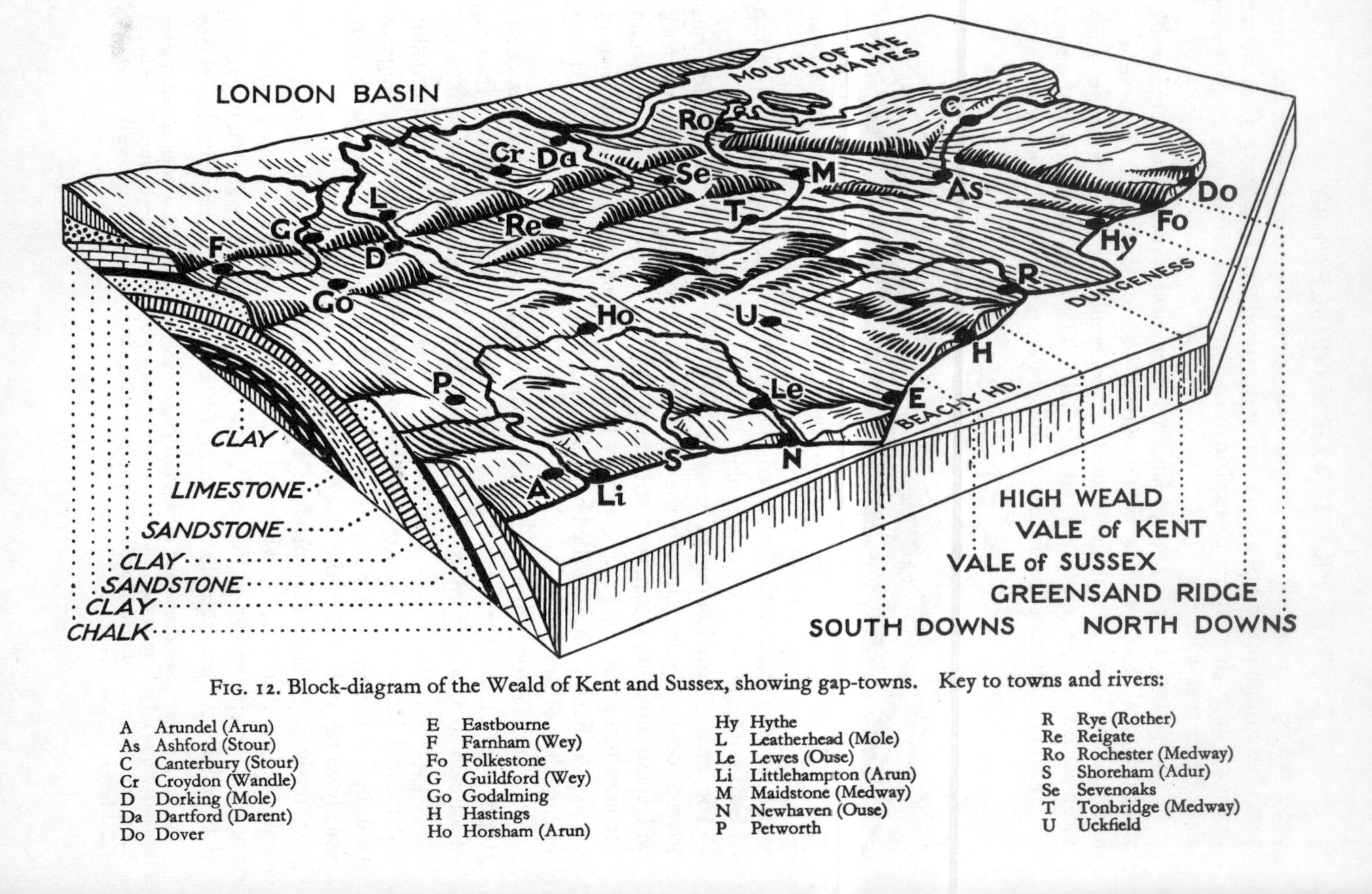

FIG. 12. Block-diagram of the Weald of Kent and Sussex, showing gap-towns. Key to towns and rivers:

A Arundel (Arun)
As Ashford (Stour)
C Canterbury (Stour)
Cr Croydon (Wandle)
D Dorking (Mole)
Da Dartford (Darent)
Do Dover

E Eastbourne
F Farnham (Wey)
Fo Folkestone
G Guildford (Wey)
Go Godalming
H Hastings
Ho Horsham (Arun)

Hy Hythe
L Leatherhead (Mole)
Le Lewes (Ouse)
Li Littlehampton (Arun)
M Maidstone (Medway)
N Newhaven (Ouse)
P Petworth

R Rye (Rother)
Re Reigate
Ro Rochester (Medway)
S Shoreham (Adur)
Se Sevenoaks
T Tonbridge (Medway)
U Uckfield

FIG. 13. Explanation of the photograph of the Purbeck Hills in Plate VI. Note that the ridge of the hills is a hog-back of chalk. This ridge continues in the Isle of Wight, where it forms the Needles in the west and Culver Cliffs in the east.

Lowlands of Scotland, which lie in a complex subsidence between the Grampians and Southern Uplands. The other formation (D) is not common in its typical form in Britain, but it should be pictured as a table-mountain surrounded by faults. It is called a 'horst', and provides a second case of the profile in Fig. 9, B, but it differs from the mesa in that the rocks on the lowland at its foot may be identical with those on its summit.[1]

Faults do not often form prominent features of the British landscape, for in our climate their edges are liable to get weathered away till they become invisible except to the trained eye, and the week-end rambler is not likely to be troubled with them. If, however, he possesses a geological map on which the faults are clearly marked (usually by heavy black lines), he may often find it worth while to look for betraying signs of them in the landscape. For example, a fault may give rise to a line of springs, or a stream may have found it out and cut itself a miniature gorge along the line of weakness (for the rocks bounding a fault are often crushed and very easily eroded by running water). There should be no difficulty in recognizing faults exposed in the faces of cliffs, of which an example is given in Plate VII, D. Rocks taken from such faults may show deep scratches or grooves ('slickensides') due to the friction of the faulting.

Much more frequently will the rambler meet with visible evidence of quite another sort of violence, and he will find it where rocks of volcanic origin, such as granite[2] and basalt, break the surface of the ground. Such rocks (which

[1] However, if the summit has suffered from exposure to the weather, its rocks may be older than those at the foot, but they cannot be younger. In the mesa, they are *always* younger. But the rambler is not to be expected to know the relative ages of the rocks; he must deduce what he can from their similarities or differences. (It is not, however, possible to judge by such criteria as hardness or degree of weathering.)

[2] To geologists granite is a plutonic, not a volcanic, rock, but in this book (until we come to Chapter V) we use 'volcanic' as a general word to indicate any association with subterranean heat. The geologically meticulous reader may substitute the comprehensive term 'igneous' wherever we have used 'volcanic'.

are further described in Chapter V) were originally forced up from the depths in a molten state, and their subsequent story depends on which of two alternative processes they have undergone. They have either reached the surface through a fissure or volcano, as at the Giant's Causeway (see sketch at head of Chapter V) and Arthur's Seat, Edinburgh (Plate VII), and have cooled after arrival, or they have failed to reach the surface at all, and have accumulated in subterranean masses where they finally cooled off and set solid.

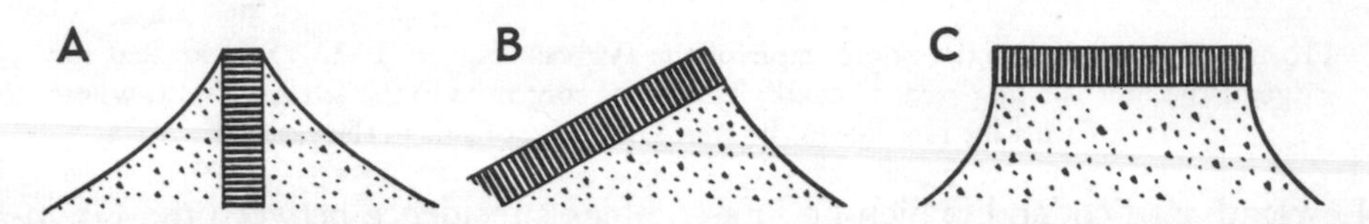

FIG. 14. A flat bed of rock, or unfolded strata, may lie vertically as at A (hog-back), be inclined as at B (escarpment), or rest horizontally as at C (mesa). These are all variations on a theme, the general term for which is 'cuesta'.

The Giant's Causeway is a quite exceptional case of a gigantic lava flow, and does not come into our story of common mountain forms, but volcanic 'necks' (or 'plugs'), like that at Arthur's Seat and those shown in Figs. 16 and 21, may produce mountains with steep sides and rounded tops, which we typify with the profile in Fig. 9, D. They are the stumps of old volcanoes, but the reader is advised to refrain from jumping to conclusions about such forms unless he has examined the rock itself or consulted a geological map.

The geological map is the best investment for the interested rambler. Costing no more than the Ordnance Survey inch-to-the-mile tourist's maps, coloured geological maps on the same scale may be obtained for every part of Britain. By comparing the geological with the tourist's map the rambler may see at once what any mountain is made of. The volcanic rocks are shown in bright red, but occur only to the north-west of a line drawn from Lyme Regis to the Humber.

In Britain, volcanic necks are the merest relics. We have no complete extinct volcanoes such as are found on the Continent, though Largo Law in Fifeshire is a moderately complete volcano with two cones, and there are several complex specimens in the Inner Hebrides, much reduced in height. What is usually found is just the solidified column of the rock which once flowed up the pipe or 'vent' in a molten state. The fiery throat of the volcano has cooled to form a solid 'neck', and all the rest of the mountain has long since disappeared. (See Fig. 17.)

Lava beds are common enough, but the lava is frequently jumbled up with fragments of other rocks, and the whole rearranged so that the original volcanoes can be reconstructed only by geologists. The rocks of Snowdonia, for

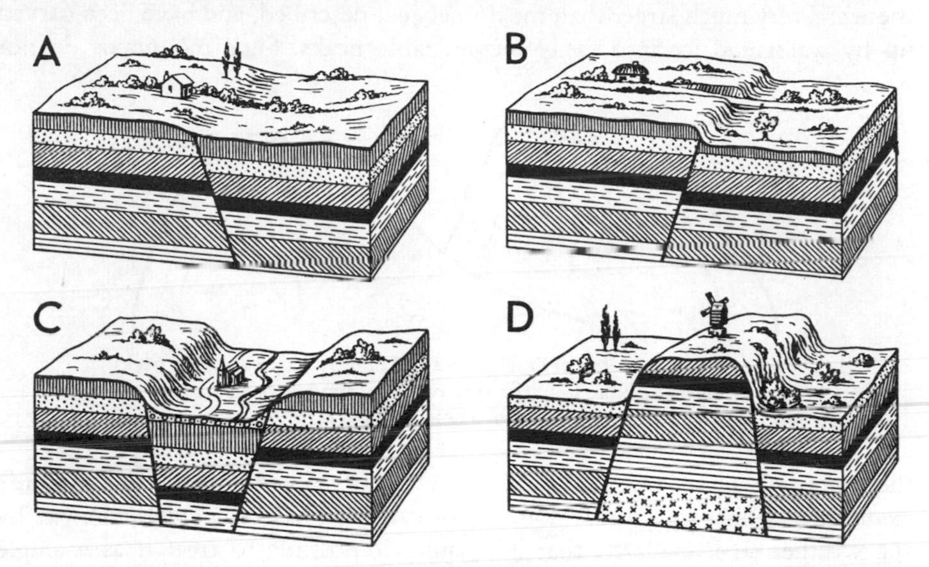

FIG. 15. Block-diagrams showing some of the effects of faulting on the surface-form of the land. A, a simple fault. B, a reversed fault. C, a trough or rift-valley. D, a horst or block-mountain.

example, are very largely lavas (poured out beneath an ancient sea), but the present form of the landscape there is due entirely to erosion, as we have described. It is for these reasons that we do not include types of volcanic cones among our common mountain profiles.

The volcanic rocks which have failed to reach the surface at all have quite a different story to tell. The force with which they came up was often sufficient to raise the overlying rocks into a huge dome—a mountain like a blister, with a granite core. In such cases the top of the granite becomes exposed only after the weather has removed the covering skin, which may be several thousand feet thick.

The general profile of *small* granite mountains formed in this way is shown in Fig. 9, E, an important feature of which is the steep angle with which its slopes meet the ground. It projects above the surface like the back of a porpoise above the sea. The dome itself is usually bare and hard, and it is not at all likely to be confused with the clothed hillock of soft rock (Fig. 4, F) whose base curves smoothly into the surrounding country. Such formations are not very common in Britain, though a few occur in Scotland, as at Traprain Law (Plate VII), and there is one in Shropshire (on the top of Corndon Hill).

The mountains illustrated in Plate IV, A, are also masses of granite, but these are very much larger than the domes just described, and have been carved up by water and ice into easily recognizable peaks. Such mountains do not

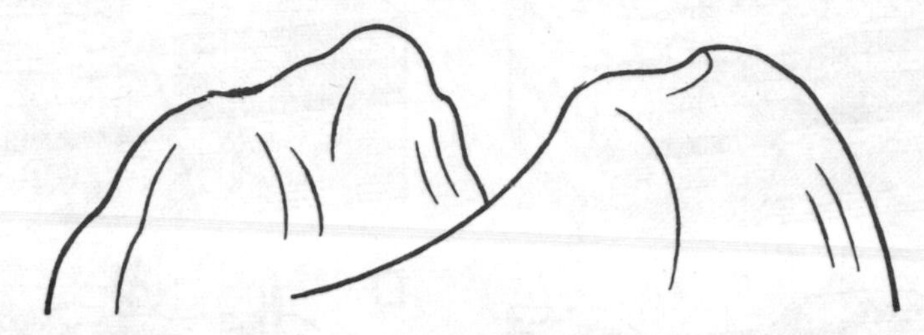

Fig. 16. Outline sketch of Dumgoyn and Dumfoyn, two volcanic necks in Stirlingshire. Note how the side of Dumfoyn has been scoured by a glacier.

therefore belong to any new scenic types. Dartmoor affords a truly gigantic example in which the granite dome is so vast, and has been chiselled away by the weather so irregularly, that it is quite impossible to treat it as a single element of scenery.

These outpourings and accumulations of volcanic rocks are more important, from the rambler's point of view, in providing the incidental features described in the next chapter. One of these must be cited in advance here, because of its relevance to mountain forms.

Salisbury Crags (Plate VII) is an example of a 'sill' (see page 37) whose profile is undoubtedly that shown in Fig. 9, C, and again in Fig. 14, B. In point of fact, this formation is simply an escarpment which owes its preservation to a fortuitous capping of hard volcanic rock. It serves here to illustrate the manner in which volcanic rocks often protect softer formations which might otherwise have long since been worn away. A much larger escarpment in volcanic rock is shown in Plate V, C, and it is to the occurrence of such features that much of the rugged grandeur of Welsh, Lakeland and Scottish scenery is due.

The framework of scenery, as we have considered it, is constructed by these four chief agencies—the surface-carvers, such as water and ice, the folding of sedimentary rocks, the faulting of rocks, and the intrusion of volcanic rocks. This is their order of importance, the first being supreme and over-ruling all the others. The action of weather, water and ice pursues its relentless and uniform course upon whatever material may be submitted to it, and, except in note-

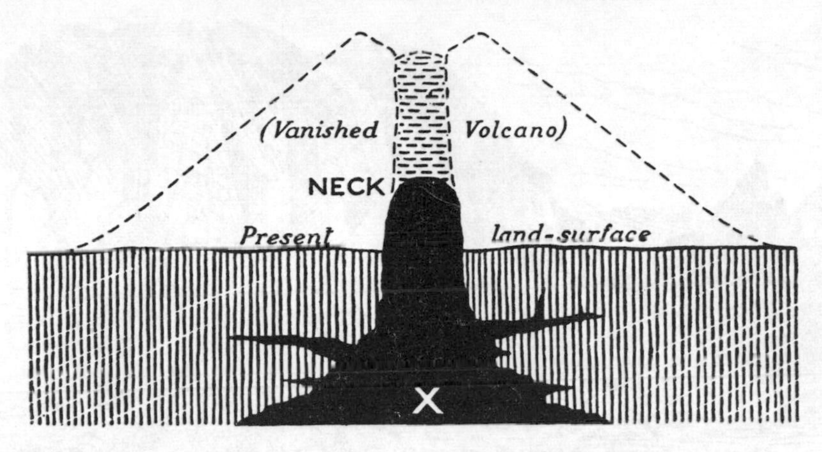

FIG. 17. Explanation of the origin of volcanic necks. The 'magma-chamber' from which the lava constituting the neck originally flowed is indicated at X.

worthy cases, irregularities in the material seldom do more than modify or ornament the results.

Nevertheless, the final landscapes produced are affected in a broad way by the general characteristics of the predominant rocks of a region. Though profiles produced by the same causes remain essentially the same, formations of volcanic rocks tend to be craggy and misshapen (Plates III, IV A, VII A, B, VIII A, B, XVI), those in hard sandstone regular but angular (Plates I A, VI B, XI A, XIII B, XXII), and those in limestone rounded (Plates V B, VI C). Chalk, which is a soft limestone, forms very rounded hills indeed (Plates V A, VI A, XIII A, XIX A, B), while in clay and soft sandstone the hills are flat and symmetrical (Plate II, C). It is also true that the older a landscape grows the softer do its outlines become; the hills, like human beings, mellow with age.

CHAPTER II

Crag and Boulder

To appreciate the true form of a mountain, and so learn something of its story, we found it necessary to ignore the smaller irregularities which break its profile. We treated these as decorative accidents of no particular interest—which is to say that we did not treat them at all. We are now to repair this omission, for it is the adventitious features which give individuality to a mountain, and, like the flourishes in a man's handwriting, afford what quality of 'character' it may possess.

The most prominent of such features are those which occur on mountain summits—the 'crags' and 'tors' and 'beacons' by which we chiefly recognize familiar peaks. It is these which tradition regards as silent monitors of the mountain deities: they point their symbolic fingers to heaven, and they alone can pierce the cloud-veil. It is these which the mountain-dweller learns first to love, and the stranger to fear, and which possess a power of *expression* unmatched in any other landscape feature.

Thus, the sublimity of mountains lies in the massiveness of their slopes, but the sanctity in the wildness of their peaks. We are to consider the carving of those peaks by the mechanical forces of nature, but in doing so we do not pretend—or wish—to explain away their magic. It is a common mistake to suppose that you can abolish the power or significance of an emotion by accounting for its origin—you can no more do so than cure your toothache by reading a treatise on caries. And if you choose to see the rising crags mounting like ladders to heaven, the knowledge that they have been carved by frost will by no means enfeeble your vision.

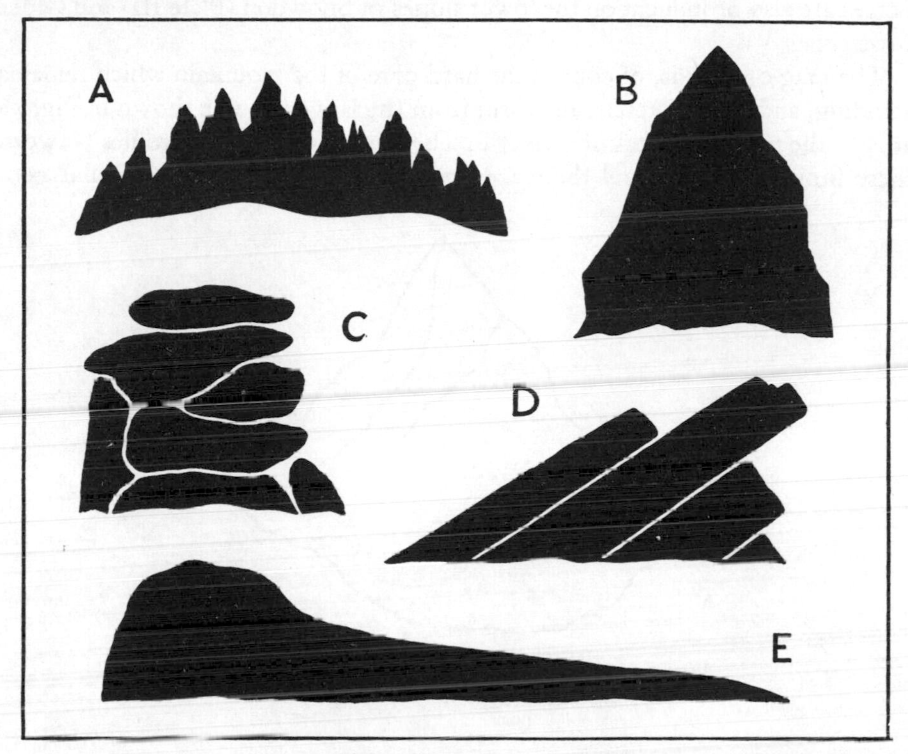

FIG. 18. Profiles of crags and tors due to weathering of the rocks. A, aiguilles. B, horn. C, tor. D, outcrop or crag. E, crag-and-tail. Such terms are used very loosely of particular topographical features.

Frost is undoubtedly the greatest of all rock-splitters, and the harder the rock the more monstrous are the forms produced. The most fantastic peaks are those carved in volcanic rocks like granite, and the jagged skyline on the distant range in Plate IV, A, is typical of such rocks, though but a moderate example. Plate VIII, B, shows the work of frost on lava.

The power of frost resides in the peculiar property of water to expand on freezing; it is the power which bursts our water-pipes in winter. A crack in the rocks becomes filled with water and sealed at the surface by ice. The deeper water then freezes, and in expanding widens the crack. The pressure exerted is about one ton per square inch, and it does not take many successive freezings to split off a small shard or 'talus' of rock. The pile of such loose, angular fragments which is found at the foot of nearly every crag is called a 'scree', and its typical appearance is shown in the sketch at the head of this chapter. Screes are also prominent on the lower slopes of Snowdon (Plate III) and Cader Idris (Plate V).

The crag or peak is, of course, the hard core of the mountain which remains standing, and it may present any form from the jagged profile shown in Fig. 18 at A to the pyramidal peak shown at B. The variety of possible profiles between these limits is infinite, and there are no rules governing their particular geo-

Fig. 19. Outline sketch of Moelwyn, N. Wales, showing aiguilles and horn or 'sugar-loaf'.

metrical shapes. Small, sharp-pointed peaks are sometimes called 'chimneys' or 'needles', especially when isolated and prominent.

Solitary pyramidal peaks large enough to be called mountains in their own right are formed by the rotting action of snow, as already described (page 8), and are sometimes called 'sugar-loaf' mountains. Their horn-like summits belong to the subject of this chapter, and are often very much sharper than the one on the right in Plate IV, A. The profile of a better example is given in Fig. 19, while in Fig. 3 the reader will find both a typical horn and a succession of *aiguilles* or needles.

In milder climates, or at lower levels, where the frost has not such continuous and drastic action, the tough, enduring blocks of volcanic rock assume another form. The level of the land around them is lowered by the normal agencies of the weather, and they project as 'tors'. They now have an ancient, monumental appearance, and seem to have been worn rather than hacked into shape.

The process of slow attrition which has left them standing as relics on the moors has been lengthy enough to find out their lines of weakness and carve them into blocks. These lines of weakness are the 'joints' which occur in all massive formations of volcanic rocks, and they are due to the cracking which resulted from the shrinkage of the rock when it cooled from the molten state. The cracks occur irregularly, but generally at approximate right-angles with one another, so that the effect after the weather has accentuated them is of crude, giant masonry. See Plate VIII, A, and the typical profile in Fig. 18 at C.

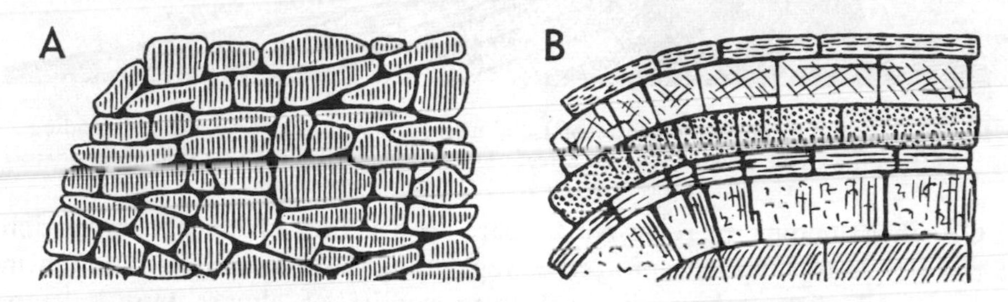

FIG. 20. Jointing in rocks. A, typical jointing in igneous rocks. B, jointing in stratified rocks.

At first glance this jointing suggests the bedding of sedimentary rocks, but the distinction (which is fundamental) is quite easily made. If the rocks were bedded, the horizontal joints would be continuous and parallel, and vertical joints on the same level would be equal in depth. They would also be much less frequent, for in bedded rocks the joints are plentiful only where the strata have cracked during the process of folding. The difference is illustrated in Fig. 20, and may be compared with the difference between rough masonry and brick-work; but doubts may always be resolved by an inspection of the rocks themselves. Compare also Plate VIII, A, with Plates VIII, D, and XI, A.

Hard beds of sedimentary rocks do, however, often form crags on mountain slopes and summits, particularly where they break the surface at a high angle. When they do so, there is generally a long succession of similar crags marking the course of the hard strata, the typical profile of such crags being shown in Fig. 18 at D. An excellent example is given in Plate VIII, C, and the rambler will expect to find others along the ridges of steep escarpments. Such exposures are frequently called 'scars' (old Norse *sker*, isolated rock) in the northern counties, and places bearing this name are illustrated in Plates VI and XVIII.[1]

Sometimes the bare rock of a summit is exposed simply because there is no foot-hold for the accumulation of soil. The rock itself is gradually removed by the weather, but exceptionally hard blocks may persist for a long time as a group of boulders without special arrangement. They are called 'residual boulders', and a group of them may be seen in the middle distance of the sketch at the head of this chapter.

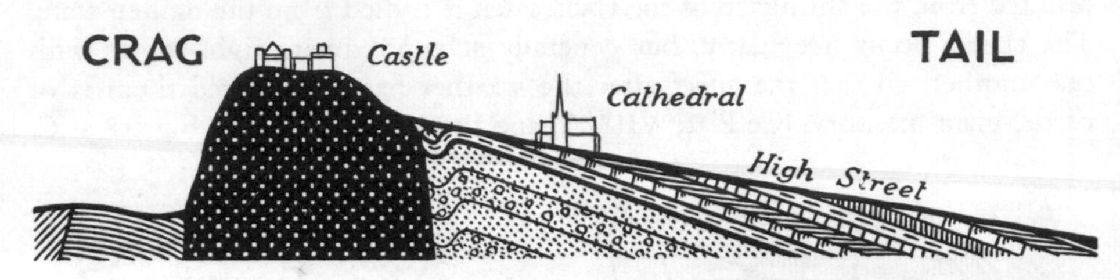

FIG. 21. Section through the centre of Edinburgh, showing the 'crag-and-tail' leading from the Castle down the High Street. The Castle stands on a volcanic neck.

On other summits the rocks remain bare because their chemical composition is too simple to support a protective vegetation. This is common enough in limestone districts, where the rock may consist of almost pure calcium carbonate. Except on occasional levels or sheltered ledges, where wind-borne material may accumulate, such rocks remain barren. Limestone is soluble in rain-water, and is therefore kept thoroughly scoured and clean. Its joints become widened by solution, and exposed surfaces often present the appearance of rough paving stones. These are called 'clints', the gullies separating them being known as 'grikes', and a good example is seen in the picture of Malham Cove in Plate V.

The steep faces of escarpments often fail to hold soil, and therefore take the form of bare cliffs. These suffer from the etching of frost and rain, and their harder portions may stand out to provide many curious features for the entertainment of the traveller and the veneration of the natives. Buttresses, stacks, shelves, chimneys, and so on, are as common in such inland cliffs as they are on the coast, and an example is given in Plate VIII, D. Large portions of a cliff may fall away and remain on the ground at the foot, as puzzling crags, long after the cliff itself has receded from the neighbourhood by the constant action of the weather.

[1] The term *scar* is also used of rocks exposed by other agencies—*e.g.* waterfalls. Its chief Scandinavian use is of solitary rocks standing out of the sea. The word has nothing to do with the 'scar' left by a wound, though it is picturesquely suggestive of it.

A unique type of large crag met with in glaciated regions is that known as a 'crag-and-tail', and a typical specimen may be seen in Plate IX. The rounded knoll to the left of this picture is a boss of hard volcanic rock which the moving

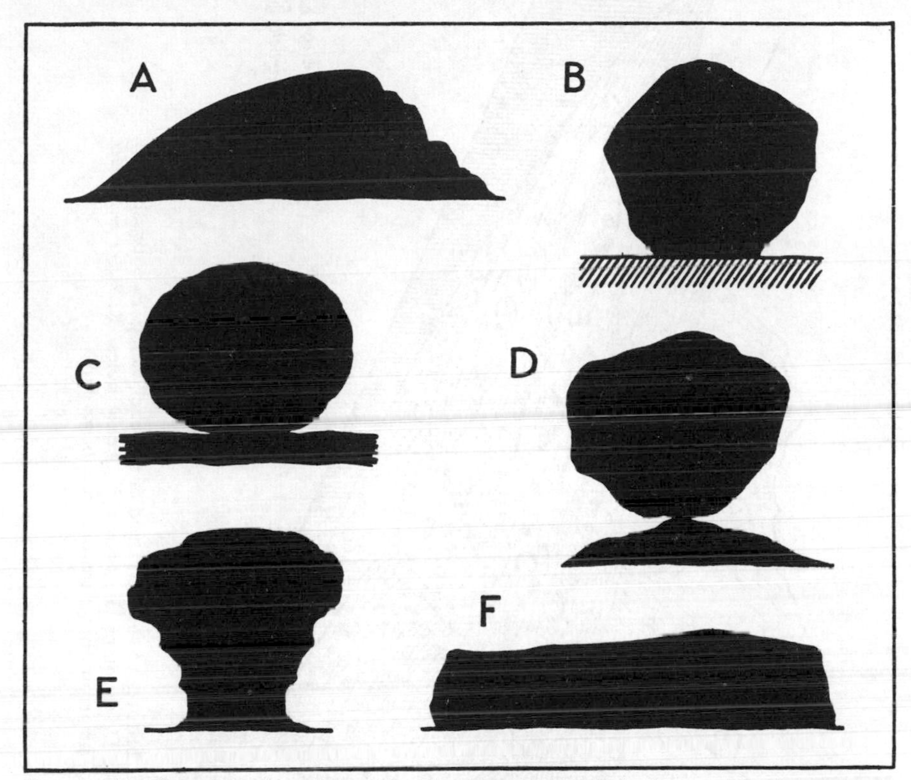

FIG. 22. Profiles of blocks and boulders having characteristic shapes. A, *roche moutonnée*. B, erratic block. C, residual boulder undergoing 'onion-weathering'. D, rocking-stone. E, weathered sandstone block. F, a typical sarsen. These forms are, of course, subject to endless variation in detail.

ice of a glacier (the Loch Lomond glacier) was unable to wear away. The ice may have been a thousand feet thick, and frozen into its base there must have been myriads of broken rock-fragments projecting downwards like chisels. With these the glacier scoured out its great U-shaped valley, removing millions of tons of softer rocks from the surface of the land, but when it came to the granite boss (a volcanic neck, in this instance) it was forced to ride up and over it.

It smoothed and rounded the granite, and descended again on the other side, the direction of its motion being from left to right in the profile in Fig. 18, E.

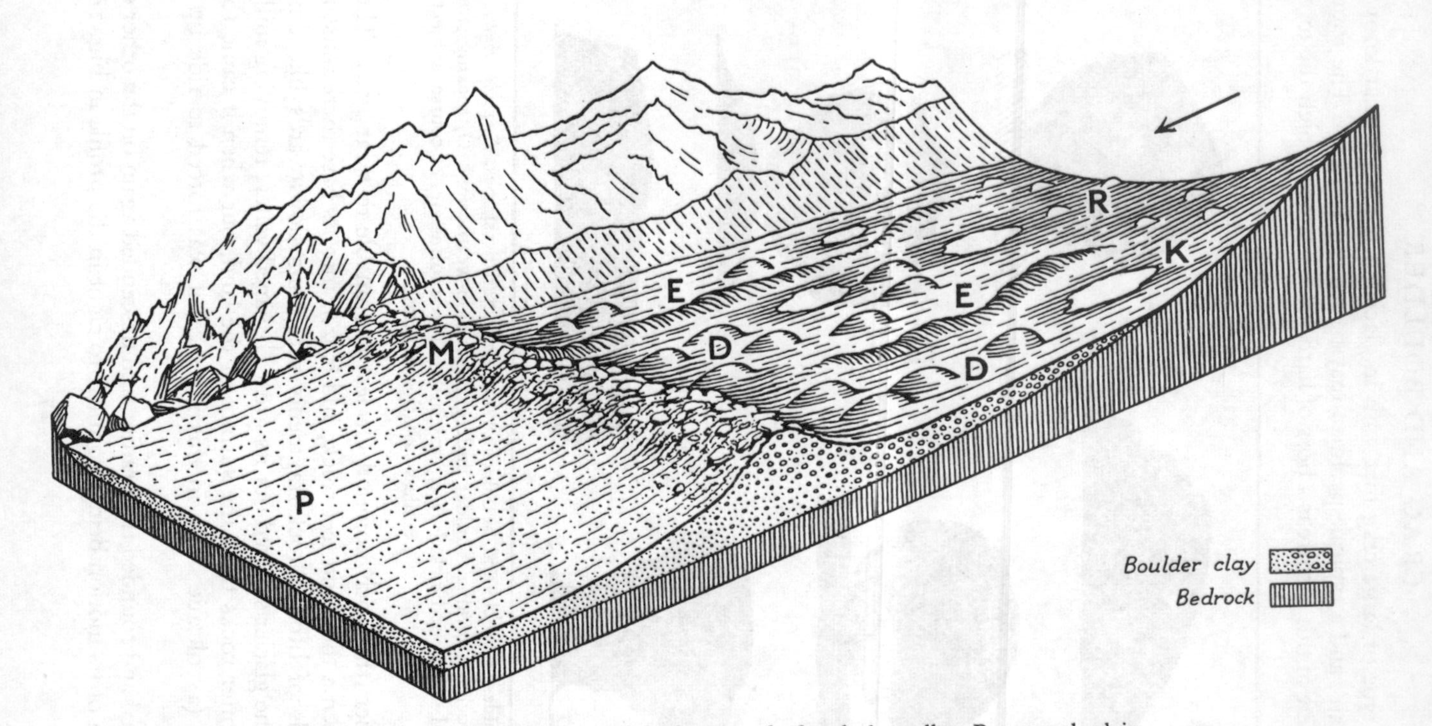

FIG. 23. Characteristic features of the lower end of a glacier valley. P, outwash plain. M, terminal moraine. D, drumlins. E, eskers. K, kettle holes. R, *roches moutonnées*. The arrow shows the direction of ice-flow.

The granite boss afforded some protection to the softer rocks immediately behind it, and it is these which form the 'tail' of the crag. Another example is given in Fig. 21, where a section through a part of Edinburgh shows that Castle Rock is a volcanic neck forming a 'crag', the High Street running down the crest of a 'tail' of sedimentary rocks.

A somewhat similar effect is produced on a very much smaller scale where a glacier has passed over any rock which is not uniformly hard. The softer areas are worn away, but the hard patches project above the general level as stream-lined hummocks of bare rock. They are smoothed and rounded by the ice, and are called '*roches moutonnées*' from their fancied resemblance to sheeps' backs when seen from a distance. Their actual shape is more like half an egg, cut lengthwise, but their disposition regarding the motion of the glacier is the reverse of that in the crag-and-tail, for in the *roche moutonnée* the ice approaches at the small end and leaves it at the large end.

The explanation is that there was originally a gradual slope at *both* ends, the highest point of the hummock being in the middle, but the motion of the ice loosened the joints in the rock and tore off blocks of it as a sort of parting gesture. Thus, it took what 'tail' there might have been with it, and terminated the hummock more or less abruptly at its original centre. This termination is often 'stepped', showing how the last pieces of rock were 'plucked' from it, and this is shown in the idealized profile in Fig. 22 at A. An actual photograph of a *roche moutonnée* is given in Plate IX, B.

All rocks over which ice has passed have a characteristic appearance which the rambler should be able to recognize. They are both polished and scratched, the polishing being due to the ice and the powdered rock which it has ground for itself on its journey, and the scratches—or 'striations'—to larger pieces of rock projecting downward from the ice like teeth. (See Plate XX, B.)

A deeply-scored piece of wood which has been only partly smoothed down again with glass-paper would give the right sort of effect, but the scores should all run in approximately the same direction. It was by mapping the directions of the ice-scratches on rocks over vast areas of the country that the movements of ice during the Ice Age were ascertained. The rambler who comes across an ice-scratched rock may at once decide the direction in which the responsible glacier moved, even when there is no surviving valley.

Another way in which the movements of ancient ice may be ascertained is by tracing the course of the rocks and rock-material carried along on the backs of the glaciers. Along the path of every glacier there is a litter of 'foreign' stones and boulders, like the spoor of the hare in a paper-chase. The original source of such material may be found by comparing it with the native rocks of the district to which the 'spoor' leads. The trail is, however, often broken and difficult to follow, and the rambler who finds a piece of granite (say) in a limestone district will usually be content to assume that it came from the nearest granite mountains shown on his geological map. He will probably be right.

At the end of every glacier, where the ice melts, there is a large deposit of mixed mud and stones, called 'boulder-clay' or 'till'. This deposit provides several features characteristic of glaciated country, and the most important of them are illustrated in Fig. 23. At the very end of the glacier the boulder clay forms a bank known as a 'terminal moraine', and this represents the bulk of the surviving material which was carried along by the ice. Moraines sometimes form considerable hills, and may so effectually dam the glacier valley as to cause a lake to form behind them. (See Plate IX.) In front of the moraine there is a comparatively level stretch of the finer material washed out by drainage streams, and this is appropriately named the 'outwash plain'.

The stretch of the valley immediately behind the moraine is full of problems, some of which have never been satisfactorily solved. The surface rises in numerous small rounded hillocks of boulder-clay called 'drumlins', and the curious hummocky landscape produced is sometimes referred to as the 'basket-of-eggs topography'. See Plate IX, D. Among the drumlins are occasional snake-like ridges or low hills known as 'eskers' (Plate XII, C) or—where they are broken into separate hills like beads on a string—'kames'. Higher up the valley where the bedrock is exposed the *roches moutonnées* appear, and where the ice has rotted out hollows in the bedrock are the small pools called 'kettle holes'. A kettle hole is shown on the left in Plate IV, A.

During the period of maximum glaciation the great moraines stretched right across England just north of the line of the Thames, and as the ice retreated towards the close of the Ice Age the corresponding retreat of the moraines carpeted large areas of the country with boulder clay. Much of this deposit, which forms the greater part of the so-called 'drift',[1] has since been removed, but the rambler should not be surprised to find eskers and other low hills of morainic material anywhere from the Thames to the north of Scotland. The typical evidence of the origin of such features lies in their stones and boulders, which exhibit the unmistakable signs of ice-abrasion.

Glaciers sometimes carry along on their backs exceptionally large boulders which have fallen on to the ice from the steep valley-sides. These may eventually

[1] The term 'drift' strictly includes all superficial deposits (except the soil) which obscure the outcrops of the 'solid' rocks, and is not confined to glacial deposits. But since almost all the drift in this country is either of glacial origin or of Ice Age date, the term has come to be used by some writers as synonymous with glacial deposits. This is unfortunate in so far as 'drift' is a geological surveyor's term, and it retains its correct meaning in the publications of H.M. Geological Survey.

come to rest many miles from their parent mountains, and may survive long after the smaller morainic material has disappeared. They are called 'erratic blocks', and the rambler encounters them as large, isolated boulders, generally on the plains and valley-sides but sometimes in more elevated situations.

They may be of any shape, for since they rode on top of the glacier they have not been subjected to the abrasion and scratching suffered by the rocks beneath the ice. Our profile (Fig. 22, B) is therefore of a chance shape, but we indicate by the shading that the block and the rock on which it rests are of different kinds. As actual examples we may cite erratic blocks of Norwegian granite which are found on the limestone of the Durham coast, blocks of pink Westmorland granite which rest on sandstones in the Vale of York, and the gigantic block of chalk half a mile long which was carried from Yorkshire and dumped on the Oxford Clay of Huntingdonshire, and which now supports the village of Catworth on its back. A typical example is illustrated in Plate IX, A.

Sometimes a small erratic block comes to rest balanced on another rock, in which case it is called a 'perched block'. An example is given in Fig. 24. Such a boulder may rock on its foundations without overturning, and many 'rocking stones' mentioned in the guide books have this origin. But rocking stones also occur in the extreme south of Britain, far beyond the reach of the ice, and these must be accounted for in a different way.

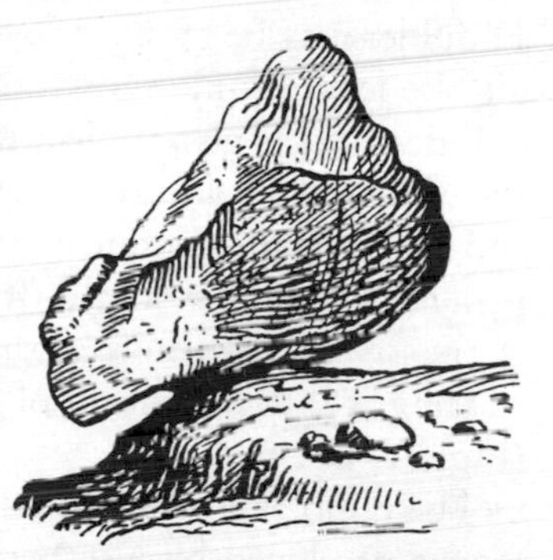

FIG. 24. A perched block in the Pass of Llanberis, N. Wales.

We saw (page 25) how the volcanic rocks are liable to weather along their joints, a habit which gives them the appearance of rough masonry. The weathering is not a simple process, but includes the effects of temperature changes, the abrasive action of sand grains blown by the wind, the splitting action of frost, and—most important of all—the chemical action of rain. Rain-water contains carbon dioxide (which it has dissolved from the air), and as it lies in the cracks of the rocks slow chemical changes take place which cause the rock to crumble away.

The weathering begins on the exposed corners and edges of the joints, so that the rectangular blocks become rounded and the entire rock is reduced first to the pile of natural 'masonry' (see Fig. 20, A), and then to a mere heap of rounded boulders. Now, if one of these residual boulders is very large, and the others small, the large one may survive long after the smaller ones have completely disintegrated.

The chemical weathering now slows down a little, owing to the absence of joint-crannies, but its continuance is assured by heavy dews and prolonged mountain rain. These may keep the rock wet for months at a time, and the moisture has ample chance to penetrate the rock through such mineral grains as are subject to its chemical action.

The depth to which it penetrates is slight but fairly uniform, and the action goes on beneath the surface long after the rock is apparently dry. It is helped by the growth of mosses and lichens, and by the expansion and contraction due to alternate sunshine and frost. The chemical products of the action are bulkier than the minerals from which they are formed, and so they swell up and force the surface layers off in flakes. Thus, the rock becomes whittled down, layer by layer, getting rounder and rounder all the time.

Because this process is reminiscent of the peeling of an onion it is called 'onion-weathering', and it is sometimes surprising how near to a perfect sphere a boulder may be reduced in this way. It is not uncommon to find one approaching the ideal profile shown in Fig. 22 at C. The rock on which this—or any—boulder rests is also subject to weathering, and its surface is gradually lowered. But the boulder affords it some protection over a small area, like an umbrella, and so the rock immediately beneath the boulder may stand above the general level as a knoll or short plinth. The boulder on top now appears to be in a precarious position, but gravity has been at work all the time, nursing it into a position of equilibrium, and the final result is a rocking stone (Fig. 22, D).

The rambler may always distinguish between the loose boulders and rocking stones produced by weathering, and the erratic and perched blocks deposited by glaciers, by examining the boulders themselves. Those produced by weathering are of the same rock as the ground on which they stand, whereas those transported by glaciers not only rest as a rule on a different kind of rock, but on rock which shows the characteristic signs of glaciation (page 29).

Our descriptions of boulders have been largely concerned with the weathering of volcanic rocks, but it is to be understood that similar boulders, produced by similar processes, may also be found in sandstone, limestone, shale, and most other sedimentary rocks. These do not require special description except in the case of exposed sandstones whose bedding is approximately horizontal. These are particularly susceptible to the action of wind-borne dust and sand grains, and yield mushroom-like rocks which are quite characteristic.

Friable sandstones succumb to the action of wind-borne sand like masonry before a sand-blast, and their softer layers get etched away while the hard bands remain. The particles removed supply further ammunition to the gales for attacking neighbouring rocks, and the whole process goes on with extraordinary rapidity on arid high land.

Only the finest particles can be raised to appreciable heights by the wind,

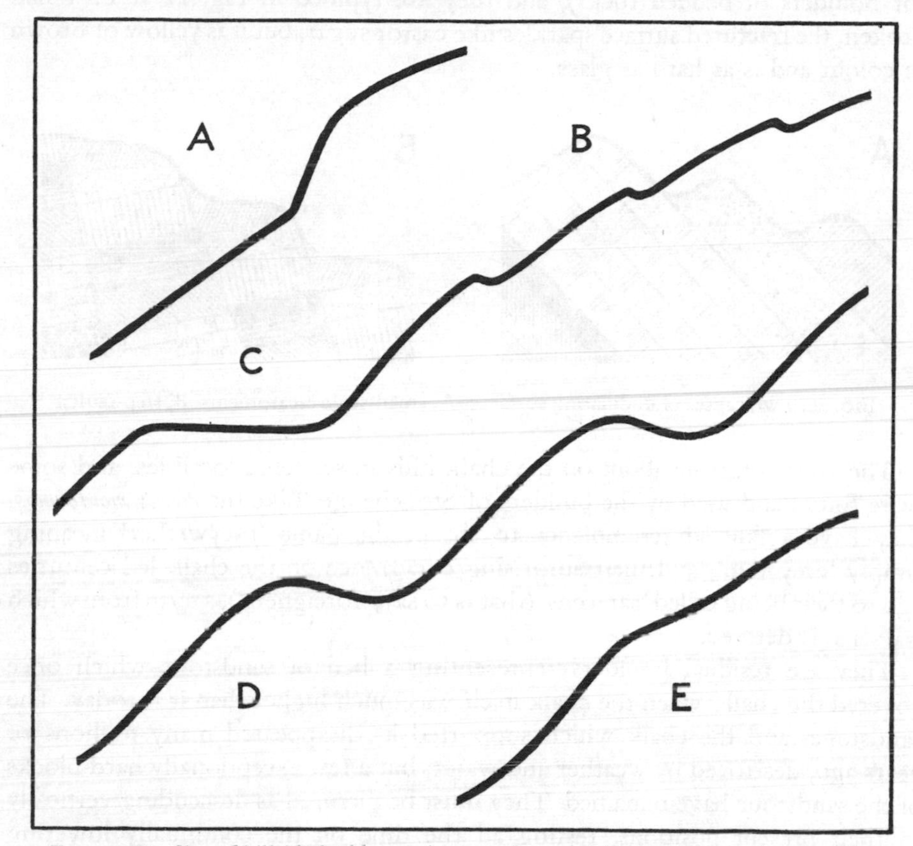

FIG. 25. Profiles of hillside incidents. Among the many interpretations described in the text are: A, scree. B, 'sheep-tracks'. C, terrace. D, step-faults. E, outcrop of hard rock. Identification cannot, however, be made from these forms alone. See the text.

and the heaviest work goes on near the ground. The result is that a block of sandstone tends to become undercut, and presents the general profile shown in Fig. 22 at E. It may even be cut right through at the base, and become yet another rocking stone. The example illustrated in Plate XV, A, is one of the many to be found in Britain, and the forms produced are often so grotesque that local fairy legends exist to account for them.

No description of the boulders likely to be found by the rambler would be complete without a reference to the 'sarsens' or 'greywethers' of the chalk downs of southern England (and particularly Salisbury Plain). These are blocks of sandstone (quartzite), often roughly rectangular in shape (a common form for boulders of bedded rocks), and they are typified in Fig. 22 at F. When broken, the fractured surface sparkles like castor sugar, but it is yellow or brown in colour and is as hard as glass.

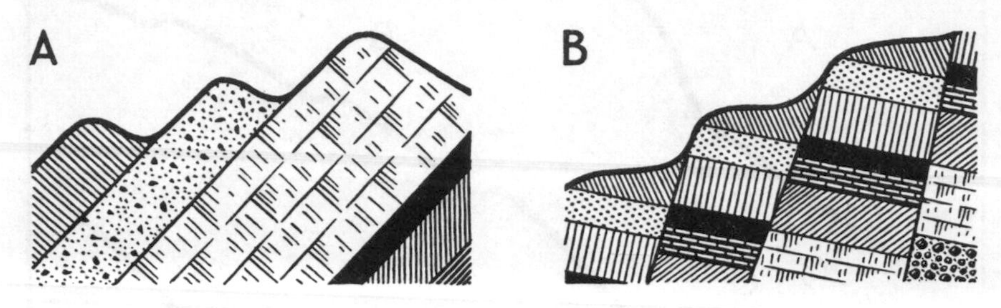

FIG. 26. Two causes of undulating surfaces. A, small-scale escarpments. B, step-faults.

The sarsens just lie about on the chalk hills in scattered localities, and some were found and used by the builders of Stonehenge. Like the *roches moutonnées*, they have a fancied resemblance to sheep, the name 'greywether' meaning simply 'grey ram', and their surprising occurrence on the chalk led centuries ago to their being called 'saracens' (that is to say, 'foreigners'), a term from which 'sarsens' is derived.

They are residual boulders representing a bed of sandstone which once covered the chalk, when the chalk itself was much higher than it is today. The sandstone, and the chalk which supported it, disappeared many millions of years ago, destroyed by weather and water, but a few exceptionally hard blocks of the sandstone have remained. They must be pictured as descending vertically to their present positions, resting all the time on the continually lowering surface of the chalk.

Crags and boulders, and other such exposures of bare rock, are liable to occur wherever ice, frost or the weather has had a chance to produce them—for instance, on any slopes exposed to the prevailing wind. In more sheltered places, such as the lee sides of hill ranges, or where the ground is well covered with vegetation, the 'decorative accidents' which give individuality to scenic forms are of a different kind.

They may be grouped together (scenically) as modifications of hillsides, and with some of them the reader of this book will be already familiar. In the previous chapter (page 15) we mentioned the occurrence of slight ridges due to faults, and in this we have referred to the screes (page 24) which may conceal the true slope of a mountain. With cliffs we shall deal in Chapters III and IV.

On steep hillsides of soft or loosely-jointed rocks, where the subsoil is fairly deep, exceptionally heavy rains may cause small landslides. The result is commonly that shown in Fig. 25 at A. There is a short cliff where the bedrock is exposed, and below it is the straight slope produced by the material which

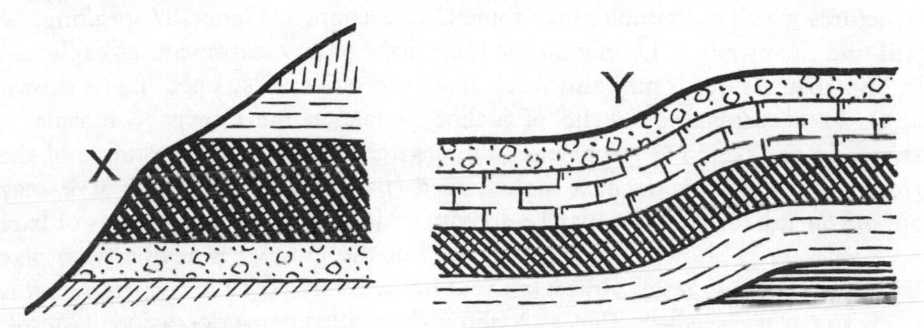

FIG. 27. Surface-effect of (X) an outcrop of hard rock, (Y) a slight fold or 'monocline'.

has fallen. This slope presents the same profile as a scree, but instead of consisting of angular fragments of bare rock it is made up of mixed rock fragments and soil, and is probably covered with grass.

Little slips of the same kind, but so small as to be confined to the top few inches of soil, are liable to occur on any steep slope. Alternate wetting and drying, and warming and cooling, loosen the grains of soil, and gravity sees to it that the minute motions of every grain, whether in expansion or contraction, are on the whole downward. This is called 'soil creep', and fortunately the roots of the grass on a hillside prevent the wholesale migration of the soil in this way from top to bottom of the hill.

But the grass-roots become effective only at intervals, and thus cause small parallel ledges to form (Fig. 25, B). These are popularly known as 'sheep-tracks', no doubt because sheep—and other animals, including man—make frequent use of them. But they are just as common where there are no sheep, and all that animals have to do with them is to accentuate favoured ones by the constant wear of their feet. A well-used sheep-track may form a level ledge a foot wide or more. The effects of soil-creep may be seen in Plates XVIII, A, and XXIII, B.

Very much wider ledges with level surfaces are also frequently seen, but these are likely to be river terraces, lynchets, or perhaps (in coastal districts) raised sea beaches. Their common profile is represented here in Fig. 25 at C, but they will be described in detail in Chapters IV, VIII and III, respectively. A possible fourth explanation of this profile is given below in connection with 'sills'.

Ledges or ridges in various forms may also occur where exceptionally hard beds of rock alternate with soft ones, or where the bedding of loosely-jointed rocks is tilted at a high angle. Such features are for the geologist to study, but the profiles given in Fig. 25 at D and E are included as examples of simple structures which the rambler may sometimes recognize. Generally speaking, he will find the profile at D only on the long slope of an escarpment, as explained in Fig. 26 at A, but it may also result from the series of 'stepped' faults shown at B. Its occurrence on a cliff of inclined strata in the Gower peninsula is shown in the sketch at the head of the next chapter. A single example of the trough at D may represent a sunken road (page 169). The profile at E may appear on any hillside, and may be accentuated by occasional exposures of bare rock. Fig. 27 X shows how it may arise, but the rambler is at liberty to play with the theme suggested almost without limit. Every possible variation on it is likely to occur elsewhere. Fig. 27 Y shows how a ledge may occasionally result from a simple fold (*monocline*), but this explanation should not be adopted unless the rocks are visible at some point and there is no room for doubt.

FIG. 28. A sharp fold in the Coal Measures at Saundersfoot, Pembrokeshire.

Other anomalies, which may appear almost anywhere, include the effects of sharp local folding, as exemplified in Fig. 28, but unless the rocks themselves are exposed the explanation of all such odd forms should be left to the experts. There remain only two easily recognized decorative features to be described in this chapter, both caused by the infilling of cracks with volcanic rocks.

We have already noted (see Fig. 20, B) that the jointing in all bedded rocks is characteristically rectangular. If we ignore disturbances due to folding we may say that joints are either vertical or horizontal; they are seldom diagonal. Now, when molten rock is forced into the crust of the earth from below it naturally makes its way into the joints, and often forces them wide apart. It is therefore not uncommon to find lavas and other volcanic rocks, and particularly the heavy black basalt, existing in sheets between blocks of natural masonry like mortar between bricks. See Fig. 29. Such rocks are appropriately called 'intrusions', to distinguish them from lava flows and volcanic blocks.

Since most volcanic rocks are considerably more durable than most sedimentary rocks, they tend to stand out above the general level of a weathered land surface, and exceptionally prominent crags, horns, needles and tors often consist of them. Again, they are sometimes responsible for damming rivers and

FIG. 29. Outcrops of igneous rocks, usually lavas. D, dyke. S. sill.

causing lakes and waterfalls (see page 68). Where the sheets are vertical they often form natural walls, which are called 'dykes' (Fig. 29, D, and Plate X, A). Where they are horizontal they may project from hillsides like shelves (Fig. 25, C) and are called 'sills' (Fig. 29, S). The sill of black rock at Salisbury Crags (Plate VII) was forced between the bedding of an old sandstone, but since it was formed the whole has been tilted and every vestige of sandstone *above* the sill removed.

And so fire has been added to frost, ice, rain and wind as the final craftsman responsible for the elaboration of scenic detail. If the crags and tors of Jack Frost are as ladders reaching to high heaven, the dykes and sills of basalt are surely visible tokens of the nether fires—petrifactions of the vapours of the pit! And as for the jointed masonry—but we fancy we hear the reader protesting in the words of Sherlock Holmes, 'Cut out the poetry, Watson. I note that it was a high brick wall.'

CHAPTER III

The Restless Sea

'A high brick wall,' indeed! Yet it will prove a useful enough description in this present chapter, for the most spectacular features of coastal scenery are just those high brick walls which keep the sea at bay—the cliffs. The architecture of cliffs is a study in itself, and we shall have more to say of it when we have made sure of the true meaning of cliffs for the enquiring rambler. With this end in view we propose first to dismiss the sea entirely from our minds.

You may stand on the Pennine moors, on Salisbury Plain, on the Wealden heights, on the mountains of Wales or Scotland, or anywhere you choose, and vainly wonder what secrets lie hidden beneath the soft carpet of turf at your feet. The vegetation itself is the merest veil, but the soil and rocks below it are impenetrable. All the knowledge that you can gather directly on viewing the landscape is purely superficial—it is confined to the thin film of surface that rolls away before you to the horizon. Your senses afford you no jot or tittle of evidence that there is anything more substantial beneath those green waves than there is beneath the cloud billows and sheets of mist that look so solid when you see them from above.

Now in moods of reverie we incline to rely utterly on the evidence of our senses, and it is then that the landscape acquires that unsubstantial fairy quality which is the bare, revealed *truth* of it, uncoloured by inference and rational belief. Such truth forms the foundation of the aesthetic appreciation of landscape, but if we require scientific information we must look beyond the appearances. It is sometimes hard to realize that the picture is but paint—that the 'green enamel' of the hills is a mere wash of chlorophyll—but it is harder still to strip off the façade of a mountain and comprehend the architecture which supports it. Almost all such work must be done by inference—and imagination.

The rambler is prone to indulge his imagination at the expense of his logic, and to wonder rather than to find out. It seems to him futile, though occasionally entertaining, to speculate on what lies beneath his feet, and for the most part he assumes that he is supported by a depressing weight of featureless stone, unbroken even by the dark vacuity of a barren cave. Yet that endless succession of dull rocks may be relieved in a hundred hidden ways, and in few localities would he be right in his hasty assumption.

Beneath the black soil there may lie bands of rich marble, beds of tropical shells, ancient coral reefs, veins of bright minerals, seams of lustrous ores, whole forests embalmed in shining coal, rivers and waterfalls, enchanted grottoes, and even the bones of creatures which lived and died in the springtime of the world. Of all these things the rambler has, of course, heard, but as he stands on the familiar hills he does not believe that he is verily in their presence.

For him, seeing is believing, and if the solid earth at his feet could be cloven as with an axe, and the deep rocks of the hills be laid bare for his inspection, he would be more than satisfied. Gargantuan task—yes, indeed! But it is just this which has been done in a thousand places by the sea, whose cliffs are no less—and no more—than sectioned mountain ranges. The rambler must learn to see them thus, and if, in his imagination, he can sometimes picture the high land continuing unbroken beyond the limit of the narrow shore, he will grasp the true significance of cliffs as elements of scenery.

This, then, is what the cliffs should be to the rambler—they are gigantic dissections across the landscape, perfectly displayed specimens of the earth's outer crust, storehouses of ancient life, and (as we shall see) marvels of natural architecture. It is only to the coastguard and the sailor that they are mere precipitous and illogical terminations to the land.

Our first observations concern the way in which the sea sets to work to demolish the land. We have said that it cleaves the solid earth as with an axe, and it verily does so, only it is with a woodman's axe, wielded horizontally—not a battle axe. Its blows are struck at the base of the cliffs, almost all of them between high and low tide levels, and the cliffs come tumbling down as surely as any forest giant at the hands of the lumberman.

The chief work of the sea is done with the pebbles which lie on the beach. Whether it hurls these at the foot of the cliff or simply washes them to-and-fro, they exercise a constant abrasive action on the rocks. They are always hard enough to leave their scratch, for the frost supplies them from the cliff-face itself. Indeed, they are often harder than the main part of the cliff, for they are likely to consist chiefly of the toughest nodules the cliff can supply. At the foot of the soft chalk cliffs, for example, they are usually flints, which are as hard as glass. If *these* lose all their sharp corners and become rounded and polished, and if some of them are reduced to mere sand-grains, you can be sure that they have done as much, and more, to the cliff-face—when they have had the opportunity. But they can do nothing without the waves, and to these we now turn our attention.

The cause of sea waves was long under dispute, but it is now known with certainty that it is the wind. The strength of the wind is an important factor,

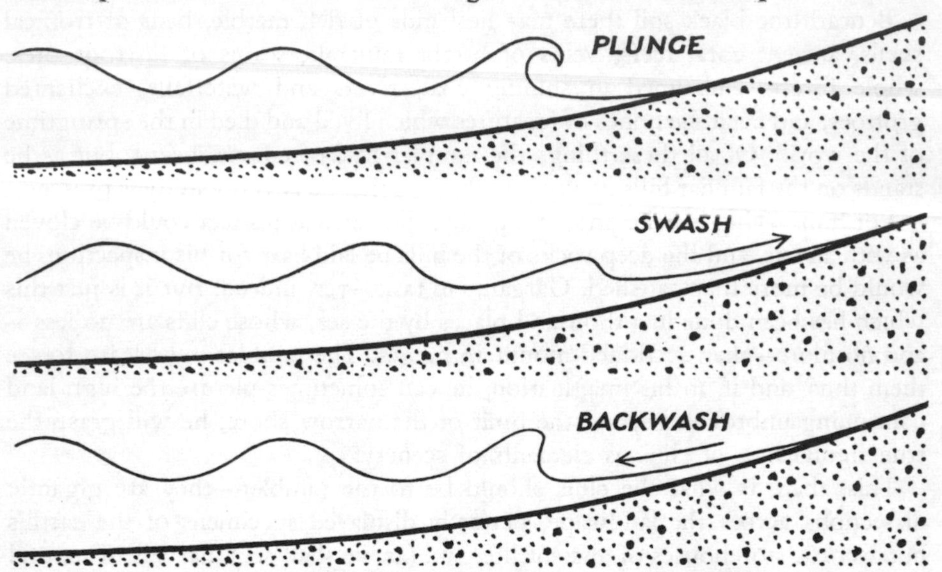

FIG. 30. Three stages in the breaking of a wave, which takes place when the height of the wave is equal to the depth of the water.

but so also is the 'fetch'. This is the distance of water over which the wind blows uninterruptedly. Quite a gentle breeze may produce large waves if it blows steadily over the surface for some hundreds of miles, the height of the waves in feet being approximately equal to half the speed of the wind in miles per hour. Thus, a breeze blowing at ten miles per hour may produce waves five feet high. Such waves, once generated, continue for some time after the wind has died down—or, if they have been produced by a local storm, they may invade channels and shores which are still enjoying calm weather. Waves thus found beyond the fetch of wind which caused them constitute a 'swell' or 'groundswell'.

At ten or more miles per hour a wind is able to blow 'spume' or 'spindrift' from the crests of the waves, and so produces 'combers' or 'white horses'. This has nothing to do with waves breaking, which can occur only along a shore or over a shoal, where the depth of the water is equal to the height of the wave. The breaking of waves is explained in Fig. 30, where the top diagram shows a breaker about to plunge. At this stage the friction between the bottom water and the beach so retards the progress of the lower part of the wave that the unimpeded top overbalances. The wave breaks for the same reason that a running man falls on his face when his feet are caught in a trip-wire. The plunge is followed by the uprush, or 'swash' of 'surf' up the beach. The water runs down again as the 'backwash', and this is sometimes drawn under the following wave with considerable force.

The size of the pebbles which are moved by this action depends upon the speed of the water, but those which are submerged are moved more easily than those which are exposed, for the buoyancy of the water reduces their effective weight by about one-third. A submerged stone five inches in diameter, resting alone on smooth sand, is moved by water travelling at two miles per hour. A group of pebbles is less easy to shift, for they protect and impede each other, but smooth stones the size of hen's eggs may be shifted on a shingle beach by water travelling at four miles per hour. It is easier to travel downhill than up, and on the whole the effect of the waves on a beach is to rake it out to sea.

If the pebbles are too large to be moved, the sea continues to pound them till they become small enough for transport. It does this chiefly by knocking them together so that they wear each other's corners off, and by the time they become small enough to be called sand they may be almost completely spherical.

The abrasive action at the foot of the cliff causes a 'nick' to be cut in it at high-water level, as is clearly shown in Fig. 31 (just below the C), while the abrasive action *beneath* the pebbles on the shore levels the bedrock into a 'wave-cut platform' (P). The extent to which the landscape has been cut into may be seen from the broken line, which indicates the original surface of the hills. Another example is shown in Fig. 42, while an actual example of a wave-cut platform with its covering beach removed (by the sea) is illustrated in Fig. 36.

The motion of the sea distributes the beach material in a more or less even layer over the platform, and at the same time grades its constituent particles according to their size. The largest stones it leaves alone, except in rough weather, but the others are found in steadily decreasing sizes as you go seaward, the smallest travelling farthest. The slightest motion of the water suffices to shift the finer sand, and this gets carried down the platform till it tumbles over the edge and settles in comparatively still, deep water. Here it accumulates to form a 'wave-built terrace' (Fig. 31, T), the outer slope of which assumes a definite 'angle of rest' with which we shall be concerned later in this chapter.

In stormy weather the waves may pick up some of the beach and throw it back at the cliffs, the smaller pebbles being flung to a height of a hundred feet or more. The stones thus cast up accumulate as a ridge of shingle above high-water mark, and constitute a 'storm beach'. This may be a bank of considerable

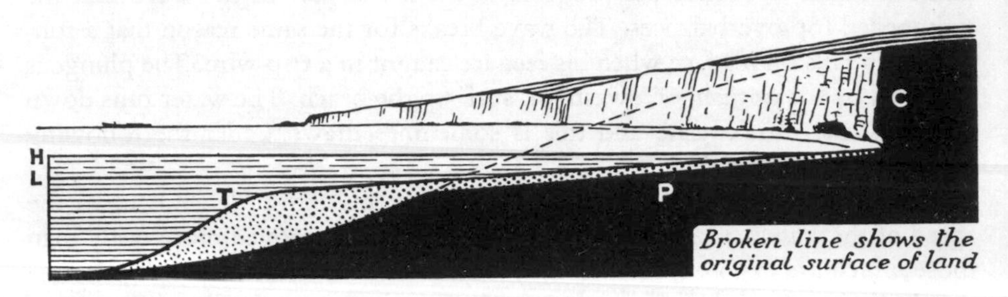

FIG. 31. Section through a typical shore. C, cliff. P, wave-cut platform. T, wave-built terrace. H-L, high and lower water levels. Note the nick at the foot of the cliff.

size, and may last for many years. The beach built up on Chesil Bank (Plate XII) by the great storm of 1852 is still clearly visible. On many coasts there are successions of storm beaches forming parallel ridges or 'fulls' along the shore, the hollows between them being called 'swales' or 'slashes'. On the wide stretch of shingle known as the Crumbles, at Pevensey, no less than sixty-five old storm beaches have been counted, though we should add that their preservation has been largely due to the fact that the Crumbles has been steadily growing seaward for many hundreds of years. We shall consider the causes of such growth in due course.

In times of storm, when the sea itself is hurled against a cliff-face, the water contributes as much to the work of destruction as the stones with which it is armed. If the large stones behave like cold chisels, and the pebbles like grape-shot, the water performs the office of battering-ram, loosening the joints in the rocks and shaking them down by the sheer weight of its blows.

In mild weather the waves commonly beat against the cliffs with the force of a quarter of a ton per square foot, and the poet did not exaggerate when he wrote:

> No rock so hard, but that a little wave
> May beat admission in a thousand years.[1]

[1] Tennyson, *The Princess*, III, 7.

During the storms the force rises to a ton per square foot, and in very heavy storms on the Atlantic coast the cliffs and rocks (and lighthouses) have to sustain a battering of three or more tons per square foot.

No wonder the cliffs are tumbling down, yet the effects of the sea on a cliff-face are, in the long run, surpassed by those due to the weather. Although—

> The sturdy rock, for all his strength,
> By raging seas, is rent in twaine;
> The marble stone is pearst at length
> With littel drops of drizzling raine.[1]

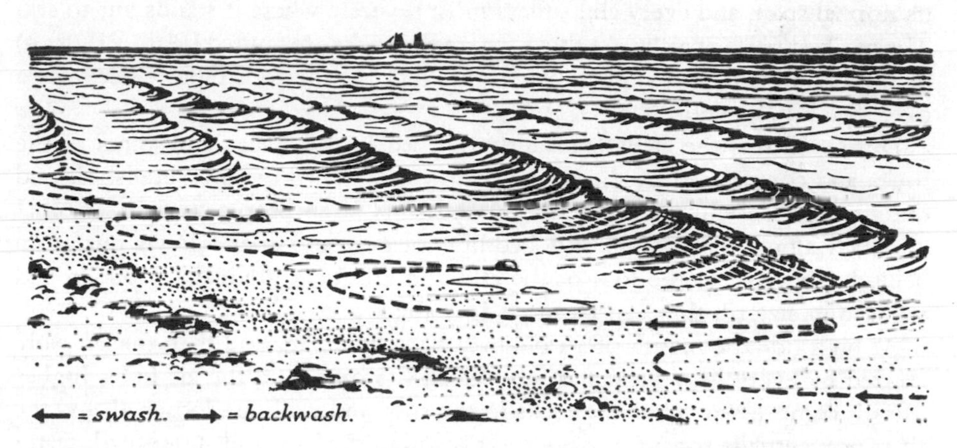

FIG. 32. Waves approaching a shore obliquely and causing longshore drifting of beach pebbles.

Frost, sun and rain are at work over the whole of the exposed portion of every cliff, in calm weather as well as rough, and if they merely keep pace with the action of the sea at its foot the cliff will rapidly recede and a wide beach will soon be formed. When this is so wide that the cliff is out of reach of even the highest tide, the work of the sea is temporarily finished. It can do no more.

It is seldom, however, that a beach is allowed to accumulate in this way. The waves approach very few shores exactly at right-angles, and when they approach obliquely, as in Fig. 32, they move the pebbles along the shore as well as up and down the beach. The diagram shows a pebble in three successive positions as a result of oblique wave action. The scale may be a little exaggerated, but it makes no difference in the end if the movements of the pebbles are measured in inches or in millimetres. The effect is the same—the whole

[1] *Anon.*—1587.

beach gradually moves along the coast, and is given no chance to form a permanent protective strand in front of the cliffs.

It is to prevent this wholesale removal of bathing and fishing beaches that 'groynes' are built out at right-angles to the shore on many coasts, and every reader will be familiar with the difference in the level of the beach on each side of every such barrier. The effectiveness of the groynes at Folkestone is well shown in Plate XV. On coasts where there are no groynes there is often no visible beach at all.

The battle of the sea *versus* the cliffs is thus liable to be prolonged beyond its normal span, and every cliff suffers most severely where it stands out to sea. The weakest parts of a cliff are those where the rocks are faulted (Plate VII, foot) or heavily jointed, and at such places the 'nick' at the foot rapidly becomes a cave. See Fig. 33 and Plate XI, A.

During storms the air is constantly trapped in the cracks and joints of the rocks and compressed by the weight of the sea. When the pressure is released the air expands with explosive force, and thus large blocks of rock are first loosened along their joints and bedding planes, and then blown out from behind. They fall to the foot of the cliff and are there gradually rounded and reduced in size till they can be moved by the waves.

At high tide the mouth of a cave may be submerged, and then the pressure exerted by every heavy roller is felt within the cave, and the air in its higher parts is compressed. Thus the rocks in the roof and walls are loosened, and the air may eventually force a passage right through the roof and spout forth water and spray to a great height. The hole from which it escapes may be a considerable distance inland, and is called a 'blow-hole' or 'gloup' (throat). One is shown in action in Fig. 33. The final result of this process is the collapse of the roof of the cave, and the formation of a deep inlet or 'geo'.[1] Examples of a blow-hole and a geo are shown in Plate X.

The picture of the geo also shows the arch known as the Needle Eye, and brings us to the long-deferred subject of cliff architecture. An arch of this sort is simply a cave which has been cut right through a headland, or it may result from the union of two caves on opposite sides of a headland. See Fig. 34, A and B. If the roof also falls in, the result is a 'stack', as at C, and in Plate XI, A.

Now, the elements of cliff architecture are caves, arches and stacks, and the styles are dependent upon the bedding and jointing of the rocks. The strata may lie horizontally, as in Plate XI, A, or vertically, as at the Needles, in the Isle of Wight. Or they may incline seawards, as in the sketch of Burry

[1] 'Geo' is a two-syllable word of Norse derivation, pronounced with a hard 'g'. Its use as a common word in Britain (for any kind of deep inlet) is confined to Scotland.

Holms (Gower) at the head of this chapter, or shorewards, as in Fig. 36. The various profiles produced in the cliffs by these forms are shown in Fig. 35.

The difference in character between profiles A and B, both in the cliffs and the stacks, is suggestive of the difference between Classical and Gothic architecture. At all events, the horizontal structure and the 'string courses' in A

FIG. 33. A cave formed by the loosening of natural joints in the rocks, and a blow-hole or 'gloup'.

contrast strongly with the pinnacled stack in B. Both these are stable arrangements, but this cannot be said of D. (We pass over C for the moment.)

A thin layer of clay or friable rock in D, which will hold water from surface drainage, is likely to become a slippery slope upon which the upper part of the cliff will eventualy crash to the beach. Such a layer is indicated at *x*, and the profile of the subsequent landslide at E. In this there are two low cliffs, an 'undercliff' and an 'overcliff', forms which are ideally displayed on the south-east coast of the Isle of Wight. The shelf separating the two cliffs is sometimes called an 'overstrand'. A landslip may set back the main cliff-face by several hundred yards, and if of very local occurrence, produces a sort of deep inlet or gorge above the undercliff—one of the many varieties of 'chine'.[1]

The profile at C is, however, stable, and Fig. 36 illustrates the sort of stack this type of cliff produces. In character it is pyramidal, but its slopes suggest a tiled roof rather than an Egyptian tomb. As a roof, it is far superior to the horizontal form shown in Fig. 34. The inclined arch shown at the head of this chapter is similarly well roofed, the bedding of the rocks being as shown in Fig. 35 D, but their uniform hardness precluding the possibility of a landslide.

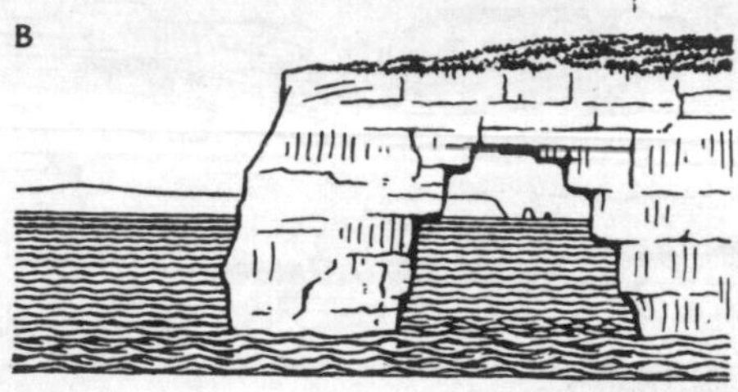

FIG. 34. The relations between the three basic forms of cliff architecture: A, cave; B, arch; C, stack.

The entrances to caves carry out these architectural principles in their general forms also. Caves in horizontal strata are prone to have a classical doorway. If there is no massive lintel, the rocks will fall and the entrance grow till a suitable one is reached—as it has been in the cave in Fig. 33. The ornamentations on such a cliff-face will consist of pediments, dados and cornices, and contrast strongly with the Gothic pinnacles and flying buttresses which decorate cliffs in vertical or inclined strata.

On coasts where the rocks are volcanic, and are not bedded, the architecture defies description. It may suggest the pagodas and minarets of the East, but is as often reminiscent of Norman castles or prehistoric ruins. The exposure of granite cliffs at Land's End to the fury of the Atlantic waves has produced the curious 'castellated' effect shown in Plate X, by accentuating the rectangular joints of the rock, but no forms are too fantastic for volcanic cliffs to assume.

We have noted that the destructive action of the sea may be checked by the formation of a wide enough beach, but that this result sometimes fails by the

[1] However, the local authorities at many coastal resorts have a habit of using the terms 'undercliff', 'overcliff' and 'chine' without attaching any very precise meanings to them; they are used as labels to attract visitors rather than to describe natural formations. A less common use of the word 'chine' is for a ridge of rock resembling an animal's back, but in this usage the word has a different derivation.

wholesale removal of the beach as fast as it forms. We now have to consider the destiny of the migrating beach. What ultimately happens to the shingle

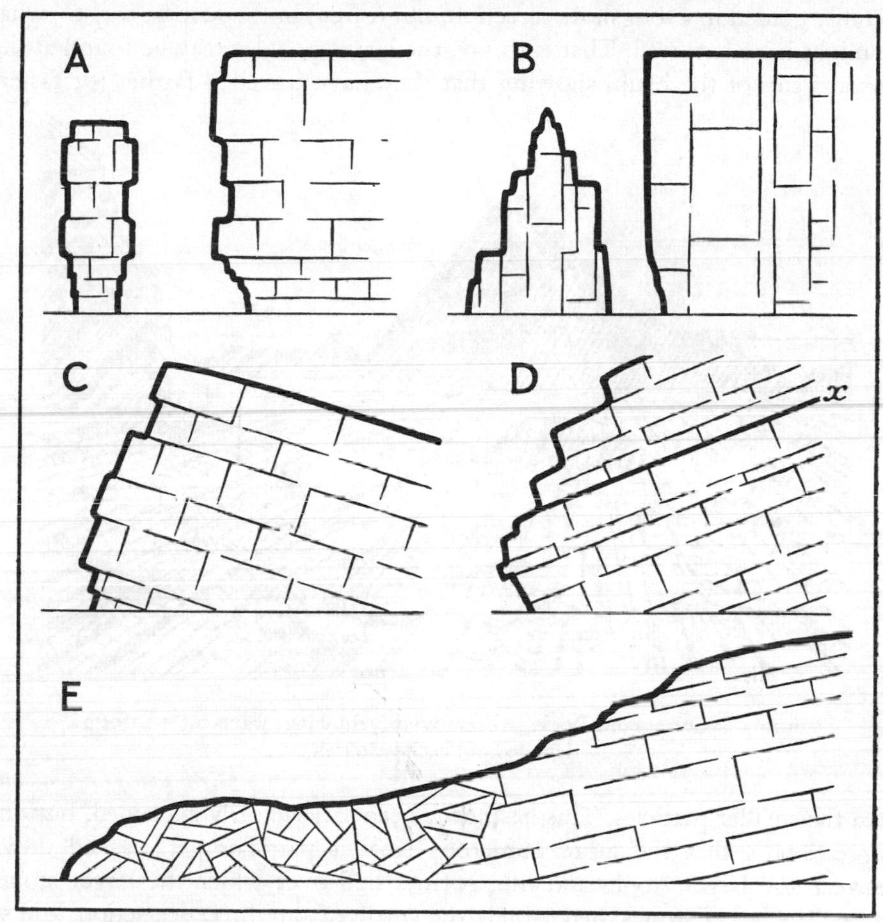

FIG. 35. Profiles of cliffs, illustrating the development of cliff architecture. A, cliff and stack in horizontal strata. B, cliff and stack in vertical strata. C, cliff in strata inclined shorewards. D, cliff in strata inclined seawards. E, landslip, showing undercliff and over-cliff. E may be taken also as a longitudinal section through a chine.

and sand which travel along a shore under the action of oblique waves?

On a comparatively straight coast they may travel for many miles, but sooner or later the shore of a bay will curve round to face the breakers, and then transportation ceases. The migrating material continues to arrive, however, and accumulates in a great bank which may project some distance out to sea. Such a bank is full of interest for the sea-shore rambler.

Perhaps the first thing he notices is the fact that the pebbles on the bank are roughly graded in a longshore direction, but (often) in the reverse way to what he might have expected. That is to say, the larger pebbles may be found at the seaward end of the bank, showing that they have travelled farther (or faster)

FIG. 36. Cormorant Rock, Aberystwyth, showing wave-cut platform denuded of beach-material.

than the smaller particles. This has never been satisfactorily explained, but one suggestion is that the more numerous smaller particles get washed down between the larger stones and thus form a bed over which the larger stones move. The larger stones then protect the smaller from direct sea action, and so finish the race alone.

Again, the rambler on a shingle bank may pick up many strange pebbles—pebbles which could not possibly 'belong' to the locality where they are found. On Chesil Bank (Plate XII), for instance, there are stones which must have come from the cliffs of Devon and Cornwall, while at the Crumbles, Pevensey Bay, the native clay is concealed by a massive shingle bank, all of which is 'derived'. Most abundant here are the flints from Beachy Head, but among them may be found pebbles of chalk and greensand from Eastbourne, of hard sandstones from Devonshire, and of various volcanic rocks which may have travelled all the way from Cornwall.

Some of these stones may have arrived in the very distant past, when the coastline differed from its present form and did not present such obstacles to longshore drifting as Chesil Bank and Southampton Water, and some may have been brought along by currents in deeper water and then been washed up. Many millions of flints have certainly by-passed the Crumbles and have not

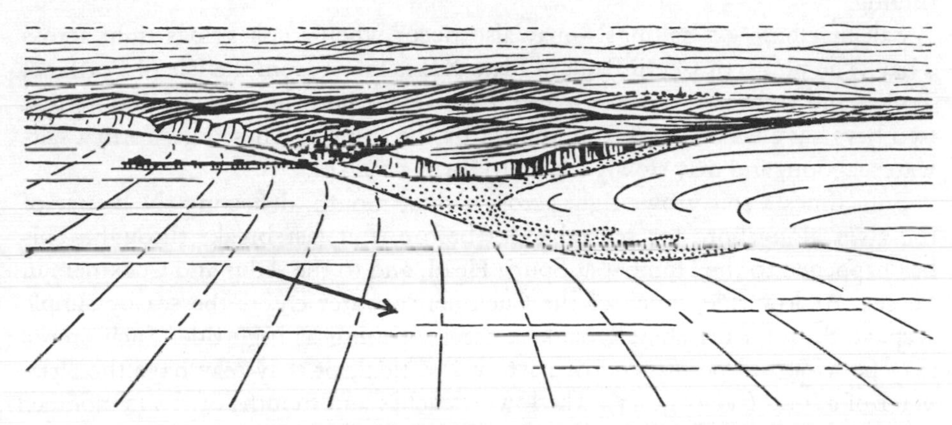

FIG. 37. The formation of a spit by longshore drifting. Note the three horns of the spit, representing old storm beaches.

come to rest till they have reached the even greater shingle bank at Dungeness, which is calculated to have taken about 2,700 years to accumulate. By such means the sea performs work of construction, as well as work of destruction.

When the curve of the shore fails to confront the waves completely, it may slow down transportation of the beach sufficiently to produce a shingle bank of a special form. This is the long 'spit', running out to sea in the way shown in Fig. 37. There is, of course, a limit to the length of such a spit, and when this has been reached the waves sweeping round its outer end give it the shape of a curved horn. In the diagram, the ends of two other horns are shown on the lee shore of the spit, and these represent the ends of storm beaches which happened to terminate the spit in earlier stages of its formation. A good example of such a spit is illustrated in Plate XI, B.

The waves now travel parallel with the arm of the horn, and in its immediate shelter the sea is comparatively calm and still. Mud and sand settle quietly here, and should a river chance to flow into the bay its load of mud would be quickly deposited. It would not be long before the shoals produced broke the surface and began to support salt-loving plants. The area would then rapidly silt up and become a salt marsh with pools of sea-water known as 'salt-pans'. Eventually these, too, would disappear, and a typical salt marsh like that shown in Plate XII, C, would mark the completion of the work. This sort of thing is likely to happen in any quiet inlet fed by sluggish streams, and it was through the silting up of a large shallow inlet that the Fens of East Anglia were formed. The present Wash is all that remains of this inlet, and the silting up is continuing.

Salt marshes—or 'saltings'—may also occur when a spit grows right across a bay. The photo of Chesil Bank in Plate XII is taken from the Isle of Portland. To left and right are open sea, but in the background the reader will note that two bays have been cut off from the sea by the shingle. These now form a salt-water lagoon, and may slowly silt up to form a marsh.

Sometimes a spit grows right across a river-mouth, deflecting the course of the river alongshore for several miles before it at last breaks through. This has happened to the Humber at Spurn Head, and to the Adur and Cuckmere in Sussex. At low tide, much of the Cuckmere's water enters the sea by simple seepage through the shingle bank, a creek opening at high tide. Such creeks may be wide and permanent, or narrow and tidal, or they may have the character of a 'gut' (see page 57). The lower reaches and mouths of rivers modified in this way are called 'pills' in Wales and 'pylls' in Cornwall. The Penard Pill in Gower, illustrated in the sketch at the head of the next chapter, is an excellent example. If the tract of brackish water behind the spit is extensive, it may be called a 'run' or a 'fleet' (a term used inland for a large shallow lake), and the general type of feature produced is idealized in Fig. 41 at F, which emphasizes the characteristic smoothness of a coast subject to extensive longshore drifting.

A sand bank may grow across a bay below the level of the water, and then it is called a 'bar', and may be a danger to shipping. Such submerged banks cannot be due to the transporting of beach material by breaking waves, but may be caused by either of two other processes.[1] The first of these is illustrated in Fig. 38.

The reader may remember what we said of the outer slope of the wave-built terrace (Fig. 31 at T), that it settles down at a definite 'angle of rest'. If this is altered through any cause, the sea gets to work to restore it. If the slope becomes too steep, the sea will soon rake off the upper layers and distribute them farther down. If the slope becomes too shallow, the sea will wash the lower layers (A in Fig. 38) up to the top of the terrace (B), and they will settle there to form

[1] We except a third process, responsible for the formation of bars across the mouths of all mature rivers. This process, being chiefly river-work, is described in the next chapter.

an off-shore bar. Disturbances able to cause these changes include exceptionally heavy storms, elevation of the sea-floor, and tidal currents.

The reader is of course familiar with some of the effects of tides, and knows that they are caused by the gravitational attraction of the moon. High tides occur at approximately every twelve and a half hours, and they are exceptionally high during periods of full and new moon, when they are called 'spring' tides.

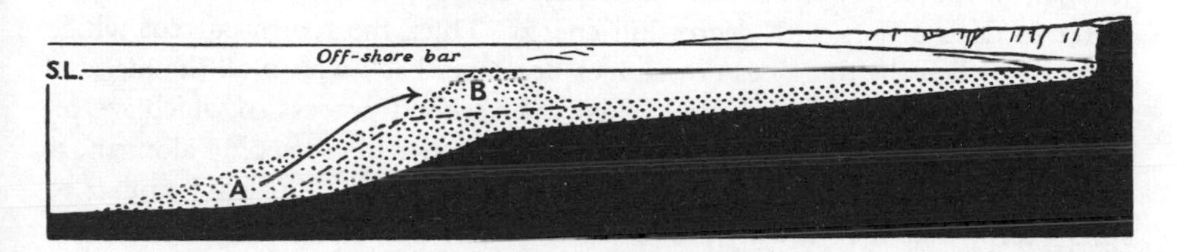

Fig. 38. The formation of an off-shore bar or shoal by wave-action. See the text.

The lower tides of the periods of 'half' moon (first and last quarters) are called 'neap' tides. It should be stated, however, that the moon is not necessarily above the horizon at the *time* of a high tide. The full explanation of the tides is very complex, and falls outside the scope of this book, but the occurrence of tidal *currents* is a matter demanding our attention.

The rise in the sea-level at high tide is due to the arrival of the crest of the tidal wave,[1] and as with all waves this happens without any extensive transportation of water. We make a digression to illustrate this. Throw a cork on to the sea, and as the waves pass beneath it it will merely bob up and down, which sufficiently demonstrates that it is not the water itself which travels along, but only its *shape*. The waves which may sometimes be seen to travel over a field of corn in a fresh breeze are precisely similar.

Nevertheless, the rise in the level of the sea at high tide *results* in a flow of water wherever the sea becomes sufficiently narrow or shallow, just as the arrival of a wave at a shore results in a flow of water (swash) up the beach. Flows due to the tides are called tidal currents, and they occur (for example) in the English Channel, the Irish Sea, and in the mouths of rivers. They may increase the natural height of the tides from a few feet to twenty feet or more, a common difference in level between high and low tides on British shores being about sixteen feet. The tidal current in the English Channel travels

[1] 'Tidal wave'—a term much abused in journalism, where it is often employed to denote a cataclysmic invasion of the land by the sea, a phenomenon which seldom has anything to do with the tides. Such a misuse of terms is to be deplored. The tidal wave is an almost imperceptible rise (of a few feet) in the level of the oceans, occurring every twelve hours twenty-six minutes.

at about two miles per hour. That in the narrower Bristol Channel travels at ten miles per hour, and when it reaches the mouth of the Severn the water advances as a breaking wave from six to nine feet high, known as the Severn 'bore'.

The effect of tidal currents is to scour the sea-floor and wash shingle and sand shorewards—where it may accumulate as an off-shore bar. Transport from deep to shallow water proceeds with increasing energy, while that from shallow water to deep occurs with decreasing energy. Thus, the return current which flows out when the tide goes down does not carry back with it all the material which the rising tide brought in.[1] This is the second process to which we referred above, and allied to it is the effect of tidal currents sweeping alongshore and thus causing off-shore drifting. Such currents build long bars similar to spits except that they usually remain submerged.

A tidal current flows through the Strait of Dover from the North Sea at about the same time that the English Channel current reaches Folkestone. The meeting of the two currents may contribute to the notorious roughness of the sea in the Strait, and it certainly leads to the accumulation of sand and shingle transported from both directions. This has formed shoals in the Channel off Folkestone, and is believed to be partly responsible for the enormous accumulation of beach-material at Dungeness.

When the surface of a sandy bar or spit stands at about high tide level, it becomes very dangerous. At low tide the surface sands are dry and firm, for their constituent grains are held in place by their own weight and are unable to slide easily over each other. But as the tide rises the water flows between the grains and reduces their effective weight by buoyancy, at the same time acting as a lubricant. The sands then yield to the slightest pressure, rapidly swallowing up anything placed on them, and are called 'shifting sands', or 'quicksands'.

The repeated piling up of water along a coast, both by wind-generated waves and tidal currents, is compensated by deeper outflowing currents known as the 'undertow'. The surplus water returns to the ocean in this way, but it does so in deep channels where it is unimpeded by incoming water. The undertow is exceedingly dangerous to bathers, who should never attempt deep diving on unfamiliar precipitous coasts.

The occurrence of spits and bars across the mouths of bays affords considerable protection to the coastline proper. The waves often break in the shallow water over the bar, and their energy is expended long before they reach the beach. Similar protection is sometimes offered by a reef of rocks due to the

[1] The reverse effect which we noticed as due to wave action on a beach is operative only where the slope is steep enough for gravity to override other forces.

geological structure of the coast. An example is given in Fig. 39, where a sloping bed of hard rock outcrops some distance from the shore. A line of rocks across the bay encloses a 'lagoon', and a particularly large rock may be selected as a suitable foundation for a lighthouse. Conditions similar to those shown in the diagram occur at Beachy Head, where a hard sandstone shelf emerges from beneath the chalk cliffs.

FIG. 39. A reef caused by an outcrop of hard rocks below high-water level.

On all coasts where the rocks vary in hardness the sea naturally takes most rapid toll of the softer formations. Every rocky headland represents a particularly resistant mass of rock. Just as the waves at the foot of a cliff find out the weak places and there excavate caves, so, on a bigger scale, they find out the softer stretches of coastline and there carve out bays and other such 'inlets of erosion'.

Now, the occurrence on a coastline of rocks of varying hardness depends upon the geological structure of the land. This may be very complicated, and in no two places will it be found to be precisely the same, but we may safely say that in any *small* area of land where the rocks vary at all, it is usually possible to detect alternate belts of hard and soft strata (or at least bands of weakness due to excessive jointing), and the general direction in which such bands run is called the 'grain' of the landscape. The character of a coast often depends on whether this grain runs at a sharp angle to, or parallel with, the shore.

Fig. 40 is an idealized map of a stretch of land in which the grain runs in the direction of the black bands (which represent the hardest rock). We suppose the waves to approach the land end on to the grain on the left side of the map (at A), but at right-angles to it on the right side (at B). The two kinds of coast produced are known, respectively, as the Atlantic and Pacific types, because they are developed characteristically on parts of the shores of those oceans. They represent extremes between which innumerable compromises are possible.

At A, the sea has made bays for itself in the softer belts of rock, and the harder belts have formed headlands with stacks (as at Reskajeage Cliffs in Plate XIII). When such bays have reached a certain depth they enjoy some

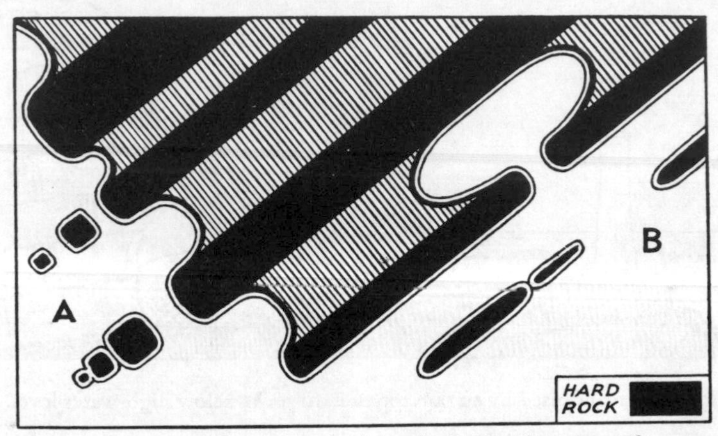

FIG. 40. Diagram illustrating A, Atlantic, B, Pacific, types of coast. In both cases the sea is imagined to attack the coast at right-angles. Compare the forms of the stacks and bays.

protection from the headlands and the work of excavation slows down. When the excavation is proceeding no more rapidly than the destruction of the headlands, the bays have arrived at their maximum development, and the coast continues to recede regularly without change of outline.

But this state of affairs does not last long, for now that the bays are no longer running inland away from the headlands, they form convenient repositories for the debris of hard shingle and sand resulting from the destruction of the headlands, and so they now begin to fill up again. The tables are turned, and the coast begins to lose its indentations. Thus, a mature coast of this kind finishes up as it began before the sea started its attack.

The coast continues to recede, however, the bays and headlands now disappearing together, and the process goes on till the original bays (with their derived infillings) have been obliterated. Then the whole cycle starts over again, beginning with the formation of new bays in the newly-exposed belts of soft rock.

Coasts of this type, in various stages of the cycle, occur in south-west England, Pembrokeshire, North Wales, and on other westward-facing seaboards, and they are typified in Fig. 41 at A. But the rambler who desires to be sure that any particular piece of coast is a genuine example is advised to consult his geological map, where the grain of the coast may usually be plainly discerned without any special knowledge of geology.

Of the other type of 'coast of erosion'—the Pacific type idealized in Figs. 40

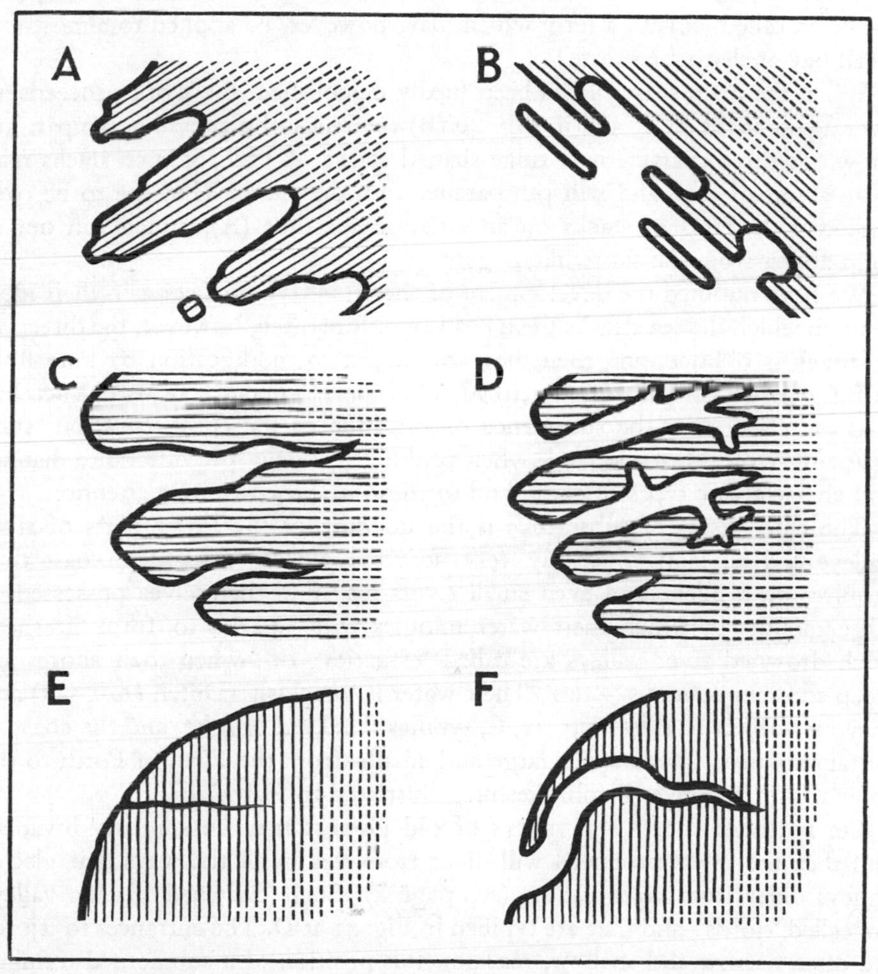

FIG. 41. 'Profiles' (strictly, formalized maps) of coastlines. A, Atlantic type. B, Pacific type. C, submerged coast with drowned river-valleys or rias. D, submerged coast with drowned glacier-valleys or fjords. E, elevated coast exposing plain of marine denudation. F, coast smoothed by longshore drifting.

and 41 at B—there is only one really good example in Britain, and that is a short stretch of the coast of Dorsetshire in the neighbourhood of Lulworth Cove (Plate XIII). In such coasts the sea attacks the protecting rampart of hard rock, and when once this has been breached it makes short work of the softer rock behind. It cuts this back to the next rampart, and at the same time works sideways so as to extend its bay behind the main sea-wall. The circular or elliptical bays produced form sheltered anchorages for small vessels, and are often called 'coves', a term which may, however, be applied to almost any small bay of sharp curvature.[1]

When the main sea-wall has been finally demolished, the work proceeds all over again at the next, and in Fig. 40 (B) the relics of a previous rampart are shown as three characteristic ridge-shaped stacks. A train of such stacks may form a sort of reef, and will run parallel with the shore. They are to be contrasted with trains of stacks on an Atlantic coastline (A), which run out at right-angles from the shore like fingers.

We have outlined the development of these two types of coast in their ideal state, in which the sea attacks them head-on. More often, however, the direction of attack is oblique, and then they are subject to modification by longshore drifting, as we have already described. Their development may also be accelerated or retarded by the subsidence or elevation of the coast itself, but such major movements of the land, when prolonged, finally provide quite distinct and characteristic types of coast, and to these we now turn our attention.

The chief result of subsidence is the flooding of the lower parts of river valleys and all land which lay very near the old sea-level. The coast thus acquires deep inlets, and even small rivers may find themselves possessed of large mouths in which their water mingles with the sea to form 'freshes'. Such drowned river valleys are called 'estuaries', or—when their shores are steep and mountainous—'rias'. Their water is 'brackish' (Dutch *brak*, salt) and they are subject to tides. Fig. 41, C, typifies this kind of inlet, and the coast of Britain abounds in examples, large and small—from the Firth of Forth to the river mouth at Solva, Pembrokeshire, illustrated in Plate XII.

On northern shores the valleys of old glaciers may be similarly invaded, and then the inlets produced will differ from rias in all the ways that glacier valleys differ from river valleys (see page 4). Such drowned glacier valleys are called 'fjords', and they are typified in Fig. 41 at D. The entrances to fjords are often narrow and shallow, marking this position of a submerged terminal moraine. As you sail up them they open out and the water becomes deeper,

[1] The word is derived from the Old English *cofa*, a chamber, and is applied inland to a cave or hollow in a mountain-side, *e.g.*, Malham Cove, a hollow in the limestone escarpment shown in Plate V.

but their sides remain precipitous. The tributary inlets at the heads of fjords often make the rectangular pattern shown in the diagram, but the reason for this is unknown.

Where the submerged land is flat, a subsidence of only a few feet may lead to the flooding of a vast area with shallow sea-water. Low hills which may have been hardly noticeable on the plain now stand out as islands. The waves roll in rapidly from the open sea and tidal currents are likely to be strong. Where they rush through narrow entrances they are often called 'races',[1] and they may scour out deep channels through which mud and sand from the main basin are raked out to form off-shore bars and shoals. These deep, narrow channels are sometimes known as 'guts' (a term used for any narrow watercourse).

At the mouths of rivers silting up begins, and the floor of the basin gradually develops a very uneven surface. The silted-up shallows are separated by channels and hollows scoured out by the tide races, and if the land should rise again the area would become a patchwork of marshes, shingle banks and lakes. The sea-water would eventually drain out, and be replaced by river-water, and the general appearance of the landscape would be that of the Norfolk Broads, illustrated in Plate XIV. We have, in fact, outlined one suggested explanation of this remarkable area, the detailed history of which has never been thoroughly investigated.

This brings us to the general characteristics of coastlines undergoing gradual elevation. They are typically smooth, as in Fig. 41, E, for the land which is emerging has already suffered the levelling and planing action of the sea. If the reader will glance at the top two diagrams in Fig. 42, he will recall what we have already said about the levelling of a wave-cut platform and the recession inland of the cliffs (page 41). It is this platform which first emerges as the land rises, and it will be unbroken except at the mouths of rivers or where it carries old stacks.

When the platform has been elevated to above high-water mark it will become a 'raised beach', and the sea will begin to form a new cliff on the new shore. This is indicated in the third diagram (Fig. 42), while we give a photograph of a raised beach in Plate XVII. The raised beach is terminated shorewards by an inland cliff, and the rambler will find many such examples round the British coast. Many of our seaside towns, with their long, straight esplanades, are built on raised beaches, and even when these have become hidden beneath other deposits (such as boulder clay, soil, turf and houses), the old cliff line is often visible behind the town as a range of low hills. When a raised beach is so

[1] 'Tide race'—any swift tidal current of local occurrence. Tide races often occur over submerged rocks off a headland.

extensive as to warrant a more imposing name, it is called a 'plain of marine denudation'. This is shown in the last diagram in Fig. 42, but its significance for the rambler will be discussed in Chapter VI.

We have considered beaches at sea-level, and beaches raised well above sea-level. It remains to look at a rising beach which is still continuous with the

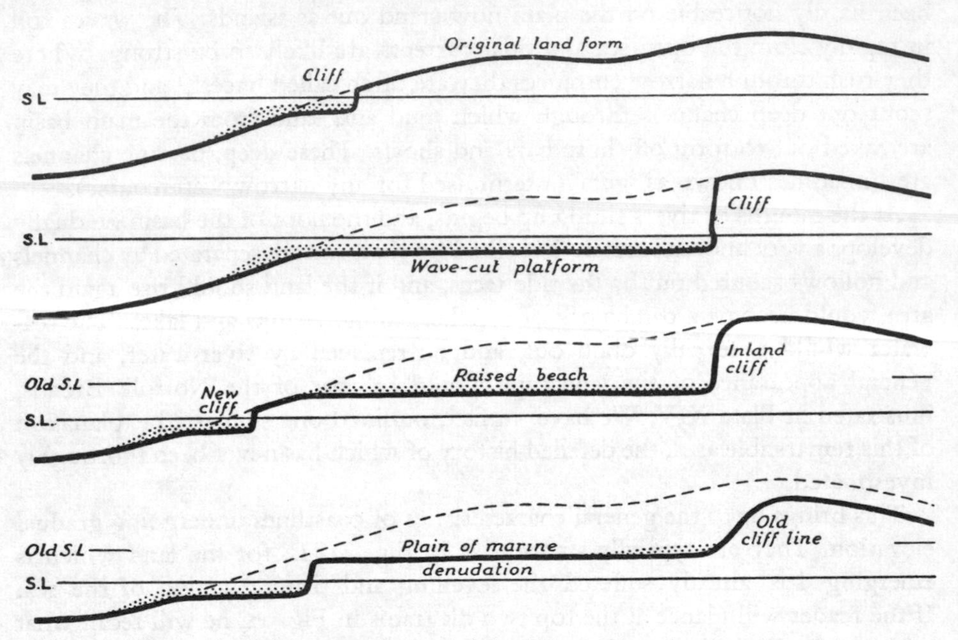

FIG. 42. The work of the sea in planing off the hills cut short by elevation of the land, thus producing a raised beach. S.L., sea-level.

foreshore. It may simply be a wide stretch of shingle at the foot of the cliffs (round the headlands as well as in the bays), but if it has been long beneath the sea it is more likely to be a wide stretch of sand.

Since this sand is no longer wetted daily by the sea, it is at the mercy of the wind and is seldom allowed to remain level. In a gale the sand may be blown up in great clouds, and at every breeze that blows the surface grains are trundled along—until they are stopped by a boulder or a tuft of seashore grass. When *this* happens a train of events is started which has far-reaching effects.

The boulder or tuft forms the nucleus of a little heap of sand. The breeze continues to blow, and fresh sand grains are rolled up its windward side, tumble over the top, and find shelter in its lee. Here they are safe, and so the sand begins to accumulate and the heap to grow. It may reach a height of several feet, but as soon as it has achieved a noticeable size it is called a 'dune'. The windward slope of a dune is gradual, but the other slope—the 'slip-face'—is steep. It assumes the steepest angle at which a heap of loose sand will remain at rest, and this is usually about 33 degrees. See Fig. 43, where the large arrow shows the direction of the prevailing wind.

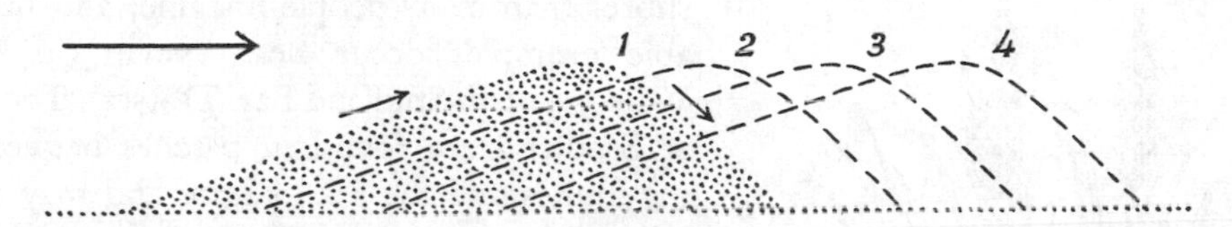

FIG. 43. How a sand-dune travels. The broken lines show the dune in four successive positions, the small arrows indicating the movement of the sand-grains. The large arrow shows the direction of the wind.

Once a dune is formed it begins to travel. The sand grains are continually being blown up one face and tumbling down the other (as shown by the small arrows), and in the diagram four successive positions of the dune are numbered in order. Presently the dune has left the boulder which first caused it behind, and then another dune will form in the same way. Thus it is common to find dunes travelling inland in serried ranks till they overwhelm vegetation and farmland once at a safe distance from the shore. (See Plate XIV, B.)

In some districts the advance of the dunes has been checked by sowing marram grass (Figs. 44 and 82) and other such plants in the sand. These grow rapidly, keeping pace with the accumulation of sand, and their roots serve to bind the sand grains together. Their foliage also acts as a windbreak, and hinders the transport of sand grains along the surface. Dunes in such regions may become turfed completely over, and thus afford permanent protection to the hinterland.

The action of the sea on sand grains is to make them round. The subsequent action of the wind is to polish them. When the rounded grains consist of quartz and are free from mineral impurities (such as the rusts of iron) they are called 'silver sand', and may be used in making glass. This sand is of no use to builders, however, who require the 'sharp sand' of river beds for making good cement. In a sharp sand many of the angles remain on the grains, and when compacted these interlock and form a firm mass, but worn or polished sands have no such cohesion. But our business here is with sandy shores, and further distinctions between the different types of sand will be found in Chapter VI.

Somewhere between the extreme of sharp sands and silver sands come sand grains which will move over one another in minute jerks, and if they are of uniform size they may give rise to a periodic vibration when disturbed. They are called 'singing sands', and as you walk over them they emit a noise which varies from a shriek to a roar.

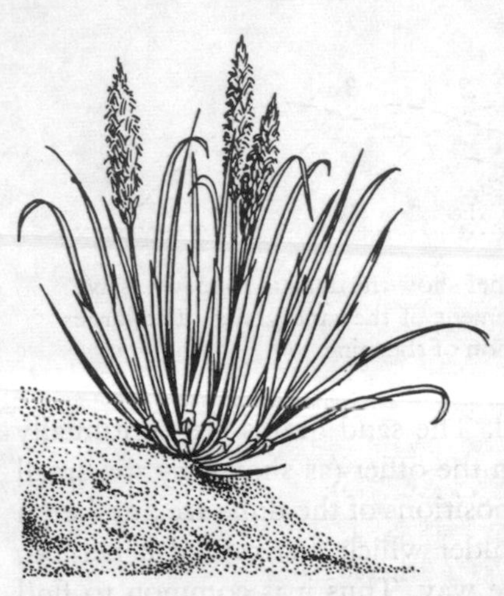

FIG. 44. A tuft of marram grass, sown to prevent the shifting of sand by the wind.

Singing sands are more common on our shores than many people imagine, and notable examples occur near Nevin (in N. Wales) and in Studland Bay (Dorset). Those at Studland are found in patches between the dunes and the sea margin, and may be 'played' by drawing a stick across the surface. Samples of musical sands will also sing if placed in a bowl and their surface struck with the handle of a wood spoon.

We cannot leave the sandy shores without a reference to ripple marks. These are caused by the to-and-fro motion of the water, and when freshly made have sharp crests and rounded hollows. Similar ripple marks may also be found on the windward slopes of dunes, where they have been caused by wind eddies, but these are usually soon destroyed again.

It remains to point out that a wide sandy shore is to a large extent immune from attack by the sea. If there are no longshore currents to remove the sand, and no subsidence of the land to submerge it, it holds the sea at bay. The sea may rake it and pound it as long as it pleases—it can do no more than grind it a little finer, and carry off the dust in infinitesimal quantities. The sand represents the final stage in the demolition of those 'high brick walls' with which we began this chapter. When a wall has been thus utterly knocked down, you can knock it down no farther.

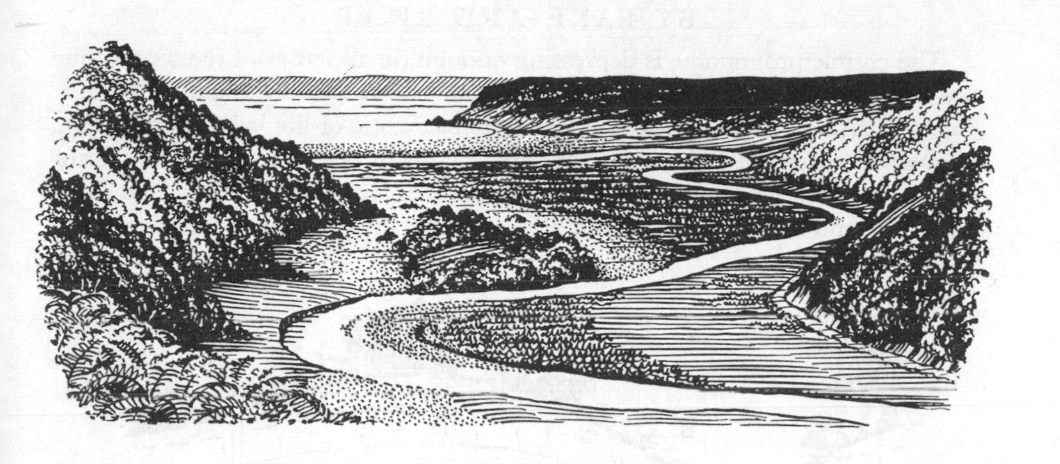

CHAPTER IV

By Lake and River

If there is a Genius behind inanimate nature, controlling the forms and processes of gross matter, he is surely the archetype of all demolition agents, an uncompromising Leveller of the First Order. At his command the mountains are laid low, the cliffs crumble away, and their very stones are ground to formless mud for the filling and obliteration of the sea. His whole object is to reduce the earth to a smooth sphere of featureless dust, to be encased—finally—in a glassy film of ice, and none can deny that he is a tireless and relentless worker.

But there is some fire in the old planet yet, and from time to time the Earth rebels against her fate, thrusting up new mountains to replace the old, and deepening her oceans that they may not be entirely choked with sediment. On the whole her efforts grow feebler with the passage of time, and science knows no reason why the Arch-Leveller should not have his way in the end. Apart from accidents, he should achieve something like it in about twenty thousand million years' time.

The reader may have begun to wonder what this has to do with the appreciation of lake and river scenery, but before this can be clearly stated we must make one more general observation. The fell course of mechanical evolution accomplishes aesthetic as well as material levelling, and if the earth should seem beautiful as a uniform, glassy sphere—fit to hang upon some monstrous Christmas-tree of the gods—it would yet be a poor exchange for the manifold beauties it exhibits in its present imperfect state. Why, we have glass globes enough already, for those who like them.

The cosmic programme is depressing enough (in all senses of the word), but we have the antidote. It is true that inanimate nature runs inevitably downhill, but the earth is inhabited, and the great characteristic of life is its ability—nay, *compulsion*—to run *up*hill, to defy gravity, to thwart destruction, to complicate nature, to raise levels, to preserve idiosyncrasies, to maintain form and individuality, and to multiply beauties. If beauty has any dynamic significance, it is

FIG. 45. Wells sunk into a hill. W, water-table. X, intermittent well. Y, permanent well. B, bourne flowing from intermittent spring.

surely of this struggle against disorganization which is the basic function of life. It is by no mere accident that the proportion of beauty in a landscape is a measure of the failure of the Arch-Leveller to accomplish his purpose. It is not by chance that the earth appears most beautiful when it seems actively to *resist* that remorseless grinding down of its surface.

Of passive resistance, by mountain and crag, we have already written,[1] and we have told of the rearguard manoeuvres of the shore. But the illusion of active resistance is most often to be seen in the ever-changing features of river scenery, which is the subject of our present chapter. The very spirit of river scenery is one of gentle refusal to bow to the inevitable. Water must, perforce, run downhill according to the Arch-Leveller's command, but it does so under protest, mischievously blocking its own course with the sediments entrusted to

[1] The undeniable beauty of fen and marsh is also passive in character, and is by no means to be credited to the cunning of the Arch-Leveller. The beauty of a marsh does not lie in the deposition of its mud, but in the fact that some clear water at least has won the struggle for independent existence. Or, if no water be visible, there must be the rising beauty of vegetation to redeem an otherwise appalling wilderness of mire. The mere *flatness* of a marsh does no more than cast a sombre tone over whatever other beauties it displays, and may be effective in this negative way even when the beauties are chiefly borrowed from the activity and variety in the sky.

Similarly, the sense of rest and peace engendered by contemplation of a fertile plain does not come from the flatness of the plain, but from the recumbence on it of living things. The mountains and crags may be bare, and all the more beautiful therefor, but strip a marsh or a wide plain of its coverings, and you will have nothing but the desolation of a desert.

its care. It may even travel *up*hill on occasion, sweeping smoothly over the back of some boulder it was its duty to undermine, as if by some mutual pact of resistance.

Its orders are to proceed by the shortest possible route to the sea, but it wanders from the straight path at the first opportunity, and delays its journey in a maze of leisurely windings before it finally and disdainfully accepts its

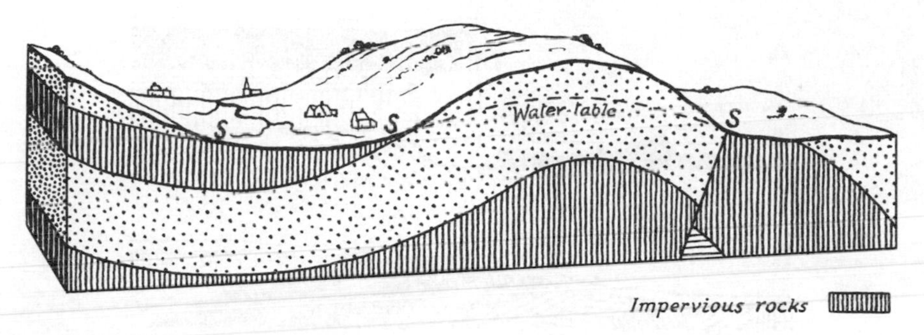

FIG. 46. Causes of springs. Note the occurrence of farmsteads along the lines of springs.

destiny. It plays pirate to neighbouring streams, robbing them of their water and hindering their work, leaving dry valleys among the mountain-tops for the Arch-Leveller to rub out if he can. For the geologist, a river is just another agent of erosion and deposition, but for the rambler its interest lies in its capricious behaviour—in the odd ways in which it defeats its apparent purpose, or goes obliquely at it to produce quaint new irregularities in place of those it was foredoomed to efface.

In order to describe and explain the vagaries likely to be met along the course of a river it will be necessary first to outline the story of an ideal stream. This story begins logically—and geologically—with the formation of springs, and if the rambler has once understood the structures which are productive of springs he may often use his observations of springs to account—geologically—for many other curious features of a landscape.

Most of the rocks at the surface of the earth are able to hold water. They may do this in the cracks and joints which they contain, or they may be actually porous, and hold water in the interstices between their constituent grains. The fissures are the more important from the point of view of water-supply, and as these occur in almost all rock formations, places beneath which there is never any underground water at all are rare. Such water is derived almost entirely from rainfall, and in regions where percolation underground is easy the water may sink to very great depths and for all practical purposes be inaccessible. But such loss may be hindered in one of two ways.

A layer of clay or other truly impervious rock may underlie the surface formation and hold the water in check, or the cracks and fissures may grow smaller or less frequent with increasing depth, so that the leakage downward is less than the supply from above. In either case there is a level in the rocks

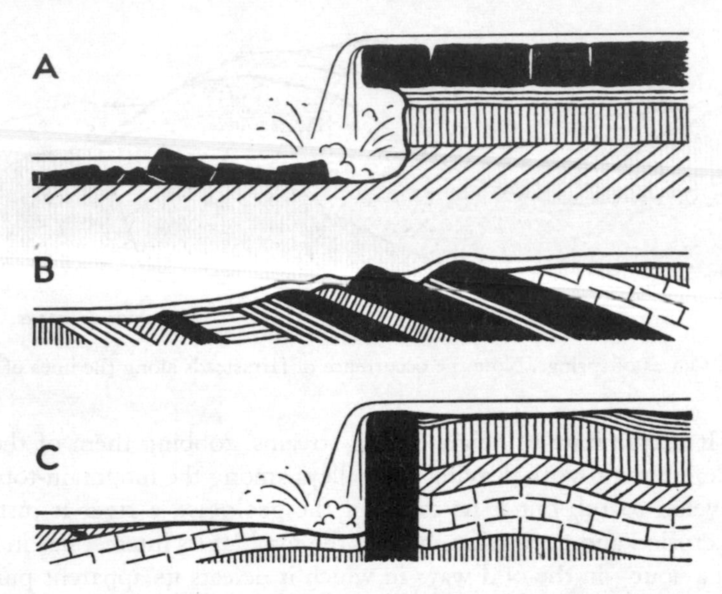

FIG. 47. A, waterfall resulting when hard rock overlies softer rock. B, cataract caused by outcropping of hard rock in bed of stream. C, waterfall due to a dyke of igneous rock running athwart the bed of the stream.

below which they are permanently saturated, and a higher level to which the saturation reaches during the wet season. Such levels are called 'water-tables', but the term is hardly appropriate because they are seldom as level as a table. The surface of a water-table is generally a milder version of the surface of the land above it, examples being shown at W in Fig. 45, and in Fig. 46.

We might point to this refusal of the water to maintain a level surface as the first manifestation of that rebelliousness which we have already noted, but while such picturesque fancies are fit enough in aesthetic discussion the time has once more come to 'cut out the poetry'. If we are not to mislead, we must observe the proprieties. It must suffice here to note that water-tables represent a nice balance between the rainfall, the speed of percolation downward, and the degree of evaporation from the surface. In any small area the depth at which saturation becomes possible is fairly uniform, and therefore the surface of the water-table tends to echo the surface of the land.

In Fig. 45 the rocks are permanently saturated below the water-table W, which means that at this level evaporation has no effect, and replenishments of rain invariably arrive before there is any appreciable loss by drainage. Thus, the well at Y will always contain water, but the well at X is sometimes dry.

FIG. 48. Gorge caused by the migration of a waterfall upstream.

In wet seasons the water-table may rise to the broken line, when X will be found to contain water, and at such times a spring will gush out at B, where the raised water-table meets the surface. Such springs are described as 'intermittent', because they flow only in wet weather, and the temporary streams which flow from them are generally called 'bournes', though in Kent they are known as 'nailbournes', in Wiltshire as 'winterbournes', in Hampshire as 'lavants', and in the northern counties as 'gypseys'.

Now, it sometimes happens that the *permanent* water-table meets the surface near the foot of a hill, as at *S* in the centre of Fig. 46, and in such cases there is a line of 'permanent' springs marking the edge of the water-table, and flowing from them is a series of permanent streams. The rambler may often be able to trace the course of a 'spring line' along a valley, by the string of farms or hamlets which have sprung up to benefit from a pure water-supply obtained without the labour of digging wells.

Spring lines also occur where a layer of impervious rock forces the accumulating water out at the surface (as on the left of Fig. 46), or where a fault obstructs its percolation downward (as on the right). There are many more complex

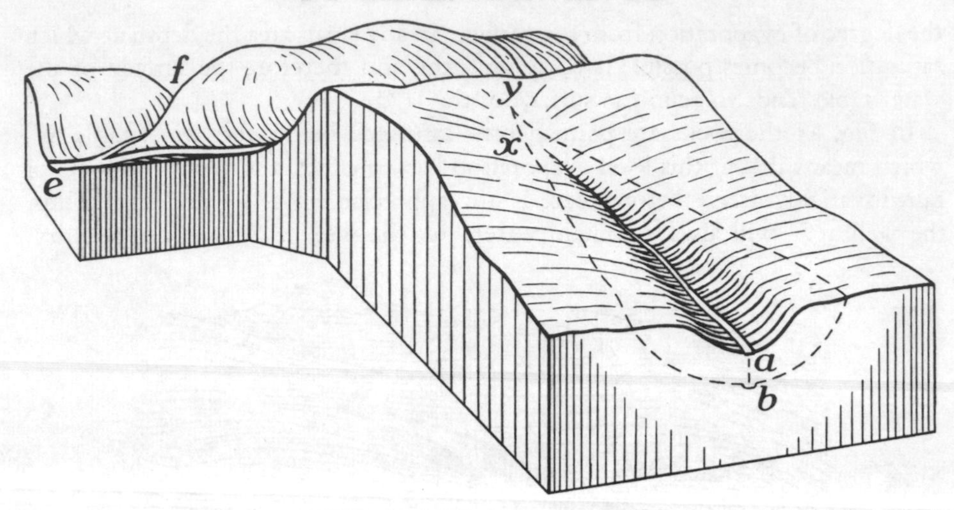

FIG. 49. River-capture—first stage. The broken line shows the growth of the valley of the river at *a*. See the text.

causes of springs, but our examples illustrate the three principal types which occur as the sources of rivers.[1] Since the waters of any considerable river are derived from the streams flowing from many springs, its source must be sought among the mountains, where water-tables frequently break the surface and supplies are plentiful. It is to the mountains, therefore, that we now turn our attention.

No river rises on the *top* of a mountain, but the first springs may appear a few hundred feet below the summit and the first few miles of the stream are characterized by a more or less precipitous descent. This is known as the 'torrent tract' of the river (see Fig. 52, A), and because the water falls swiftly it rapidly cuts for itself a fairly straight, steep-sided valley (see Fig. 2, A), which may even become a gorge (Fig. 2, E). Down-cutting proceeds apace, as we described in Chapter I (page 3), and waterfalls may frequently occur even if the mountain-slopes themselves are not particularly precipitous.

Any bed of exceptionally hard rock running athwart the bed of a stream may produce a waterfall or a rapid, but (if we except irregular bosses of volcanic rock) such beds must lie in one of three ways. If they are not horizontal, they must be either diagonal or vertical. There is no other geometrical alternative. The three types of waterfall produced are illustrated in Fig. 47, and it should be

[1] Artificial springs may sometimes be made by boring a hole through impervious strata so as to tap water-bearing rocks below. The water in these rocks may be under sufficient natural pressure to rise to the surface, or even to spout forth like a fountain. Such springs are called 'artesian wells'.

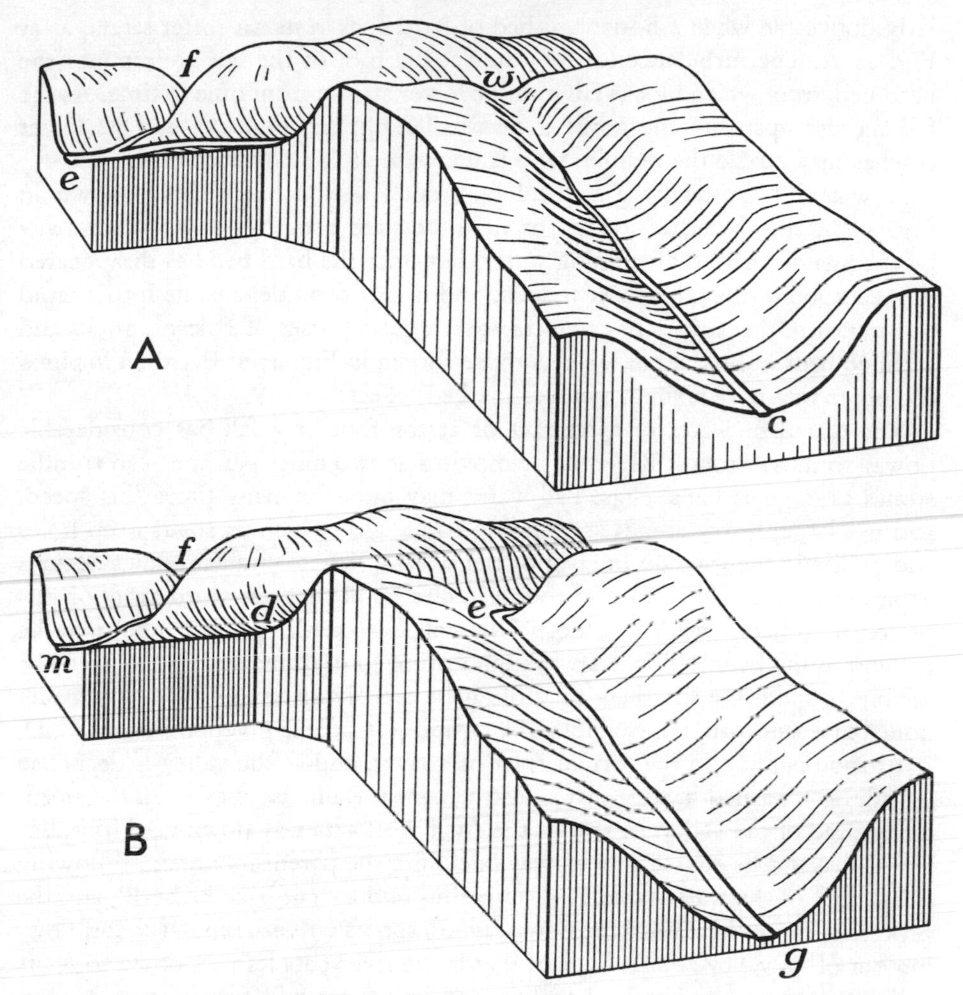

FIG. 50. River-capture—second and third stages. At A, the breaching of the watershed between the two rivers has begun at *w*. At B, the capture of the slower stream is accomplished.

pointed out that the beds of hard rock, which are shown in solid black, *may* be volcanic sills or dykes (see Fig. 29). The sudden drop of level at a waterfall usually means that for some distance below it the river flows through a gorge (Fig. 2, D), the cutting of which is due to the exceptional force of the falling water.[1] (See Plate XV, D.)

All waterfalls gradually migrate upstream, and the evidence for this is particu-

[1] The northern name 'force' for a waterfall is, however, from the Icelandic *foss*, waterfall.

larly noticeable when a horizontal bed of hard rock rests on softer strata, as at Fig. 47 A. The turbulence of the water at the foot of the fall undermines the hard bed, from which blocks fall into the lower stream from time to time. As the fall recedes upstream the gorge grows in length (see Fig. 48), and its lower reaches may puzzle the rambler who is unaware of the existence of the fall.

A waterfall caused by a vertical bed, such as the basalt dyke shown in Fig. 47 C, travels more slowly, for here the hard rock has to be worn away by the unaided action of running water, but once the hard bed has disappeared the recession of the fall proceeds apace and it may soon degenerate into a rapid or cataract. Other causes of cataracts are irregular bosses of volcanic rocks and inclined beds of hard strata such as those shown in Fig. 47 at B. Strata inclined the other way have a similar (if less marked) effect.

The turbulent water of a cataract or at the foot of a fall has considerable power to move stones. River-water moving at two miles per hour can trundle stones as large as hens' eggs. Fall-water may move at many times this speed, and use large, heavy stones as grinding tools with which to scour deep holes and gullies in the rock on the bed of the stream. Where circular eddies occur a group of stones may be carried round in circles till they are worn away or displaced by others, and here a deep hole called a 'kettle' or 'pot-hole' may be ground in the bedrock. It is always interesting to examine such holes, and the pebbles responsible for them may often be seen lying within like eggs being boiled in a saucepan. An example of a typical pot-hole is given in Plate XV, D.

Erosion is rapid in the torrent tract of a river, and as the valley is deepened its sides get washed in so that it is also widened. Rain also washes in the steepening head of the valley, so that as the river works its way downward its valley lengthens, and its source cuts its way back into the parent mountain, following the surface of the water-table. A river is thus said to 'cut back its head', and the process is called 'headward erosion'. Fig. 49 shows a river rising at *x* and flowing out of its valley at *a*. It is plain that if the river cuts its way down to *b*, its valley will spread to the broken line and its source will recede from *x* to *y*. A river may in this manner cut its way back right through a mountain range, and invade the valley of a neighbouring river, such as that at *e*.

The chief condition necessary for this to happen is simply that the stream *a* should be cutting its way downward more rapidly than stream *e*, and this might be the case if either the gradient (slope) of *a* were steeper than that of *e*, or if the rocks beneath *a* were softer than those beneath *e*. It is not at all necessary for *a* to be the bigger river, and in point of fact *e* is more likely to become a victim if it is larger than *a*, for then it will probably be the slower stream.

The half-way stage of the process is shown in Fig. 50 A, where the valley has become deepened to *c* and lengthened sufficiently to cause a depression in the dividing range at *w*. A depression of this sort is called a 'saddle', 'col', or 'wind-gap', the terms applying to the scenic form whether caused in this manner or by some other process.[1]

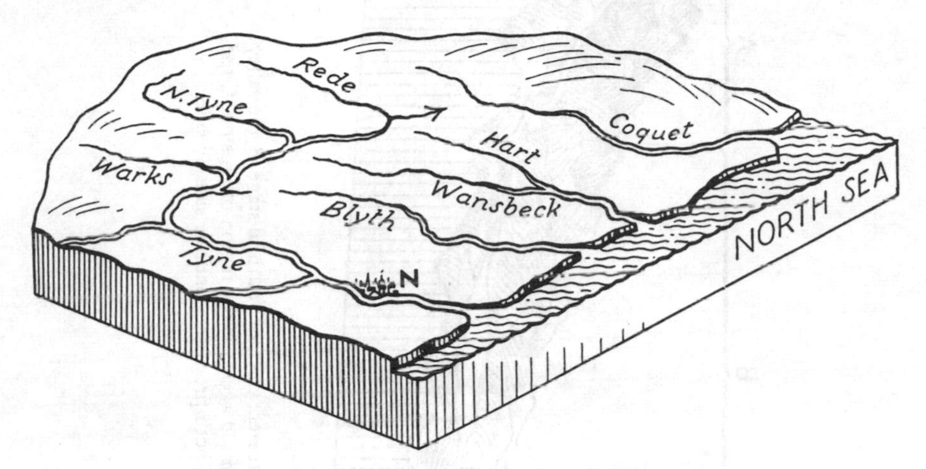

FIG. 51. Block diagram of part of Northumberland, showing examples of river-capture by the river Tyne. N, Newcastle.

The final stage is shown in Fig. 50 B, where the valley has been lowered to *g* and lengthened so as to breach the range completely. The head-waters of *e* now forsake their old course and flow down the deeper valley, the angle at *e* being called the 'elbow of capture'. The old valley of *e* has become a 'dry valley' for the stretch marked *d*, but lower down it is still occupied by the small tributary stream *f*. This little river now flows (from *m* onwards) in a valley very much too big for it, and it is therefore called a 'misfit' or 'underfit'. The whole process is called 'river-capture', and the original river *e* (Fig. 49) is said to have been 'beheaded' by *a*.

We may now imagine the steady deepening of the occupied valleys, while the dry valley at *d* (Fig. 50 B) remains at its present level. It is evident that its scenic form will be that of another col or wind-gap. Such wind-gaps are plentiful on the downs and moors of Britain, for river-capture is a very common phenomenon. Our purpose in this book is to explain scenic forms, and not to dwell upon large-scale processes requiring to be studied on maps. Nevertheless, we give in Fig. 51 a block-map of a part of Northumberland to show how the

[1] Another cause of wind-gaps is mentioned below, and the rambler in glaciated regions will often find 'cols' or 'saddles' caused by two corries (see page 9) encroaching on each other back to back.

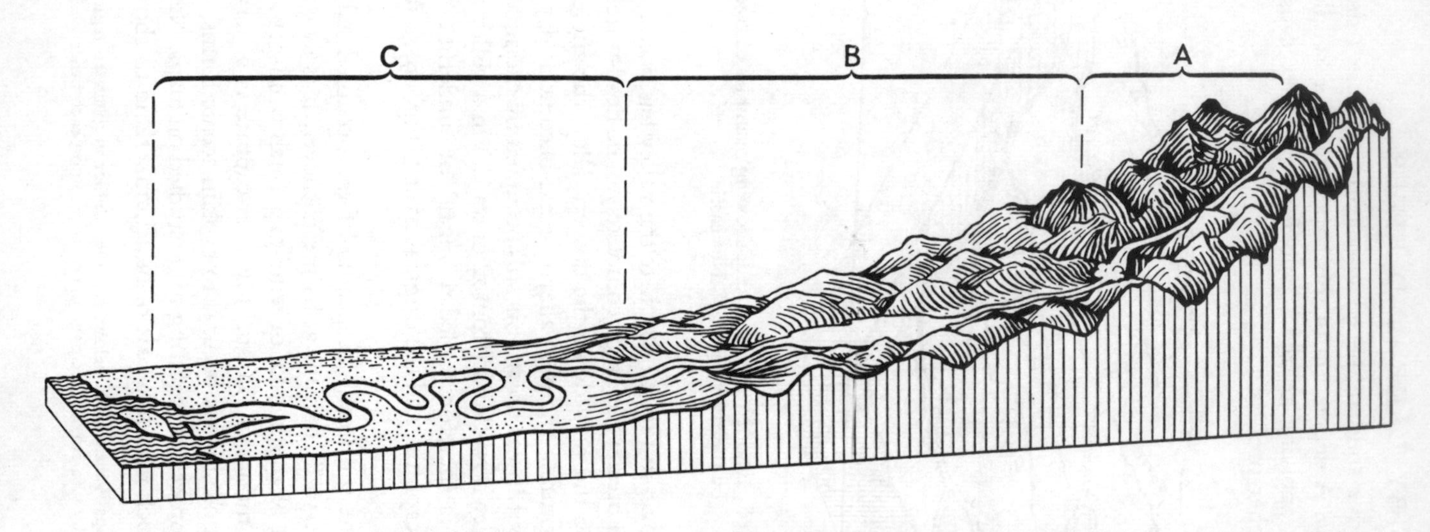

Fig. 52. The three stages of a river's course. A, the torrent tract, or youthful stage. B, the valley tract, or middle stage. C, the plain tract, or stage of old age. A is the region of erosion, C the region of deposition, and B the region where both processes continue side by side.

river Tyne has cut back its head (along a belt of exceptionally soft strata) and so captured the head-waters of three large rivers. The Rede formerly flowed into the Hart Burn, the North Tyne into the Wansbeck, and the Warks Burn into the Blyth. The old courses of these rivers can be traced in a succession of

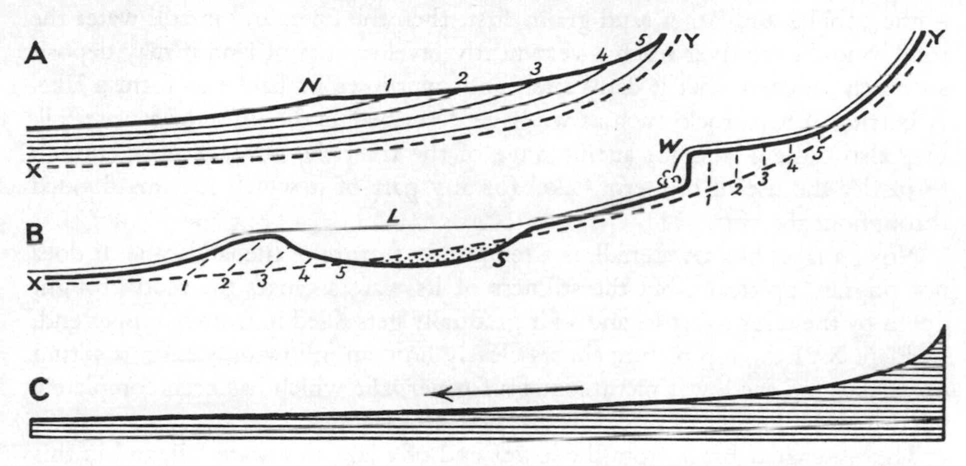

FIG. 53. Profiles of rivers. A, headward erosion from a knickpoint. B, elimination of a lake and a waterfall by headward erosion and deposition. C, the profile of the river Mole, Surrey, at the end of the Ice Age.

wind-gaps. A small head-stream of the Tyne, the Otter, is now cutting back in the direction of the arrow to behead the Coquet.

In Chapter I (page 14) we showed how a river may cut a gap for itself through an escarpment, and all such gaps which are still occupied by their rivers are known as 'water-gaps', to distinguish them from the 'dry-gaps' which we have been describing. In the block-map of south-eastern England shown in Fig. 12 the reader will find many gaps of both kinds, and in most of them (as we have already noted) a 'gap-town' has arisen on the site of an old camp or fortress, built (in mediaeval or Roman times) to guard the way through the hills. Roads and railways now make free use of these gaps, which, in more mountainous regions, would be dignified by the name of 'passes'.

The features we have described so far in this chapter belong properly to the torrent tract, or first stage, of a river's course from the mountains to the sea. Its precipitous descent does not, however, continue indefinitely. Sooner or later the land becomes more level and the river itself larger by the contributions of streams and runnels flowing in from the valley-sides. It pursues a more sedate course in a larger valley, and it has not only lost its power to move large stones, but it now begins to drop some of the heavier sediments which it has washed down from the mountains of its origin. This stage of a river's course is called the 'valley tract', and it is illustrated in Fig. 52 at B.

Swift water is able to hold sand and mud in suspension, and to roll stones along its bed, but as it slows down the sediments begin to settle on the bottom —the pebbles and larger sand-grains first, then the finer, and in still water the mud. Should the river reach a very nearly level stretch of land it may deposit so much sediment that it dams itself and overflows its banks to form a lake. A barrier of hard rock, such as we have described as the cause of a waterfall, may also cause a lake, for at this stage of the river the valley is wide enough to justify the use of the term 'lake' for any part of it which remains flooded throughout the year.

Now, a lake, like a waterfall, is a temporary feature of the landscape. It does not migrate upstream, but the stillness of its waters causes the mud brought down by the river to settle, and so it gradually gets filled in from its upper end. In Plate XVI the top picture shows clearly how an inflowing stream is silting up a lake, and the lower picture is of a former lake which has been completely filled with sediments.

The water may break from the lower end of a lake in a waterfall, and in this case the lake is gradually destroyed at the lower end as well. Here there is a recession of the waterfall as we have already described, and a form of 'headward erosion' (page 68) occurs. The river, having set itself a problem, proceeds at once to solve it, and the fact is that in spite of all its tricks every river is destined finally to smooth every irregularity from its bed, and to descend from source to mouth in one long, even curve.

Sometimes the bed of a river steepens after crossing a hard stratum of rock, and its curve therefore has a 'bump' in it, as shown by the thick line in Fig. 53 A. A curve which indicates in this way the varying gradients of a river is called the 'profile' of the river, and 'bumps' of the sort indicated at *N* (whether abrupt enough to cause waterfalls or not) are called 'knickpoints'. Knickpoints may be caused in many ways, including changes in level due to the faulting or folding of the strata over which the river flows, or the sudden acquisition of new water from a rapid tributary.

The water runs steeply downhill after passing a knickpoint, and its downward cutting is thereby accelerated. It behaves as if it has acquired a new torrent tract, starting at the knickpoint, and some headward erosion occurs. In the diagram, its down-cutting is indicated in five successive (numbered) stages, and it will be seen that the knickpoint recedes upstream (like a waterfall) till it is eventually eliminated. The river finally acquires the smooth profile indicated by the broken line X—Y.

Fig 53 B shows the profile of the river illustrated in Fig. 52, and indicates the fate of both the waterfall and the lake. The recession of the waterfall upstream is shown in five numbered stages, and so is the similar headward erosion at the lower end of the lake. Meanwhile, the upper end of the lake is being filled in by sediments (*S*), and the final profile is shown by the broken line X—Y. Fig. 53 C presents the ideal type of curve to which all rivers tend to conform, and it is definable by a precise mathematical formula.[1] For convenience the vertical scale has been exaggerated, but if this curve be imagined two hundred times as long as it is shown (the height remaining the same), it represents the actual profile of the river Mole, in Surrey, during the Ice Age. (Subsequent changes in the level of the land have caused the present river Mole to forsake the curve in its lower reaches.)

But we have not yet finished with our valley tract. We have now to describe those stretches of it which are not broken by knickpoints, waterfalls or lakes, but in which the stream pursues a steady course at, perhaps, one or two miles per hour. At such speeds a river tends to wind about a good deal, seeking the lowest land or cutting for itself the softest bed available, and—incidentally—providing many features of interest to the rambler. The river is said to 'meander' (from the winding river Maiandros in Phrygia), and its windings are called 'meanders', the stretch of water between each curve and the next being known as a 'reach'.

When a river begins to flow in a curve the first result is that the water on the outside of the curve, having farther to travel, puts on speed, while the water on the inside of the curve 'marks time'. The swifter water rapidly wears away the outer bank and cuts a deep channel for itself, while the slower water deposits some of its sediment on the inner shores. There is thus erosion and deposition going on side by side. So nice a balance is struck between these two processes, that in any river which is already carrying the maximum amount of sediment possible for it, the new land washed from the outer bank is exactly equal in weight to the amount being deposited on the inner. This must be so if the river maintains its volume and speed throughout the meander.

Once a meander has been initiated, it grows. The outer curve acquires a wider and wider sweep, while the inner shore—known by the grotesque name

[1] The non-mathematical reader may be surprised that the forms of landscape are amenable to any sort of mathematical treatment, yet it is plain enough that the processes which provide us with scenery are the physical ones with which engineers are familiar. The principles of hydraulics, friction, gravity, and so on, are formulated mathematically in engineering and in the laboratory. They operate just as precisely in the larger laboratory of the landscape. The difficulty in applying them to scenery is due wholly to the complexity of the subject. For those who are interested, the ideal profile of a river is the simple logarithmic curve: $y=a-k.\log(p-x)$, where the values of a, k, and p depend upon local conditions and are obtained by direct observation of the river concerned.

of 'slip-off slope'—accumulates a steadily widening 'strand' of gravel, sand, or mud. The process is illustrated in Fig. 54 at A and B, where the arrows indicate the course of the swiftest water and the dots the deposits of sediment, and

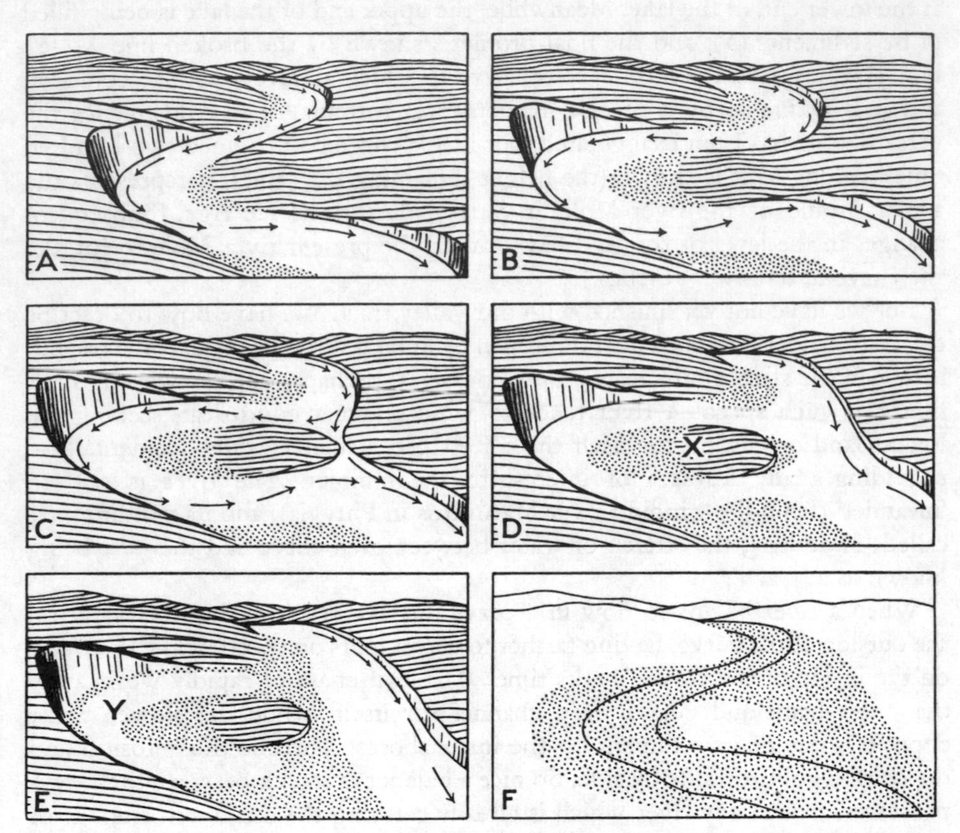

Fig. 54. The development of meanders and the formation of an ox-bow lake. See the text. F shows the extent of the gravel distributed by the stream during the processes illustrated in A to E.

again in section in Fig. 55 A. The swift water is rapidly cutting into a hillside and producing a river-cliff or 'bluff', while the curve of the river is becoming a loop into which the slip-off slope projects as an isthmus. (See Plate XVII, A.) The cross-profile of the valley is now the asymmetrical one of Fig. 2, E (page 5).[1]

[1] It should be added that just as the river widens its valley by its sideways sweeping, so the reaches which *traverse* the valley tend to sweep downstream; that is, the meanders themselves migrate slowly down the valley.

The two limbs of the loop eventually unite, as in Fig. 54 C, and the swift water begins to race through the breach, which it widens till it is able to take the whole of the current (D). The isthmus has now become an islet or 'eyot' (pronounced, and sometimes spelt, *ait*), as at X, while the water in the loop forms a quiet and almost stagnant 'backwater'. The course of the swiftest water

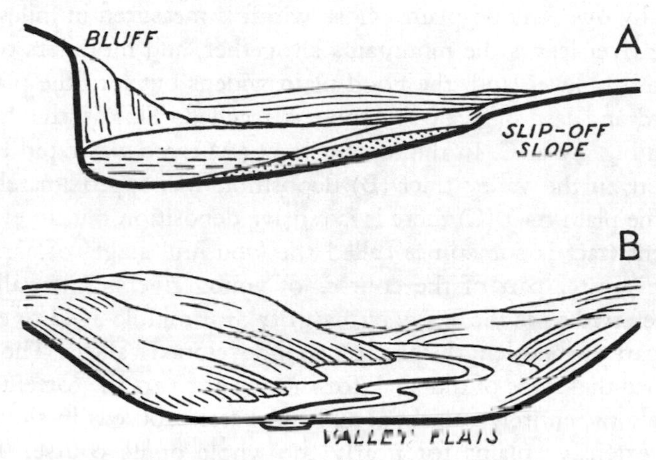

FIG. 55. Cross-profiles of valleys of meandering streams. A illustrates the cause of the asymmetrical valley shown in Fig. 2 E. B shows the development of valley flats or a flood-plain.

is now shown in E, and it will be seen that sediment is being deposited across the entrances to the backwater, to produce the 'ox-bow lake' marked Y. This lake may be kept supplied with water for a long time by seepage through the sandy bars across its mouths, but when the new stream has lowered its bed sufficiently the water will drain out of the lake by the same route. It will be noted that the new course of the river is once more very nearly straight, and that the whole story affords another example of a river setting itself a problem and then proceeding to solve it.

Fig. 54 F shows the original course of the river (as at A) superimposed on a map of all the sediments deposited during the process illustrated from A to E, and indicates how a comparatively narrow stream may lay a very much wider belt of sediment over the floor of its valley. Material thus deposited by rivers is termed 'alluvium', and its effect on the valley profile is to give it a flat bottom, as in Fig. 55 B. This must not be thought of as a very deep valley filled up to the level of the flats, but as any of the valleys shown in Fig. 2 widened by simply drawing their walls apart without increasing their depth. Level stretches of alluvium on such valley floors are called 'valley flats'. In times of flood, the flats may be entirely covered with water, and if they are very extensive they are dignified by the title of 'flood-plain'. An old flood-plain of the river Mole is shown in Plate V, A, where the stream lies at the foot of the hills.[1] A better small example is shown at the head of this chapter, but a river a few yards wide may eventually own a flood-plain whose width is measured in miles.

When the river leaves the mountains altogether, and meanders over a wide expanse of nearly level land, the flood-plain widens out into the plain proper, and the third and last stage of the river is reached. This is the 'plain tract' illustrated in Fig. 52 at C. In the torrent tract (A) there was rapid erosion but no deposition; in the valley tract (B) deposition was approximately equal to erosion; in the plain tract (C) there is extensive deposition but no erosion.

The torrent tract is sometimes called the 'youthful stage' of a river, for it occupies the greater part of the courses of young rivers. The valley tract is sometimes referred to as the 'stage of maturity', for middle-aged rivers flow for the greater part of their length through well-developed valleys. The plain tract is often termed the 'stage of old age', for in ancient rivers the torrent and valley tracts have almost entirely vanished, and the water proceeds in slow meanderings across extensive plains for nearly the whole of its course. The simple profile[2] of a river plain is given in Fig. 105 at D, while the relation between the river tract and its age (which is also the age of the landscape it has produced) is shown in Fig. 104.

The plain tract marks the river's final struggle against the inevitable engulfment by the sea. All the features associated with meanders are now carried to extremes and multiplied in numbers till the course of the river becomes a maze of interconnecting channels. And it is here that the river actually succeeds in raising the level of its own bed, and—in flood time—that of the surrounding plain, by dropping the remainder of the sediments it has been carrying down from the mountains. The quantity of these sediments is often staggering, the Thames (to cite a moderate example) bringing down in suspension about a quarter of a million tons per year—which is one ton every two minutes.[3]

The cause of the steady deposition in the plain tract is the slowing down of

[1] 'Old' flood-plain, the river having since cut itself a deeper channel (see page 140).

[2] Scenic profile, or cross-section.

[3] The deposition of Thames mud is largely prevented by the artificial restriction of the river to a relatively narrow channel by means of embankments, a measure which increases the speed of flow. In many rivers (such as the Mersey) the effect of such measures has to be augmented by constant dredging to maintain a channel for shipping. In prehistoric and early historic times the lower course of the Thames conformed to the description here given of the plain tract of a natural river.

the river, and this is at first due simply to the level form of the land. The deposits themselves raise the river bed and the stream becomes wide and shallow, and is bounded by marshes. Not infrequently a stream—aided, perhaps, by a natural dam of driftwood—will completely choke itself, and turn off on a new course. When this has happened, the 'abandoned water-course'[1]

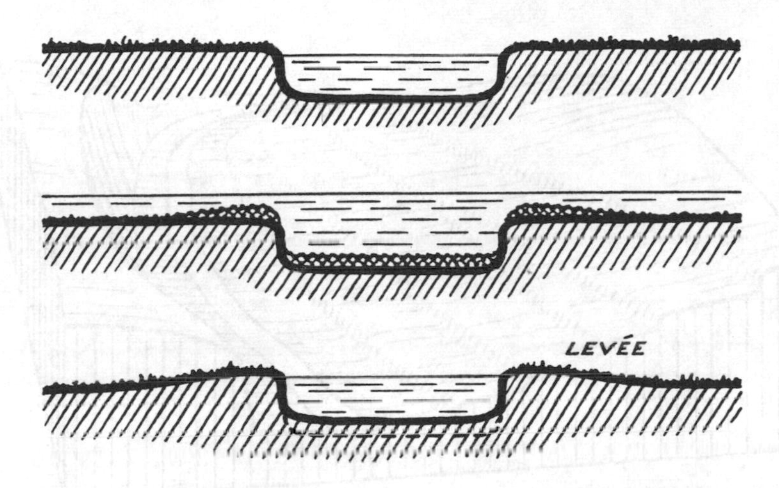

FIG. 56. How a river may raise its bed. During a flood, sediment is deposited not only on the bed of the river but also on its banks.

may often be traced as a sinuous strip of sand or gravel. In the sketch at the head of this chapter an old course of the Penard river, complete with eyot and ox-bow lake, is clearly visible in the sandy tract in the centre of the picture.

In the rainy season such a river may overflow its low banks and flood the plain, which becomes a great, still lake through which slow currents may be seen drifting lazily along over the drowned watercourses. Mud is now dropped not only on the bed of the river but also on its banks where the currents meet the still water on either side. Fig. 56 shows in section a river flowing across its plain (top) and the same river in flood (centre), the dotted area indicating the deposits of mud. The bottom diagram shows what happens when the floods subside. Both the bed of the river and its banks have been raised by the deposition, and its new water level is now actually higher than the level of the surrounding flood-plain.

The raised banks soon become grassed over, and are called 'levées'. In inhabited country it is often necessary to reinforce the levées artificially to prevent

[1] The 'dry valleys' (pages 69 and 82) afford other examples of abandoned water-courses.

the river from bursting its banks and laying waste valuable land. The banks of untended rivers are usually riddled with breaches and the neighbouring parts of the flood-plain are more or less permanent marshes or water-meadows.

It should be mentioned here that although the occurrence of levées and marshes is a characteristic of the plain tract, or of any ancient river, they may

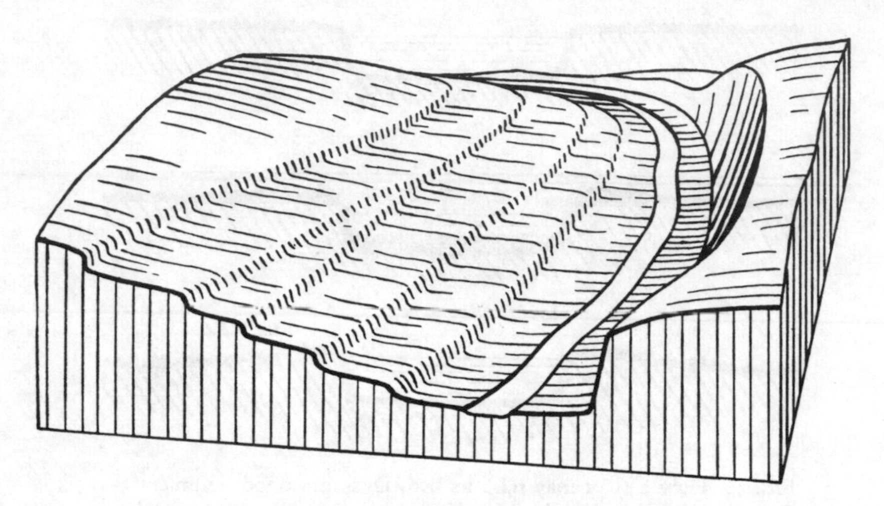

FIG. 57. A series of river terraces caused by rejuvenation in several successive stages.

sometimes be found on a smaller scale in a valley tract where the flood-plain is wide, and particularly where a river begins to approach the still waters of a lake.

As the river approaches the sea there is a further check on its speed. This is caused by the sea itself, for though a river may continue to flow for some distance out to sea (through the surface-waters), it is eventually brought to a complete standstill. The last of the sediments are then deposited on the sea floor, and they may there accumulate till they form a submerged bank across the mouth of the river. This is the river 'bar' which is so often dangerous to unpiloted shipping, but which also breaks the ocean waves before they reach the shore and thus provides a sheltered anchorage. The river bar may be added to by longshore drifting, and a spit may develop which turns the mouth of the river in the way described in the previous chapter (page 50).

If the coastal lands have subsided the tides may flow for some distance up the mouth of a river and periodically cause heavy deposition of sediment within the river mouth itself. In this way an island of mud is liable to form and block the normal course of the river, which then finds new channels on both sides of the island, as shown in Fig. 52 C. The river virtually divides into two diverging streams ('distributaries') and the resulting triangular shape of the whole mouth gives it its name of 'delta' (from the Greek letter for D, Δ), though a large delta may have many islands, and depart considerably from the ideal shape. Elevation of the coast also may cause a delta by prematurely checking the flow of the river and at the same time raising its bar above the surface, while a river which is very heavily laden with mud indeed (like the Nile) is likely to form a delta in any circumstances.

The general effect of coastal elevation, or—what comes to the same thing—of inland subsidence, is to stagnate and prematurely age the rivers involved, but inland elevation gives the rivers a new lease of life by increasing their speed of flow, and thus accelerating the process of down-cutting. It often causes intensive down-cutting to start again in reaches hitherto given over to deposition, the sudden increase in the gradient at such places giving rise to knick-points (page 72). The general effect upon rivers of inland elevation is known as 'rejuvenation'.

The signs of rejuvenation may often be spotted by the rambler, and perhaps the most common of them is the occurrence of 'terraces' along the sides of a valley (Fig. 25 C). The cross-profile of a terraced valley is typified in Fig. 105 at E, where the upper broken line indicates the original plain of a river which has later passed through two successive stages of rejuvenation. After the first period of renewed down-cutting the river made itself a new plain, shown by the second broken line. This plain would gradually have widened till it was as extensive as the first, but before this could happen the down-cutting began again and produced the present valley. The remains of the old plains exist as ledges of gravel or sand.

When a shelf of this sort is seen to run along one side of a river valley, it is always interesting to look for signs of its counterpart on the other. But these may have disappeared, and in cases like that illustrated in Fig. 57 they may never have been present. Fig. 57 shows a river which has enjoyed five successive periods of rejuvenation while occupying the same meander, but it is only on the slip-off slope that the terraces have had a chance to appear. See also Plate XVII, B, which shows two terraces and the present flood-plain of the river Findhorn, in Scotland.

Terraces may also mark the site of an old lake, whose water-level may have changed many times from any of a number of causes. For instance, rejuvenation may have caused a temporary increase in the supply of water, particularly if it has resulted in river-capture among the head-streams, or the water-level may have been lowered by a change of climate to more arid conditions. The increase in average temperature towards the end of the Ice Age caused such extensive flooding by melt-water that most of the rock-basins in northern Europe became lakes of exceptional depth. Many of the old beaches of these lakes exist today as terraces, the famous 'Parallel Roads' of Glen Roy, in Inverness, being the

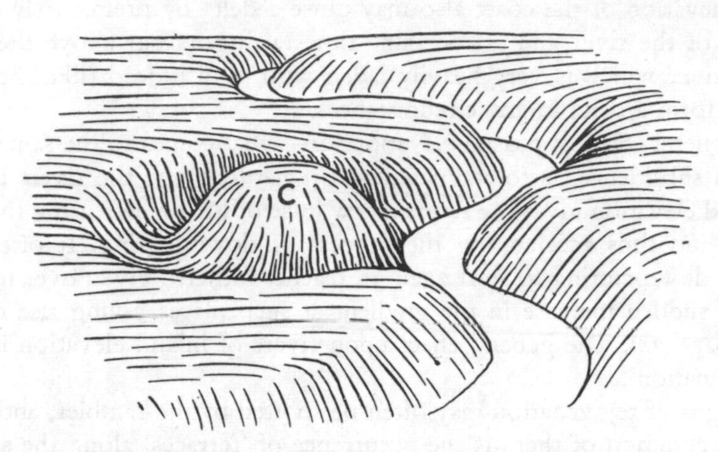

FIG. 58. Entrenched meanders, and an old meander-core (C).

best-known example in Britain. These are three lake terraces running for many miles high up along the sides of the glen, which now contains no more than a small river.

The general effect of rejuvenation on a meandering stream is to cause it to cut its meanders deeper. A river does not normally meander unless it is flowing across a level plain, and if meanders are ever observed to occupy steep-side winding valleys then the river has cut the valleys after the meanders were formed. Such deep windings are called 'incised' or 'entrenched' meanders, and they are a sure sign of rejuvenation. An islet such as X in Fig. 54 D may appear in a rejuvenated river valley as an isolated round hill, appropriately termed a 'meander core', and it may well puzzle the rambler if the ox-bow lake has dried up or lost its connection with the main stream. (See Fig. 58.) The rate of down-cutting in a rejuvenated river may be sufficiently rapid to deepen its valley into a meandering gorge or canyon, the depth of which goes on increasing as long as the land continues to rise.

We close this chapter with a brief account of the peculiar behaviour of rivers flowing over limestone country. River-water, being exposed to the air, contains a small amount of carbon-dioxide in solution, and this gives it the power to dissolve limestone. The river Thames, which we have already mentioned as bringing down a quarter of a million tons of sediment in suspension per year, removes half a million tons (chiefly of chalk) by solution in the same period. The widening and deepening of joints in limestone rocks (which include chalk) by the dissolving action of rain-water was mentioned on page 26, and the same

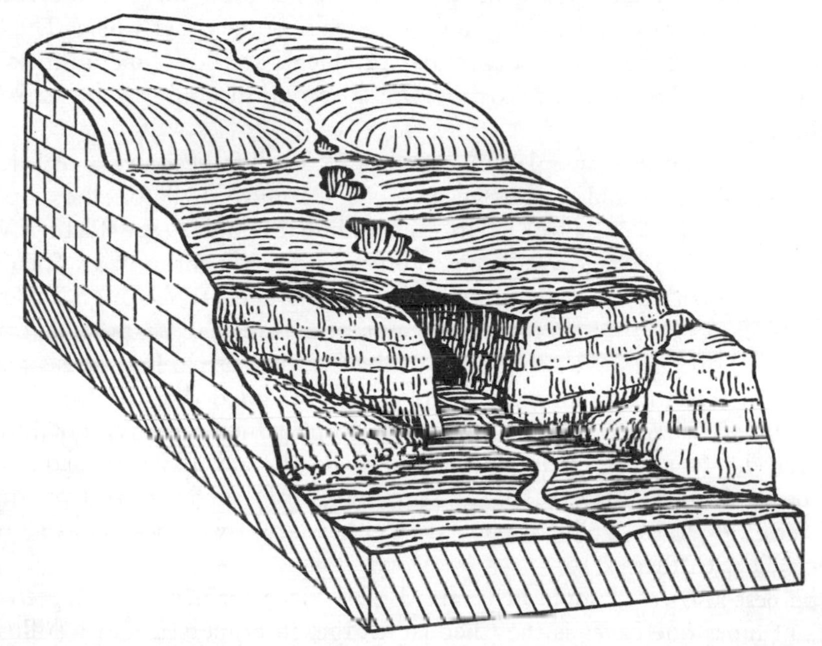

FIG. 59. Block-diagram illustrating swallow-holes, limestone caves, underground water-courses, and a type of gorge produced by the collapse of the roof of a cave.

process goes on very much more rapidly in the beds of rivers. The hollows dissolved out of limestone river-beds may measure several yards across and several feet deep, and their floors be riddled with deep fissures able to swallow up much of the water flowing over them. Such hollows are therefore known as 'swallow-holes', 'swallets', or 'sink-holes'.

Normal rivers grow larger as they proceed along their courses, but a river flowing over a bed punctured with swallow-holes usually dwindles in size and sometimes disappears below ground entirely—at any rate during the dry season. The river Mole in Surrey (with its oddly appropriate name) dives underground during the summer months, some twenty swallow-holes in the chalk between Dorking and Mickleham (a distance of two miles) sufficing to engulf it. Examples abound in the limestone district of Derbyshire, and elsewhere, and in some cases the rivers have permanently forsaken their old surface courses, which the rambler encounters as otherwise inexplicable dry valleys.

Underground, the river descends to the level of the water-table, and there dissolves out a channel which may become enlarged here and there into a chain of caves. It finally emerges again where the water-table meets the surface at some point lower down its old valley—or even in some other valley. The occasional collapse of the roof of a cave may produce a swallow-hole on the slopes of a mountain, this type of sink providing a second meaning to the term 'pot-hole' (see page 68).

Constant solution may enlarge a swallow-hole till it becomes a real danger to the incautious rambler, and we may cite Gaping Ghyll (on the slopes of Ingleborough, in Yorkshire) as an outstanding example. (See Plate XVIII.) This great circular swallow-hole communicates directly through an open shaft 365 feet deep with a vaulted chamber 480 feet long and 110 feet high. From this the water flows through an intricate system of fissures and channels to emerge at the Ingleborough Cave a mile away as the Clapham Beck. Fig. 59 is a general diagram of this sort of formation, and it will be noted that the front part of the cave has collapsed to form a type of gorge which we have not hitherto mentioned.[1] This gorge is usually a deep *cul-de-sac*, and may be called a 'cove' (see page 56 *n.*); in Plate V, B, the view looks into such a cove from above. The term 'ghyll' or 'gully' is applied to either large swallow-holes or ravines associated with them.

The best-known example in England of a gorge formed by collapse of the roofs of limestone caves is the Cheddar Gorge, in Somerset, and we illustrate another in Plate XVIII. Sometimes the collapse of the roof is incomplete, and then the result is a ravine with overhanging sides, bridged here and there by natural arches. Such ravines are often dry, the streams which once occupied them having gone still farther underground. Small caves may often be found running back from the walls of limestone gorges, and in these the cautious rambler may find much to interest him. They may be known locally as 'holes', 'grottoes' or 'caverns', and their contents are described in the next chapter.

[1] Eight quite distinct causes of gorges (or ravines) have been described in this book, and for the convenience of the reader we may recapitulate them as follows: (1) The gorge produced in the torrent tract of a river owing to rapid flow and excessive down-cutting (page 66). (2) The river valley with vertical sides due to arid climate or exceptionally hard rocks (Fig. 2, D, and page 4). (3) The gorge due to a fault (page 17) or system of faults (Fig. 15, C, and page 15). (4) The deep valley cut across an escarpment by a river older than the escarpment (page 14). (5) The gorge cut by a receding waterfall (Fig. 48 and page 67). (6) The deeply incised meander (Fig. 58, page 80). (7) The collapsed limestone cave with which we have just dealt. (8) The local landslip or chine (page 46). We might add a ninth to this list, for the upper reaches of fjords (page 56) are sometimes called gorges.

CHAPTER V

The Earth Beneath

Ramblers may be divided into two broad classes. There are those who like a set course to follow, and take with them a map and a guide book, and there are those who decide merely upon a general direction of travel and then proceed in the spirit of explorers. The former rely upon the discoveries of others, and work their way through a list of noted objects of interest. The latter do their best to forget that they are not the first of mankind to tread their chosen track, and strive to see the country as a *terra nova*.

In the British Isles, and indeed in Europe, genuine exploration of this sort is no longer possible *on the surface of the ground*, yet there are many caves and subterranean water-courses which have still to be visited by man. Various societies of 'speleologists' (Greek *spelaion*, cave) exist in order to explore this underground country, but such exploration can be as dangerous as any expedition to polar or tropical lands. We cannot conscientiously recommend the ordinary countrygoer to do more than peer into unknown caverns unless he has first sought expert local advice and taken all the prescribed precautions, but we can offer him an alternative kind of exploration which is a genuine breaking of new ground.

'Breaking of new ground'—the phrase is to be taken quite literally. The sole equipment required is a geological (or any other) hammer (Fig. 60) and a pocket magnifying glass, and the hammer may be conveniently carried in the belt. For it is undeniably true that every time a fossil or mineral collector strikes a flake from the surface of a rock, he gazes upon something never before seen by man. As an unexplored part of the country it is admittedly small—a few square inches or so—yet it holds excitement for those who find joy in discovery.

To lay bare a new surface of rock, and at the same time to be fully aware of the nature of your act, is an experience common only to geologists, but it is open also to the layman. And with it go tangible rewards—treasure trove, in literal truth, though not to be assessed in pounds sterling. The rambler who thus becomes a 'rock-hound'[1] will soon appreciate why Tennyson wrote in *The Princess*—

> . . . that sport
> Went hand in hand with Science.
>
> . . . and then we turn'd, we wound
> About the cliffs, the copses, out and in,
> Hammering and clinking, chattering stony names
> Of shale and hornblende, rag and trap and tuff,
> Amygdaloid and trachyte. . . .

and he may soon come to share the enthusiasm of Robert Dick:

> It's good to be breaking a stone,
> The work is lucky an' braw;
> It's grand to be finding a bone—
> A fish-bone the grandest of a'.
>
> Hammer an' chisels an' a',
> Chisels an' fossils an' a';
> The deeper we go, the more we shall know,
> Of the past an' the present an' a'.

The hammer is to the geologist what the pen is to the writer, or the scissors to the tailor. For ramblers like ourselves it is invaluable if we wish either to collect specimens or to read the story of the rocks on which we stand. This can be done, in the simplest sense in which we mean it, without any study of geology. One lucky blow of the hammer, and we may know whether the spot we now occupy was once desert, tropical forest, a river bed, a lake, a shallow sea, the ocean deeps, or perhaps the very throat of a volcano. It is the purpose of this and the succeeding chapter to show how this may be done.

[1] A colloquialism especially among oil engineers, and applied by them to prospectors.

The distinction between igneous ('volcanic') and sedimentary rocks has already been made, yet it is well to remember that both kinds of rock are derived from the same parent material. We may picture the earth as a molten iron ball with a crust of slag floating on the surface, and it is this dross on the metal which is the fundamental stuff of which all rocks (except limestones) are formed. It contains many different minerals, but only a few of these occur in sufficiently large quantities to affect the form and colour of the landscape. Of these few the red oxide (rust) of iron, and the three ingredients of granite—quartz, mica and felspar (Fig. 61)—are all that the rambler needs to note.

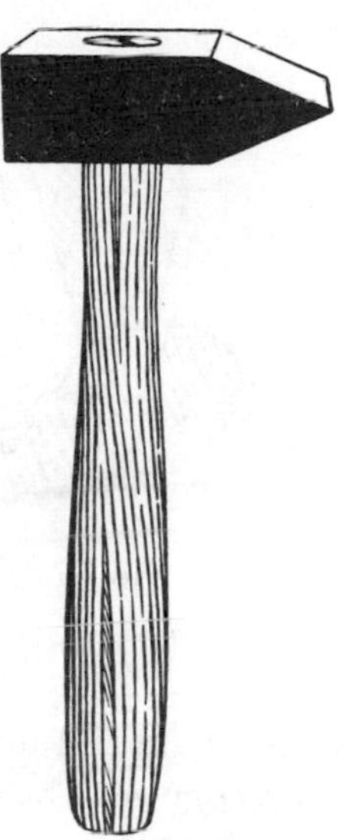

FIG. 60.
A geological hammer.

When simply cooled from the molten state the slag on the earth-ball forms 'igneous' ('fiery'—a wider term than 'volcanic') rock, in which the minerals are generally visible as crystals irregularly matted together. (See Fig. 62.) When it has also suffered weathering and its constituents have been thus altered or rearranged by wind or water, it forms 'sedimentary' rock, in which the crystals have lost their clearness and distinctive forms or have disintegrated into powder. Thus quartz, which exists as recognizable crystals in granite, occurs as rounded sand-grains on the sea-shore, while the crystals of felspar weather away to form a fine clay. Little plates of mica may be seen sparkling in sandstones no less than in granite, but most of the crystals found in sedimentary rocks are quite clearly not part of the rock, but simply occupy holes or cracks in it. They often have very perfect forms, and are of secondary origin, having been deposited from solution in water after the rock was formed.

The hall-mark of sedimentary rocks is their occurrence in layers or 'strata' (see Figs. 33, 66 and 80), but in small specimens stratification may not be apparent. In this case the rambler must rely upon the non-crystalline, granular structure of the rock, which should be revealed by his magnifying glass. On the other hand, the crystals in an igneous rock may be indistinguishable because of their small size, and then the rambler must be guided by the absence of stratified layers in the formation he is examining.[1]

These simple tests will often be sufficient but are by no means always so. For example, many a hard sandstone (of the type known as 'quartzite') will

[1] A few igneous rocks are neither crystalline nor granular, but glassy, but the rambler need not bother his head with them.

glitter like castor sugar and appear quite obviously to be a crystalline rock of some sort, while some limestones are so dark and compact that the amateur might easily mistake them for the igneous basalt. The rule for ramblers in such cases has already been given in this book. Consult the geological map, where outcrops of igneous rocks are shown in bright red; but if you have no

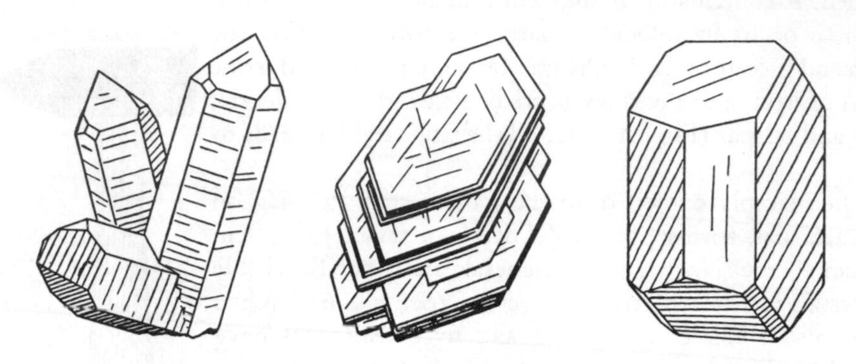

FIG. 61. Well-developed crystals of the three constituents of granite. *Left*, quartz. *Centre*, mica. *Right*, felspar.

map, or are still unconvinced, drop the problem and hunt for something you *can* recognize. The fun in rambling lies in recognizing things you know, not in worrying too much over those which baffle you. For all you can tell the experts themselves may be as puzzled as you are over your particular problem, which may not be solvable without hours of microscope work or chemical analysis.

In the specimen of granite illustrated in Fig. 62 the felspar is indicated by diagonal shading, and the mica by solid black, the quartz being left clear. None of the crystals is perfect, yet the fact that they *are* interlocking crystals whose interstices are filled with the glass-clear quartz is evident enough. The perfect crystal forms of these substances were shown in Fig. 61, and sometimes such crystals are found lining the cavities of hollow stones. In granite, the felspar may be an opaque white or pink, and the mica transparent or black. The mica occurs in sheets or leaves, and these can often be splintered off with the point of a knife.

Igneous rocks similar in general appearance to granite, but commonly of finer grain, are also abundant enough. Many of them have a greenish tinge due to the mineral olivine, many are densely speckled with black hornblende, or appear dark because they are deficient in quartz. The rambler's name for them is 'crystalline igneous rocks', and he should compare them with granite only in order to distinguish them from that notable variety of their class. In both granite and many other crystalline rocks very small crystals of a clear, ruby red sometimes occur. These are not rubies but garnets, and they are of no commercial value.

The only other common igneous rock which the rambler should learn to recognize is the heavy, black basalt which so often forms the dykes (page 37) which cause waterfalls in the northern counties. Basalt—pronounced, by the way, '*bass*-alt', with the accent on the first syllable—is a very fine-grained, hard rock of a uniform dark grey or black colour, its crystals being too small to be distinguished by the naked eye. It is really a lava, poured out from a volcano or a fissure in the crust of the earth, and it has cooled rapidly on or near the surface. The smallness of its crystals is evidence of this, for large crystals (such as those in granite) occur only in rocks which have cooled slowly. Thus, the rambler with a chip of igneous rock in his hand may know whether he stands on the site of an old lava flow, or has come across a mass of rock which cooled slowly far beneath the surface and has subsequently become exposed to view.

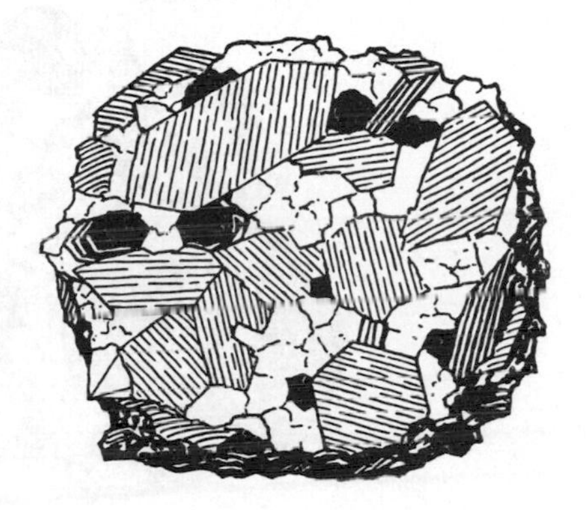

FIG. 62. Granite, polished to show constituent crystals clearly. (Slightly enlarged.)

In some localities the basalt has shrunk and cracked on cooling to form hexagonal pillars which cannot be mistaken for anything else. The finest display of these occurs at the Giant's Causeway, in northern Ireland, illustrated at the head of this chapter, but they are to be seen also at Fingal's Cave in the island of Staffa, at Kinghorn in Fifeshire, and elsewhere.

Igneous rocks usually contain many ingredients of diverse chemical composition, but the sedimentary rocks derived from them are by comparison remarkably pure. Compare Fig. 62 with Fig. 64. The mixed debris resulting from the weathering and decay of the original rocks is automatically sorted out by the flow of the rivers which wash them away, and by submergence beneath the sea. Thus, quartz sands are often pure enough to use as quartz in glass-making, and kaolin (a clay derived from felspar) for the manufacture of porcelain. Even coarser clays, pure enough only for brick-making, may accumulate in enormous beds of astonishingly uniform colour and texture.

We have already described how this purification is accomplished. The reader will remember that the heavy grains of quartz or silica (as it is usually called in its granular form of sand) settle down in shallow water, the finer grains of clay remaining suspended until they reach deep or very still water, where they accumulate as mud.[1] Far out at sea, beyond the reach of sediments from the

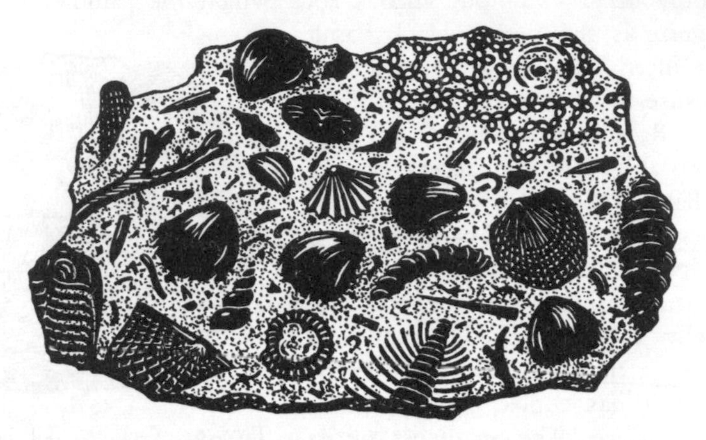

FIG. 63. A shelly limestone consisting largely of fossils.

land, the only deposits on the bottom consist of the shells and skeletal remains of sea-creatures, and sometimes insoluble matter precipitated chemically. These form the limestones, of which there are several different kinds.

Some limestones consist almost entirely of the calcium carbonate secreted by certain red and green seaweeds, and deposited—in the first instance—in their cell-walls. Others are consolidated deep-sea oozes, such as are now accumulating on the bottoms of the Atlantic and Indian oceans, and others again are 'bacterial' oozes (see page 126). Banks of sea-shore shells, and old coral reefs, also form limestones, and occasionally a limestone rock is easily seen to consist of nothing else but such remains cemented together. A shelly limestone is illustrated in Fig. 63, but the shells in such a rock are not in their original state, but have become mineralized by the action of water. They consist of the same chemical substance as fresh shells—calcium carbonate—but in a crystalline form. Shells altered in this way are called 'fossils', but the term

[1] The international standard employed to determine whether a deposit is to be called stony, sandy or muddy (clayey), is based on the diameter of its particles, thus:

Stones	2 mm. or more in diameter.
Coarse sand	0·2 to 2 mm. in diameter.
Fine sand	0·02 to 0·2 mm. in diameter.
Silt	0·002 to 0·02 mm. in diameter.
Clay	less than 0·002 mm. in diameter.

covers many other methods by which the relics of ancient life have been preserved.

The cementing of sedimentary rocks—shells into limestones, sand into sandstones (Fig. 64), mud into clay or shale—probably begins while they are still beneath the sea. As the deposits accumulate the weight of the upper layers

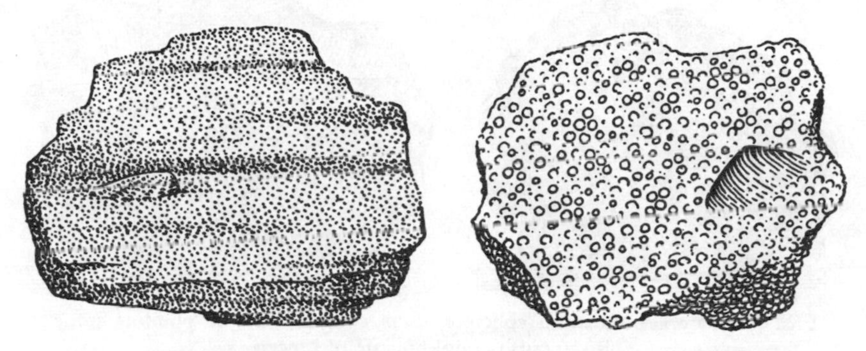

FIG. 64. Sandstone (*left*) and oolitic limestone (*right*), formalized for easy comparison. Note the impressions of fossil shells.

compresses the lower layers into a hard, compact mass, which the water partly dissolves. It sets into a hard rock much as a heap of salt or sugar will set into a lump if it is allowed to get damp.

Further changes, and more cementing, often occur long after the rocks have been raised above sea-level. Rain-water percolating through massive formations dissolves minerals from the upper layers and deposits them between the particles of the lower layers. In this way a soft, friable sandstone may become a solid mass of crystalline quartz, as hard as glass and dignified by the special name of 'quartzite', and a limestone which was once as soft as chalk may set into a dense, hard 'marble' capable of taking a high polish.[1] Marble-topped tables are often made of such limestones, and fragments of fossil shells, corals and sea-lilies provide the ornamental detail. (See Figs. 91 and 92.)

Limestone formed by the deposition of lime from solution may have a granular structure, so that it looks like the hard roe of a fish. In a magnifying glass the grains on a freshly-broken surface look like tiny eggs, so that this sort of limestone is called 'roe-stone' or 'oolite' (Greek *oon*, egg, *lithos*, stone). This word ought to be pronounced 'o-o-lite', in three syllables, but alas! even some geolo-

[1] 'Marble' by courtesy only. The nature of true marbles is given on page 104. Polished igneous rocks are also sometimes called 'marbles' by architects and monumental masons, and it must be admitted that the term 'marble' is, etymologically, appropriate to anything which sparkles.

gists may be heard to call it 'oo-lite' in unguarded moments. Microscopic examination shows that each 'egg' consists of a tiny particle of sand (or a shell fragment) thickly coated with lime. A piece of oolitic limestone is illustrated in Fig. 64, and the famous Portland building stone affords a common example.

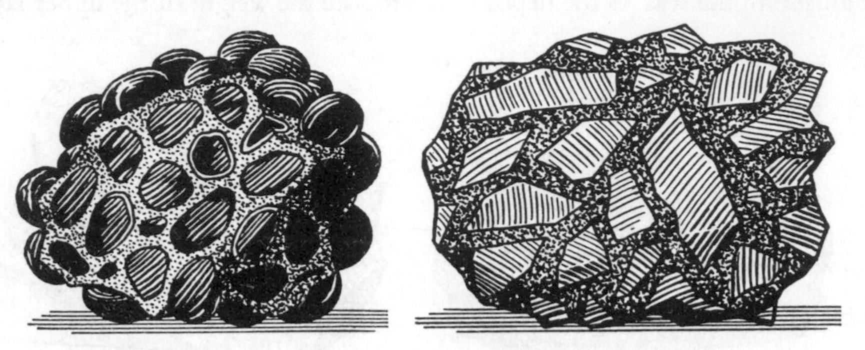

FIG. 65. Examples of natural 'concrete'. *Left*, conglomerate or 'pudding-stone'. *Right*, crush-conglomerate or breccia.

It sometimes happens that cementing materials get washed in between the pebbles of sea-shore shingles or river gravels, and then the result is 'pudding-stone' or conglomerate (Fig. 65). This is a hard rock as full of pebbles as a Christmas cake is of currants, and it looks like a concrete-maker's dream. The rambler who finds a deposit of conglomerate may know at once that he stands on an old shore or river-bed, and it is by mapping such deposits that geologists have sometimes been able to determine the outlines of seas and lakes many millions of years old.

Small chips and fragments of rock, such as are produced by frost (page 23), by a landslide, by the rupture of a fault (page 15), or even by an erupting volcano, are similarly liable to become cemented into a solid mass. This type of natural concrete is called 'crush-conglomerate' or 'breccia', which is an Italian word for the fragments of a broken wall, and is pronounced (in English usage) '*brech*-ya'; in the north breccias are locally called 'brockrams'. Breccia is distinguished from conglomerate by the angularity of the fragments it contains, and the great variation in their sizes. (See Fig. 65.) If you find a breccia along a shore, look up at the cliffs to see if the rocks are faulted. You will probably find that the lines of bedding are broken, and that there are springs—or a cave—at the foot of the rupture.

It is evident from the foregoing paragraphs that the comparative chemical purity of sedimentary rocks *is* only comparative after all. A sea-floor covered with mud will produce a clay or shale, but if it supports many shell-bearing creatures (molluscs) the clay or shale will contain the lime[1] of their shells and will be called 'marl', or it may get compressed into a 'mudstone'. Sand may get mixed with the mud to form a 'loam', or its grains may become cemented by lime to produce a 'calcareous sandstone'.[2] This may occur in a quarry as a band of exceptionally hard rock which can be dislodged with a crowbar. Blocks of stone thus easily levered out of a softer bed are called 'burr-stones' or 'doggers' by the quarrymen, and often need very little trimming for use in rough masonry. Similar doggers of iron-cemented sand are also common.

Again, the constituent grains of a sandstone may consist of other materials besides quartz. They may include some of the felspar and mica from the original granite, and minerals contributed by longshore drifting (see page 43) while it was still a sea-shore. Sandstones containing the little flat plates of mica (Figs. 61 and 66) often split very easily into slabs of even thickness suitable for paving, and they are then called 'flagstones' by quarrymen. Massive sandstones (or limestones) which do not split, but may be hewn into blocks of any shape or size, are called 'freestones' and are used for building and sculpture. Sandstones containing sharp, angular grains (often of felspar) are known as 'grits', and these are used for grindstones and millstones, while a very pure, hard, fine-grained sandstone used for lining blast-furnaces is known as 'gannister'.[3]

[1] 'Lime'—a term used conveniently for calcium carbonate, the stuff of shells and limestones. In chemistry and commerce the word applies to calcium oxide ('quick lime') or hydroxide ('slaked lime' or 'hydrated lime'), neither of which substances occurs free in nature.

[2] An attempt was made some years ago to introduce the word 'marm' or 'malm'—compounded from 'marl' and 'loam'—to describe calcareous sandstones, but it was never generally adopted. In any case, it might have become confused with a term spelt variously by Cobbett 'maume', 'mame', or 'malme', which is used on the Hampshire-Surrey border for puddled chalk. This is a sticky, clay-like mud, 'very much like *grey soap*' (Cobbett's phrase), produced by the trampling of cattle on wet chalk. Another term, 'malmstone', is used in Wiltshire for an impure sandstone containing both clay and lime, while clayey bands in the chalk are known to geologists as marls. To make matters worse, some of the sandy clays were called marls by the early geologists, and the word has become a permanent proper name for those particular deposits. By extension, it is also used of the 'brick clays' (used for brick-making), which are characteristically clay containing sharp sand or grit. We should not, therefore, be surprised to find that though the word 'marl' is still used as a proper name (*e.g.*, Keuper Marls, Plenus Marls, Marlstone), it is being dropped as a general term.

Shales with fibrous lime are called 'beef' in Dorset, while clays or sands containing rubble from an underlying limestone are known as 'brash', a word cognate with 'breccia'. Other terms of more or less local use included 'gaize' (Wiltshire) for a soft sandstone, 'rag' (Wiltshire) for a hard sandstone, 'rag' or 'ragstone' (Kent to Dorset) for a sandy limestone, 'cornstone' (Welsh border) for limy sandstones, and 'crag' (East Anglia) for shelly sandstones. A limy sandstone from which most of the lime has been removed by solution, leaving a sort of rock-skeleton of silica, is often called a 'rotten-stone', while the top bed of the Portland limestone, which is full of holes left by dissolved shells, is termed 'roach'.

[3] Ordinary 'fire-brick' is made in kilns like other bricks, but from 'fire-clay', which is a variety of clay devoid of lime and alkalies.

The cementing of the grains of a rock into a solid mass by lime or silica (of which quartz is the crystalline form) is, as we have said, the work of percolating rain-water, but though this process may result in the intermixture of minerals, it very frequently leads also to their purification. When substances are deposited from solution in water they often show a tendency to settle on particles (especially crystals) of their own kind. Thus, if silica and lime are both contained in the water, the lime may gather in the form of crystals of pure calcite in one place and the silica as crystals of pure quartz in another. As the water continues to flow, these crystals are more likely to grow in size than new ones are to form. Further, water containing one mineral may, on reaching particles of the same substance, add its quota to the deposit and take up a different mineral in exchange. This often happens in compact rocks where there would be no room for fresh deposits unless some of the old material were removed.

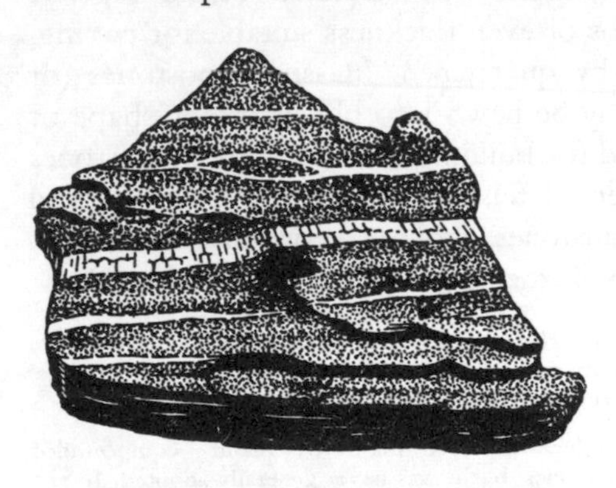

Fig. 66. A piece of liver-coloured Old Red Sandstone, showing bedding and veins of quartz.

Such processes take place extremely slowly, for most minerals are only very slightly soluble in water. Nevertheless, nature works on such a vast scale, and continues without ceasing for periods measured in millions of years, that the results are truly amazing. It would take you a very long time to dissolve a pebble in a reservoir of water, yet the river basins of England are lowered one foot every 13,200 years *by solution of their rocks alone*! And as for the deposition from solution, single crystals of quartz and calcite sometimes weigh several pounds (or even hundredweight) apiece, while water-deposited lime may form beds four or five hundred feet thick and be quarried for ornamental building stone ('travertine').

Crystals deposited by water are often to be seen filling cracks in the rocks. They grow across from each side of the crack till they meet the middle, and thus appear to knit the rock together. Fig. 66 shows a piece of Old Red Sandstone with cracks infilled by veins of quartz, and many of the valuable mineral ores are deposited in veins in precisely this way.

Lead, iron, zinc and copper ores scattered in small particles throughout the rocks would be of no use to man. But the percolating water has first collected and dissolved them, and then separated and concentrated them for use in the masses of crystals which fill the 'lodes'[1] and 'veins' of the miners. Such crystals are not always glass-clear; many are of opaque substances. The sulphides of lead ('galena') and iron ('pyrites'), for instance, form heavy, dense crystals looking very much like lumps of pewter and brass, respectively.

Sometimes the crystals are impure, and this often adds to their beauty if not to their usefulness. Thus, quartz crystals not uncommonly contain a trace

FIG. 67. The interior of a limestone cave, showing stalactites and stalagmites.

of manganese which gives them a mauve colour, and then they are known as 'amethyst'. Quartz containing a trace of iron is yellow, and is called 'cairngorm', and so on. The most striking variations in colour occur in the crystals of calcite which are so abundant in limestone caves, and these we shall now consider.

Limestone is exceptionally soluble in natural water, and the moisture which constantly drips from the roofs of limestone caves is highly charged with lime. Before each drop falls it partly evaporates, and so deposits a minute crystal of calcite on the rock. The next drop adds its mite, and the next, year in and year out, till at last a long pendant of crystalline lime hangs from the roof of the cave. This is called a 'stalactite', and it looks very much like a soft, pink icicle. (See Fig. 67 and Plate XVIII, C.)

Meanwhile, each drop has fallen to the floor and there evaporated a little more, and deposited another little crystal of lime, so that a heap of crystals has also been growing upwards to meet the stalactite. This heap is called a 'stalagmite', and presently it may reach the stalactite and join it to form a complete

[1] 'Lode'—an ore-bearing fissure-vein, as distinct from veins in marble, etc.

pillar. Often, a group of such pillars will coalesce and produce the effect of a set of organ-pipes. Where the water flows from cracks in the walls of the cave it encrusts the rock with pink 'icing'. This may assume many fantastic forms and mimic frozen waterfalls, guttering candles, honeycombs, and so on. A sloping crack in the roof may give rise to a series of wavy curtains which, in the light of a torch, suggest a petrified aurora.

All kinds of architectural detail may be imitated, including stained-glass windows in several colours, for the predominant pink colour of the crystalline lime varies according to the traces of 'foreign' minerals which have found their way into the water. The pink itself is due to iron, and may deepen into red or brown, but even blues and greens (due to lead and other metals) are not as rare as the pure, waxy white of unadulterated calcite. The curtains, stalactites, and other pendant forms may ring out like bells when struck lightly with a wooden mallet—but strike carefully, for they are very brittle.

The rate of growth of stalactites varies enormously. Those in the Cheddar Caves are said to require about three thousand years to grow an inch, but in Moravia a specimen as thick as a pencil was broken off in 1880 and grew an inch and a half in twelve years. A stalactite an inch and a half in diameter, and of about the same length, was reported to have grown beneath an Edinburgh bridge in a hundred years, but there is no doubt that the rapidly grown specimens are poor in quality owing to the small size of their crystals, and are generally opaque. Very rapid deposition does not appear to result in stalactites, but in the cauliflower-like encrustations of 'tufa' (see below).

You do not, of course, have to go underground to see lime deposited by water. It is true that good stalactites and stalagmites have no chance to grow save in the seclusion of a cave, but all water flowing from the limestone hills carries a burden of lime which it is ready to get rid of at the first opportunity. It may do this in your kettle, encrusting it with 'fur', or it may deposit it with surprising rapidity on articles placed at the mouth of the spring from which you draw your water. These 'petrifying' springs and wells are common enough, and are sometimes advertised to attract tourists. Birds' nests and other such objects coated with lime may be sold on the spot as souvenirs, but the deposits have not the pure quality of those in the limestone caves. They are dull and opaque, and crumble when roughly handled. They are known to geologists as 'tufa', a hardened variety of which—travertine—has already been mentioned.

Lime may be deposited in fissures and hollows in many other crystalline forms, and sometimes large, perfectly formed single crystals may be found. Of the two hundred varieties known to mineralogists the two most common are illustrated in Fig. 68, and both are usually glass-clear or stained pink with iron. The first is known as 'Iceland spar', in which the calcite assumes the form of a rhombohedron (a sort of solid parallelogram). Iceland spar possesses the peculiar property of polarizing light, dividing a ray into two parallel beams, so that if a crystal be laid on a printed page the letters seen through it appear double. The other variety is 'dog-tooth spar', the pyramidal crystals of which suggest (to the fanciful) canine teeth. At first glance, crystals of dog-tooth spar

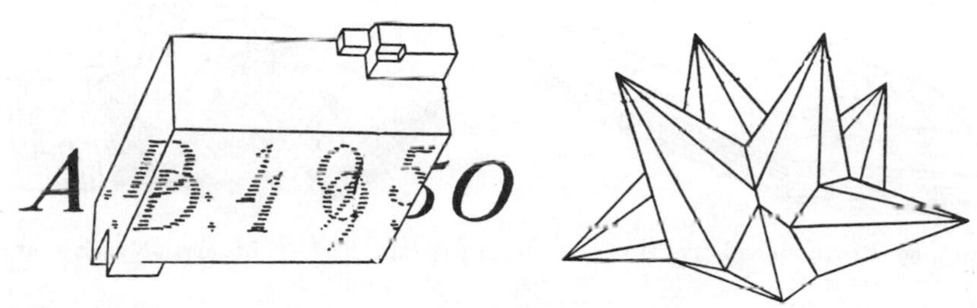

FIG. 68. Two of the common forms of calcite. *Left*, Iceland spar, showing double refraction. *Right*, dog-tooth spar.

may be confused with those of quartz (Fig. 61), but the points of its pyramids are very much sharper. In cases of doubt a pocket-knife provides a ready test: dog-tooth spar is easily scratched, while quartz isn't.[1]

Other salts of lime besides the carbonate are also found as mineral crystals, the most common being 'selenite' (the sulphate) and 'fluor-spar' (the fluoride). (See Fig. 69.) Large, water-clear crystals of selenite are often found in clays. They may be scratched very easily (even by a finger-nail), and split into flakes when pressed with the point of a knife. When they occur in commercial quantities they are mined as 'gypsum' and ground and roasted to produce 'plaster of Paris'. Sometimes the crystals are very fine and packed into a rock-like mass which can be carved and polished. This is often stained and streaked with coloured impurities, and has a waxy appearance. It is called 'alabaster', and is used like marble for ornamental work.

Fluor-spar is found in mineral veins, particularly in limestone regions. It occurs in perfect cubes of transparent violet or royal blue, and occasionally green, but it is also found in crystalline masses large enough to carve into vases, bowls and other ornaments. In this form it is called 'blue-john' or 'Derbyshire spar'. Fluor-spar can be scratched with a knife, but it is much harder than selenite and a little harder than calcite.

[1] An infallible test for all carbonates—including limestones—is a drop of any dilute acid, spirits of salts (hydrochloric acid) being commonly used. The effect is an immediate and copious effervescence of bubbles of carbon dioxide.

Most mineral crystals have easily recognized forms, but their forms alone are not always sufficient to identify them. Thus, both rock-salt and iron pyrites crystallize in cubes, and the illustration of fluor-spar in Fig. 69 would do equally well for either of them. Rock-salt, however, is neither blue nor green, but something near to white (though it may be stained brown with iron), and it tastes salt, while iron pyrites looks like cubes of polished brass.

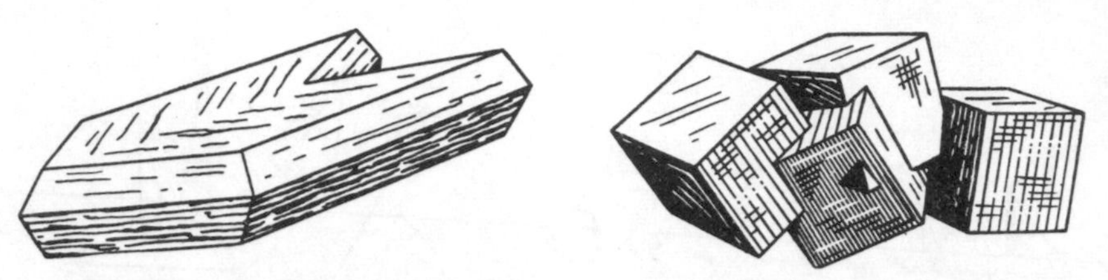

FIG. 69. *Left*, twinned crystal of selenite or gypsum. *Right*, cubic crystals such as are formed by fluor-spar (transparent blue).

Again, many minerals exhibit different forms in different circumstances. We have already mentioned some of the forms assumed by calcium carbonate, and iron sulphide affords us another common example. Lumps of coal often contain it in the form of thin plates of pyrites which people have sometimes mistaken for gold. The popular name for pyrites is, in fact, 'fool's gold'. But it is most commonly met with in the form of heavy rounded nodules in both clay and chalk (which is a soft white limestone), and then it is known to mineralogists as 'marcasite' but to country-folk as 'thunderbolts'.[1] A small nodule of marcasite is illustrated in Fig. 70, and a broken section shows that it is made up of radiating brassy crystals. The surface of the nodules decays and weathers until the metallic lustre is lost, and their external colour may be anything from a clayey yellow to dark brown. Twinned crystals of marcasite resembling brass arrow-heads ('cockscomb' or 'spear' pyrites) are sometimes found, and in Kent they were traditionally regarded as Roman weapons!

The very pale colour of marcasite crystals has also earned it the name of 'white pyrites', and has led some people to imagine that it is meteoric iron. Meteoric iron, however, is very rarely found, and even then only in very small pieces of rusty metal which bear no resemblance to marcasite. A magnet will attract meteoric iron but not marcasite or pyrites.

Pyrites is not used as an iron ore because of the sulphur it contains, but it is mined (in Spain and elsewhere) for the conversion of its sulphur into sulphuric acid. The most important commercial iron ores consist of the oxides of iron,

[1] There is, of course, no such thing as a 'thunderbolt' apart from the flash of lightning which strikes the earth. There is no connection between thunderstorms and falling meteorites.

Ia. V-shaped valley. Ramsden Clough, Yorkshire.
(Ramsden reservoirs in middle distance.) (*Pp. 4, 9, 21, 176*)

Ib. U-shaped valley. Pass of Llanberis, N. Wales.
(See Fig. 5.) (*Pp. 4, 8, 9*)

IIA. Convex mountain-slopes. Malvern Hills. (*Pp. 7, 10, 157*)

IIB. Concave mountain-slopes. Schiehallion, Perthshire. (River Tummel in foreground.) (*P. 7*)

IIC. Low hill of clay. Guildford Cathedral, Surrey. (*Pp. 11, 21*)

IIIA. Peak, corrie and tarn. Snowdon and Glaslyn. (*Pp*. 7, 8, 14, 21, 24)

IIIB. Arête. Striding Edge, Helvellyn. (*Pp*. 7, 9, 21)

IVA. Mountains carved in granite. Red Hills, Skye. (*Pp. 7, 20, 21, 23, 24, 30*)

IVB. Folded strata (anticline). Plynlimmon. (See Fig. 8.) (*P. 11*)

Va. Escarpment in soft rock (chalk). Box Hill, Surrey. (*Pp. 13, 21, 76, 139, 140*)

Vb. Escarpment in harder rock (Great Scar limestone), with clints in foreground. Above Malham Cove, Yorkshire. (*Pp. 13, 21, 26, 82*)

Vc. Escarpment in hard rock (volcanic). Cader Idris. (*Pp. 13, 20, 24*)

VIA. Hog-back. Purbeck Hills, Dorset. (See Fig. 13) (*Pp. 14, 17, 21*)

VIB. Mesa or tabular hill. Pen Puch, Glamorgan. (*Pp. 15, 21*)

VIC. Fault-scarp. Giggleswick Scar, Yorkshire. (*Pp. 15, 21, 26*)

VIIA. Sill and volcanic neck (left background). Salisbury Crags and Arthur's Seat, Edinburgh. (*Pp. 18, 20, 21, 37*)

VIIB. Mountain of igneous rock. Traprain Law, Haddington. (*Pp. 20, 21*)

VIIC. Folded strata. Stair Hole, Dorset. (*P. 14*)

VIID. Fault. Black Point, Pembroke. (*P. 17*)

VIIIA. Tor. Bowerman's Nose, Dartmoor. (*Pp. 21, 25*)

VIIIB. Frost-shattered rocks. Tryfan, N. Wales. (*Pp. 21, 23*)

VIIIC. Outcrop of hornstone. Charnwood, Leicestershire. (*Pp. 25, 99, 125*)

VIIID. Inland stack. Devil's Chimney, near Cheltenham. (*Pp. 25, 26*)

IXa. Erratic block. Norber, Yorkshire. (*P. 31*)

IXb. *Roche moutonnée*. Glen Nevis, Inverness (*P. 29*)

IXc. Crag-and-tail. Duncryne, Gartocharn, Dumbarton. (*P. 27*)

IXd. Glacial lake and moraines. Llyn Llydaw, N. Wales. (*P. 30*)

XA. Dyke. South-east coast of Arran. (*P. 37*)

XB. Castellated granite. Land's End. (*P. 4*

XC. Blow-hole or gloup. Holborn Head, Caithness. (*P. 44*)

XD. Arch and geo (foreground), Needle E from Ashey Geo, Wick. (*P. 44*)

XIa. Stack, arch and cave. Covesea, Elgin. (*Pp. 21, 25, 44*)

XIb. Spit and salt marsh. Scolt Head, Norfolk, from the air. (The south side of the area is at the top.) (*P. 49*)

XIIA. Drowned river-mouth. Solva River, Pembroke. (*P. 56*)

XIIB. Drift-beach. Chesil Bank from the Isle of Portland. (*Pp. 42, 48, 50*)

XIIC. Salt marshes. Morston, Norfolk. (Blakeney esker in background.) (*Pp. 30, 50*)

XIIIA. 'Pacific' type of coast. Lulworth Cove, Dorset. (*Pp. 21, 56*)

XIIIB. 'Atlantic' type of coast. Reskajeage Cliffs, Cornwall. (*Pp. 21, 54, 140, 141*)

XIVA. Broads. Ormesby Broads, Norfolk, looking south. (*P.* 57)

XIVB. Dunes. Culbin sand-hills, Elgin. (*P.* 59)

XVA. Weathered sandstone. Rombalds Moor, Yorkshire. (*P. 33*)

XVB. Dry river-bed. Anglezark Moor, Lancashire. (*P. 3*)

XVC. Groynes checking longshore drifting of beach. Folkestone. (*P. 44*)

XVD. Waterfall, gorge and pot-hole (foreground). Tintagel, Cornwall. (*Pp. 67, 68*)

XVIa. Infilling of a lake. Derwentwater. (*Pp. 21, 72*)

XVIb. Infilled lake. Borrowdale. (*Pp. 21, 72*)

XVIIA. Meander, bluff and slip-off slope. Tidenham Bend and Longhope Reach, river Wye. (*P. 74*)

XVIIB. River terraces. River Findhorn, Nairn. (*P. 79*)

XVIIC. Raised beach. North coast of Islay. (*Pp. 57, 140*)

XVIIIA. Swallow-hole. Gaping Ghyll, Ingleborough. (*Pp. 35, 82*)

XVIIIB. Limestone gorge. Gordale Scar, Yorkshire. (*Pp. 26, 82*)

XVIIIC. Limestone cave with stalactites and stalagmites. Gingling Hole, Fountain's Fell, Yorkshire. (*P. 93*)

XIXA. Clump or cap of beeches. Chanctonbury Ring, Sussex. (*Pp. 21, 107, 167, 177*)

XIXB. V-shaped hanger on the side of a coombe. Near Plumpton, Sussex (planted to commemorate Queen Victoria's jubilee, 1887). (*Pp. 21, 107*)

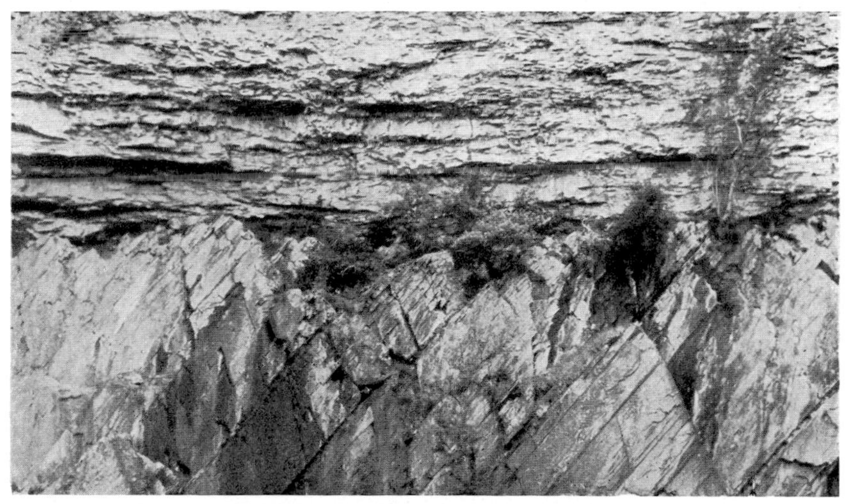

XIXC. Fossil land-surface (unconformity). Near Helwith Bridge, Yorkshire. (See Fig. 103.) (*P. 133*)

XXA. Ripple-stone (*p. 113*). B. Ice-scratched rock (*p. 29*). C. Fossil bivalve shell (*p. 114*). D. Outside and inside of 'potato-stone' (*p. 99*). E. Ammonite or 'St Hilda's serpent' (*p. 128*). F. Fossil sponge in flint (*p. 124*). G. The 'Devil's toe-nail' (fossil bivalve) (*p. 114*). H. 'Shepherd's crown', a fossil sea-urchin (*p. 123*). I. 'Dudley locust', a trilobite (*p. 119*)

XXIA. Fossil islands (monadnocks) on a plain of marine erosion.
St David's, Pembroke. (*Pp. 132, 137, 140*)

XXIB. Dissected plateau. Rhinog Fach and Rhinog Fawr, Merioneth.
(See Fig. 106.) (*Pp. 7, 138, 140*)

XXIC. Conical waste-dump at a colliery. (*P. 170*)

XXIIA. Destructive work of the sea. Pakefield, near Lowestoft, 1936. (*Cf.* Plate XXVIIIC.) (*P. 143*)

XXIIB. Buried forest. Little Galley Hill, near Bexhill. (*P. 149*)

XXIIIA. *Left*: Long barrow and bowl barrow. *Centre*: Disc and bell barrows. *Right*: Three bowl barrows. At Winterbourne Crossroads, near Stonehenge. (*Pp. 160, 162*)

XXIIIB. Green road, near flint mines at Findon, Sussex. (*P. 35*)

XXIIIC. Covered way or cross dyke. Highden Hill, Sussex. (*P. 169*)

XXIIID. Standing stone. The second 'Devil's Arrow', Boroughbridge. (*P. 171*)

XXIVA. Prehistoric mound. Silbury Hill, near Avebury. (*P. 164*)

XXIVB. Iron Age fort. Maiden Castle, Dorset. (*P. 167*)

XXVA. Strip lynchets. Norton, near Bishopstone, Sussex. (*Pp. 169, 170*)

XXVB. Stone circle. Merrivale, Dartmoor. (*P. 173*)

XXVC. Slag-heap engulfing a house. Near Swansea. (*P. 170*)

XXVD. Scarp-like face of a rubbish-tip. Derbyshire. (*P. 170*)

XXVIa. Celtic fields. Fyfield Down, Wiltshire. (*P. 170*)

XXVIb. Dolmen. The 'Devil's Den', Marlborough. (*P. 172*)

XXVIc. Dew-pond. South Downs, near Wilmington. (*P. 174*)

XXVId. Windbreak. Great Bookham, Surrey. (*P. 177*)

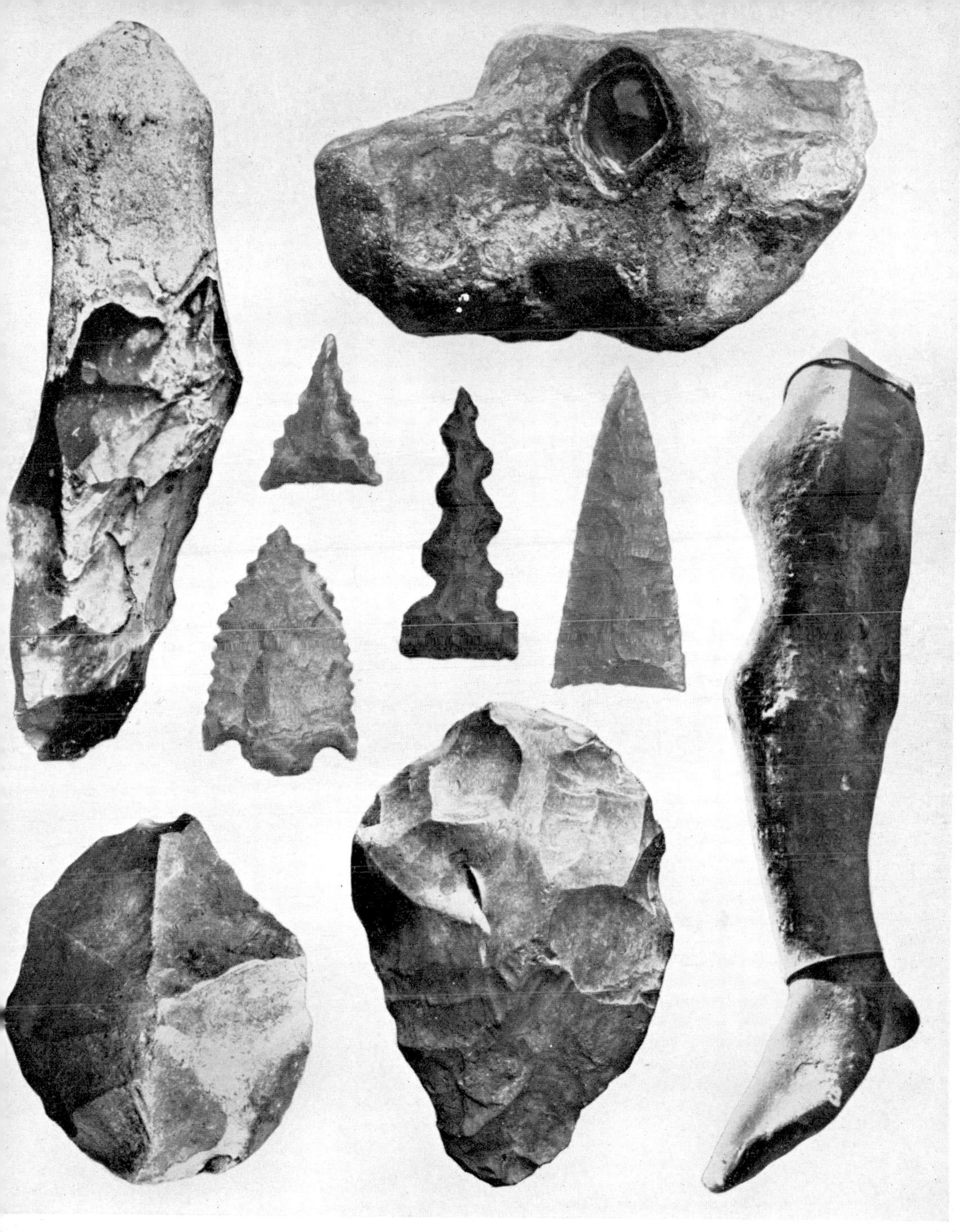

XXVII. *Top and right*: Accidental flints resembling a dog's head and a human leg. (*P. 126*)
Left and foot: Old Stone Age pick and hand-axes. (*P. 181*)
Centre: New Stone Age arrow-heads. (*P. 186*)

XXVIIIA. Slate quarry a mile long and 1,200 feet deep. Penrhyn, N. Wales. (From a diorar at the Geological Museum, London.) (*Pp. 102, 157, 188*)

XXVIIIB. Cliff-protection work in beach pebbles and concrete. Brighton. (*P. 189*)

XXVIIIC. Sea-wall to protect cliffs. Pakefie near Lowestoft. (*Cf.* Plate XXIIA.) (*P. 18*

and these occur in varying quantities almost everywhere. They are responsible for the yellow colour of sands and weathered clays, for the deep browns and reds of sandstones, for the red of building bricks, and for dark red and black deposits in many kinds of rock. The carbonates are also worked.

One of the most valuable iron ores is called 'haematite' because of its red colour (Greek *haima*, blood), but it is often so dark as to appear black. It occurs (in England chiefly in the north-west) in smooth spherical masses looking very much like bunches of kidneys, so that the miners' name for it is 'kidney ore'.[1] (See Fig. 71.) Along with the bunches of iron 'kidneys' there often appear masses of small, black, sparkling crystals, like little plates of black glass set on edge, and these are simply an alternative form of haematite called 'specular iron'. Specimens are often studded with large quartz crystals, and handsome pieces may be used as paper weights, for they are very heavy.

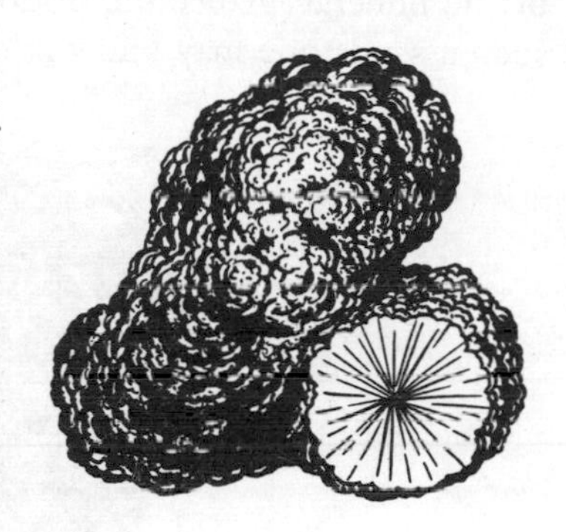

FIG. 70. A nodule of marcasite (sulphide of iron) from the Chalk.

All these iron minerals—and the quartz—have been deposited by water, and in sandstone districts, where the water percolates rapidly, the iron is often found in yet another form. It occurs in bands of dark green or purple-black rock consisting of sand grains thickly coated and cemented together by a nearly black hydrated iron oxide (not the red oxide of haematite). This mineral is known as 'limonite', and the hard blocks of sand cemented by it are called 'carstone', 'hard-pan', 'iron-pan', or 'ironstone', the last term being also applicable to any low-grade iron ore. They are quarried and used for paving and for building walls and cottages. In some sand-pits you may see the beds of carstone projecting from the face like shelves, and quite often they assume fantastic forms suggesting drain-pipes, corrugated iron, warped and split ply-wood, massive honeycombs, and so on. (See Fig. 80.) The occurrence of limonite in 'iron-shot' sands is described on page 111.

Traces of various minerals are often deposited in sandstones separately in different layers, each mineral staining the sand a different colour. Thus, manganese gives a fine series of pinks and purples, iron yellows, browns and

[1] Occasionally lumps of marcasite may be found which would conform to this verbal description of kidney ore, but nobody who has once seen both minerals would ever again confuse them. The broken surface of haematite is red and has no metallic lustre; it is quite different from the brassy rays of marcasite. The rambler will find no haematite in the east or south of England, where marcasite is abundant. The most notable counties for haematite are Cumberland and Lancashire.

reds, and also blues and greens, lime white and grey, carbon black, and pyrites blues and greys. The famous coloured sands of Alum Bay, in the Isle of Wight, exhibit such a wide range of brilliant colours that in George III's reign some remarkable pictures were 'painted' by dusting them on to gummed boards.[1] Some sandstones are of a particularly vivid green colour, due to the deposition of the mineral 'glauconite' round their grains. The rambler who comes across such a sandstone may know at once that it was a sea-sand and not a river or a

FIG. 71. A piece of haematite or 'kidney-ore', with quartz crystals and specular iron.

desert one, though the *absence* of the green colour proves nothing, for there are many marine sands which contain no glauconite. Further ways of detecting the origin of sands were given in Chapter III (see page 59), and we shall have more to say on the subject in the next chapter.

The concentration of minerals in well-marked layers is little understood, even today. It occurs in limestones and clays as well as sandstones, and the deposits are not necessarily crystalline in structure, but may be granular, laminated, or massive and structureless like glass. Silica, which can crystallize as quartz, is actually more often deposited in this structureless form, in which it is familiar to everybody as 'flint'. (See Fig. 134.)

All flints originate in bands of irregular nodules of various sizes in the chalk, and in their unaltered state are black in appearance.[2] However, they acquire a white porous crust through partial solution, and those which have been carried away by rivers or torn from the chalk cliffs by the sea are more often worn down to small, rounded pebbles, and stained brown by iron. Occasionally

[1] There were four notable sand-painters, the chief being Zobel, and their pictures were often copies in full colour of famous masterpieces. Their palette of sands was augmented by marble dust, but the exact method they used is still a mystery. About one hundred examples of their work are known—and many inferior imitations.

[2] Due to their translucency; a thin slip is straw-coloured. For their origin see page 123 *et seq.*

a hollow flint may be found lined with quartz crystals. Nodules of silica similar to flint, but more splintery, are found in older limestones and are known as 'chert'; a more splintery variety still is called 'hornstone'. Both chert and hornstone sometimes form quite massive layers (see Plate VIII, C). .

In cavities in igneous rocks, in mineral veins, and sometimes in the older

FIG. 72. Agate, showing concentric growth lines.

sedimentary rocks or lining hollow flints, silica may be deposited in the semi-translucent mass known as 'chalcedony' (from *Chalcedon*, a town in Asia Minor, and pronounced 'kal-*sed*-on-y'). Though it has a waxy look it is exceedingly hard. Several successive deposits may be made, and if each layer happens to be stained a different colour the mineral is known as 'onyx' or 'agate'. Specimens of agate, cut and polished, show concentric rings like the growth-rings in tree-trunks—and they are indeed growth-rings. (See Fig. 72.) When this non-crystalline form of silica is stained a vivid red by iron it is called 'carnelian', or—with sufficient iron to make it quite opaque—'jasper', and pebbles of both these minerals may sometimes be picked up on a shingle beach. 'Opal' is a much rarer form of silica which the rambler would be really lucky to find.

Many of the softer rocks through which water cannot percolate very easily—such as clays—become cemented locally into hard lumps called 'concretions', and these are always worth breaking open to see what they contain. There may be a fossil at the centre, or a cavity lined with crystals. The example shown in Plate XX, D, is known as a 'potato-stone' because on the outside it resembles a potato. Another type, common in the London Clay, contains a network of veins filled with calcite, and is called a 'cement stone' or 'septarian nodule' (Fig. 73). Yet another is the 'coal-ball' described on page 131.

Concretions may be formed in concentric layers of varying solubility, and one of the interior layers may later be dissolved away leaving a hard core loose inside a hollow ball. These are known as 'rattle-stones'.[1] In limestone which contains a lot of magnesia[2] large round concretions are often found, particularly along the bedding-planes, and this has given rise to the name 'cannon-ball limestone'. Similar round balls, cemented this time by iron, are found in some

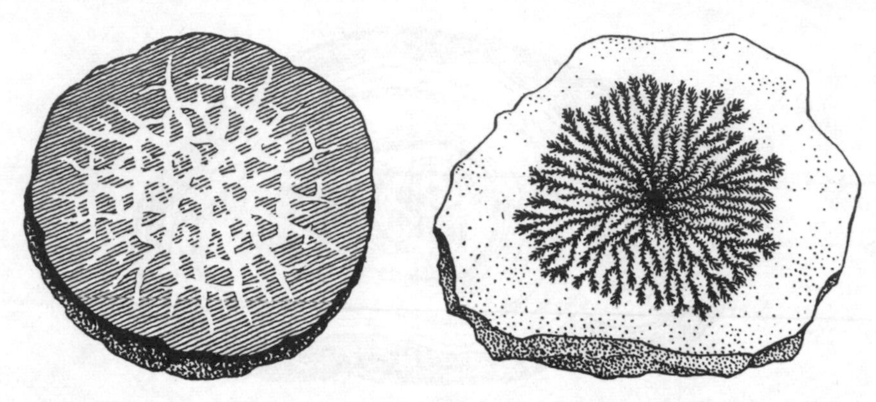

FIG. 73. *Left*, a cement-stone or septarian nodule from the London Clay. *Right*, dendrite, a deposit of manganese resembling vegetable growth, on a joint-face in a piece of limestone.

of the older shales and are called 'clay-ironstone nodules'. The nodules of flint and marcasite which we have already described are also classed as concretions.

The last group of curious mineral deposits likely to arouse the curiosity of the rambler is typified in Fig. 73 (right). This looks like some sort of fossil moss, but it is really a fine crystalline deposit of manganese on the face of a block of limestone. Because of their resemblance to the forms of plant-life, deposits of this type are called 'dendrites' (Greek *dendron*, a tree), and in a variety found near Bristol the outlines and foliage of trees and hedgerows are so well imitated that the stone is called 'landscape marble'. The imitations are, of course, in miniature (the 'trees' are usually about an inch and a half high), but dendritic markings of various sorts found on the joint-faces of limestones may measure anything from a millimetre to a foot or more across. Occasionally a dendrite of the kind shown in Fig. 73 appears on an agate, and provides the jewellers with the 'moss-agate' of Victorian brooches.

[1] Other hollow and 'lucky' stones are described on pages 124 and 125.

[2] Magnesian limestone is abundant in Durham, and York Minster and the Houses of Parliament are built of it. Unfortunately, the sulphurous fumes in the London air (due to the burning of coal in half a million grates) attack the magnesia in this stone, converting it into Epsom salts, so that the Houses of Parliament are under almost continuous repair. Portland stone, which contains no magnesia, is immune from this form of attack and is therefore very widely used for city buildings.

We have described so far in this chapter the general characteristics of igneous and sedimentary rocks, and the more common minerals deposited in them by water. But a miscellaneous group of rocks—the 'metamorphic'—remains to be described. These were originally normal igneous or sedimentary rocks, but were later subjected to some form of physical violence which changed their structure or chemical composition. The physical violence may have been excessive pressure or excessive heat, or both, but the technical nature of the subject forbids us to give more than a few notes on the most common examples.

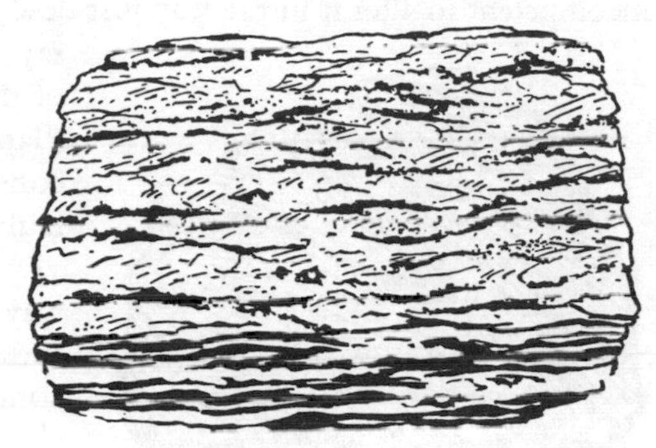

FIG. 74. A hand-specimen of gneiss, showing flow-structure.

The normal effects of great pressure are first the consolidation of the rocks and then the folding of the strata. All this we have described, and it occurs without any radical change in the rocks themselves. But there is a limit to what even the hardest rocks will stand, and when this is exceeded new processes are set in motion. One of these is that the rocks may begin to flow like very thick liquids.

In the Highlands of Scotland (and elsewhere) some mountains consist largely of an igneous rock containing the same constituents as granite, but they appear to have been mixed in a toffee-factory and then drawn out while still sticky. This effect was not produced by the flowing of molten rock, however, but was achieved long after the original rock (granite) had set cold. The evidence for this is that the crystals in the rock are themselves distorted which means that they were formed first (by cooling) and were later pushed out of shape. Moreover, they are not distributed entirely haphazard throughout the rock as they are in granite, but the different kinds have been partly separated into layers which show the direction of the cold flow.[1]

This rock is called 'gneiss' (pronounced 'nice') and is illustrated in Fig. 74, but many rocks other than granite (both igneous and sedimentary) are subject to similar changes, and the general name for this type of metamorphic (altered) rock is 'schist' (pronounced 'shist') which indicates their proneness to splitting (Greek *skhistos*, split). The layers or 'foliations' of different materials may be distinguished from sedimentary bedding by their irregularity. It should be

[1] That rocks can yield to pressure in this way was observed during the driving of the St Gotthard Tunnel, and has been demonstrated in the laboratory.

added that heat from nearby molten rock often *assists* in the formation of schists, for these have been observed to become more and more plentiful in the neighbourhood of ordinary igneous rocks, which must have come into place in the molten condition. The arrival of these rocks must, indeed, have applied both heat and pressure simultaneously to all the surrounding country.

If the pressure applied to a sedimentary rock is insufficient or otherwise incompetent to alter it in the way just described, it may yet crush it. That is to say, apart from the folding and faulting of the strata as a whole, the small layers ('laminations') of which the rock itself consists may suffer intense folding and faulting on a miniature scale. (See Fig. 75.) Rocks which have suffered in this way are appropriately described as 'contorted', and common examples include contorted shales, limestones, boulder-clay and even gravel-beds (contorted by the movements of glaciers). Sometimes a rock which has already been altered into a schist becomes further altered into a contorted schist, and the reader is at liberty to imagine every possible combination of the processes we are describing.

FIG. 75. A hand-specimen of contorted schist.

In the case of fine clays, the particles of which are flat plates of microscopic size, moderate vertical pressure converts them into shales. These look like what they are—hardened clays which split easily into slabs along their bedding-planes. But when subjected to intense horizontal pressure a remarkable change occurs in their internal structure.

Fig. 76 A shows a deposit of clay with its particles all lying flat, just as they settled down in a river delta or off a muddy shore. We now imagine them covered by other deposits and subjected to lateral pressure as shown at B. The flat particles leave their beds and begin to stand up, and when the process is complete they are all vertical, as at C. To accomplish this result the pressure has to be much greater than that which produces shale, and the final rock is therefore very much harder. It is slate, and Fig. 76 D shows how roofing slates are split off the rock—they come away at right-angles to the bedding instead of parallel with it. See Plate XVIII, A. This unique property is called 'slaty cleavage', and the process described has been imitated in the laboratory by subjecting blocks of wax containing flakes of shellac to horizontal pressure.

We have already mentioned one of the effects of the intense heat and pressure to which rocks may be subjected when molten granite or lava is forced up to the surface of the earth. This was the conversion of many rocks into schists, and it may begin to occur as far as a hundred miles from the source of the heat. When water or steam is also present, chemical as well as structural alterations may be brought about. Details of the complex processes which may take place

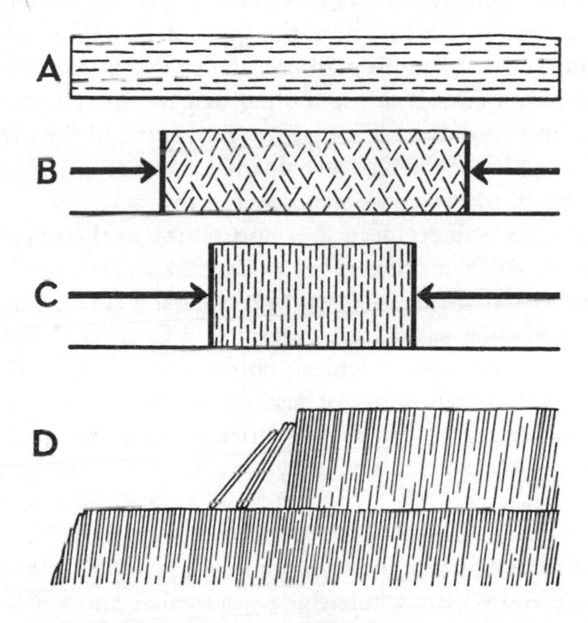

FIG. 76. The formation of slate from a deposit of mud. See the text.

are not likely to interest the average rambler, but a few of their results may claim his attention.

For instance, the visitor to the Lizard, Cornwall, may be offered souvenirs in the form of little vases and other ornaments carved from the local rock—a beautiful variegated stone in red, black or green. This is called 'serpentine', and it takes a high polish like marble but is more easily scratched. Serpentine is produced by the action of heat and water on igneous rocks rich in magnesium. A very soft form of it, pale pink, yellow or white in colour, is known as 'soapstone' because of its soapy feel, and this also is carved into ash-trays and other *bric-a-brac*. Soapstone ground to a fine powder is the 'talc' or 'French chalk' of beauty specialists and tailors.

Intense moist heat is able to convert limestones and sandstones into hard rocks of uniform crystalline texture, limestones becoming true marbles and sandstones quartzites—indistinguishable from the quartzites we have already described as formed by percolating water. The true marbles (those used for the finest sculpture, for example) sparkle like castor sugar when broken, and unlike the so-called 'marbles' described on page 89 they contain no fossils, though they may be veined in many colours by traces of 'foreign' minerals.

Heat converts coal into coke below the ground as well as at the gasworks, and further changes the coke into graphite. It also cracks and splinters rocks of all kinds, and injects minerals in the molten or gaseous state into the fissures, where they cool and crystallize. Tin ore, sulphur, some of the ores of iron, lead and zinc, and possibly the Cornish arsenic ore known as 'mispickel', are among the minerals believed to have been deposited in this way.

But let us leave the subterranean fires and return to the open air, where all rocks are liable to suffer a quite different sort of interference. The constant attack made on them by the weather has two results: it carves out of them some of the forms of landscape, as we have described in Chapters I and II, and it also changes their structure and chemical composition, converting them into soils. Common soils contain more or less of 'humus', a dark brown or black product of vegetable decay, but in this brief account we shall consider only those characteristics of soils which they owe to the rocks from which they are derived.

Fig. 77 shows a section through a typical soil—a 'soil-profile'—the bed-rock being marked X. Immediately above X there is a layer of broken fragments of this rock (C—B), and on the whole these get smaller and smaller towards the surface. This layer used to be called the 'subsoil'—and still is by ordinary folk. The top layer, A, consists of finer particles still, and a great deal of humus, and this is what is usually referred to as the 'soil'. In clay regions the soil will be yellow, brown or black, in limestone districts grey or black, in sandstone areas brown, red, or dirty white.

These colours are not infallible guides, but the rambler cannot fail to notice the difference between the light grey soils of the chalk country, the red soils of Devon, and the sticky yellow soils of the London Basin, and he should have some idea of the causes of such differences. In all cases the colours are more or less those of the 'country-rock', save in the case of clay and some sandstones.[1]

[1] The general nature of the rocks is also reflected in the predominant colour of the older buildings. Before the age of mechanical transport local stone was used for most manor houses, churches, and old boundary walls (less durable materials sufficing for cottages). Thus, we notice the predominance of grey granite in Aberdeenshire, of greenish slates in the Lake District, of warm-coloured limestones in N. Yorkshire and Gloucestershire, of red sandstones in Herefordshire, and of red bricks in the clay vales and plains.

The true colour of our largest formations of clay is blue-black, or blue-green-black, and this is due to dark-coloured compounds of iron.[1] It is the colour of the London Clay, of the Gault of the Weald, of the Oxford Clay, and of the Lias of Dorset. But in the surface soil the black compounds become changed into the red oxide (rust), and so the clay as a whole takes on a yellow or brown colour. The soil over a yellow or red sandstone may become whitened by the removal of its colouring matter (iron oxide) by percolating rain-water. It may consist of nothing but white sand grains dirtied to an ashy grey by particles of humus, and in this poor condition is known as a 'podsol'. The colour of loams and marls (see page 91), and all other mixtures in which no one ingredient predominates, may be generally described as brownish black.

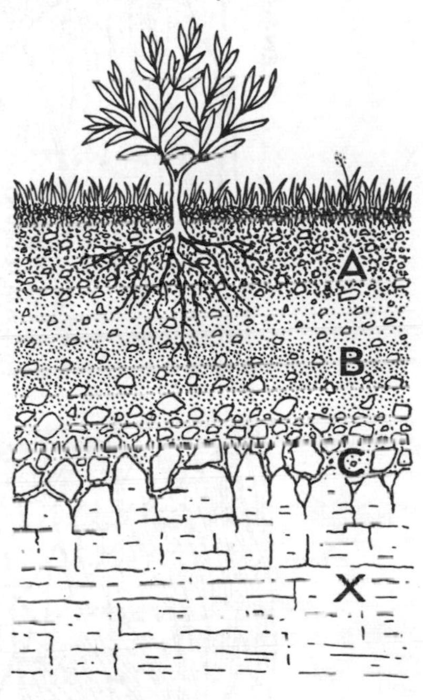

Fig. 77. Typical soil-profile, showing chief zones (A, B & C) and bedrock (X).

In the finely-divided state of a soil the soluble minerals of a rock are especially subject to solution in rain-water, so that the top layer (Fig. 77 A) is usually divided into two sub-sections. There is the surface layer which is rich in humus and dark in colour, and a paler layer immediately beneath it from which many of the minerals have been leached out by percolating rain-water. In layer B some of these minerals may be redeposited as a 'hard-pan' (see page 97), which interferes with further drainage and often makes cultivation difficult. So effective is this leaching action of the rain that even on the chalk hills, where there is only nine inches or so of soil, the actual surface may become completely devoid of lime.

The rambler's acquaintance with soils is practically confined to freshly-ploughed fields, yet he may often know the nature of the 'country-rock' by the type of vegetation which grows in its soil. Lime, for instance, is poison to rhododendrons, and the rhododendrons which may be seen growing in private hedges almost at the foot of the chalk downs are trustworthy evidence that the boundary

[1] Bands of pure white clay, deposited by rivers, are sometimes found, and this is called 'pipe-clay' from its use in making tobacco pipes. A fine greenish-grey clay which falls to pieces when immersed in water is also found in narrow seams in some rocks. This is called 'fuller's earth' and is used for cleaning cloth because of its power to absorb grease.

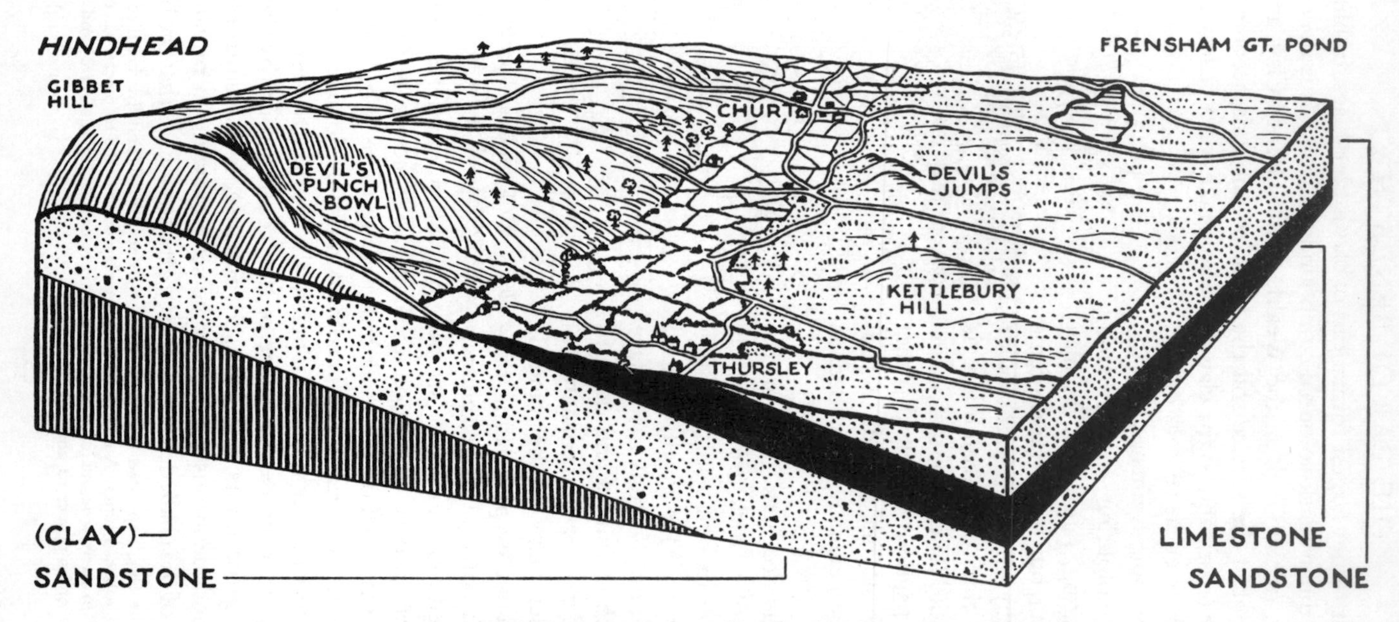

Fig. 78. Block-diagram of a part of west Surrey, showing the effect on vegetation of a narrow outcrop of limestone traversing barren, sandy country.

of the chalk has been passed and that clay or greensand here forms the bed-rock.

Other plants which avoid lime but flourish in sandy or gravelly soils include heather, broom, gorse, sorrel, bracken, foxglove, pine, and sweet chestnut. These may grow on soils derived from igneous rocks, or on clay, but not as a rule on limestone. If such plants are met with on, say, the top of a chalk hill, it is a sure sign that the hill is here capped with 'clay-with-flints'.

'Clay-with-flints' is an interesting deposit of the kind sometimes called 'residual'. The chalk hills were once much higher than they are today, but they have been lowered by the action of weather and water. Much of their lime has been removed by solution, and from their steep slopes the insoluble materials—chiefly flints and traces of clay—have been washed down to the plains below. But on the flat summits these insoluble materials have just accumulated, and they exist today in isolated patches which are often betrayed by the presence of a group of trees called a 'cap' or 'clump', such as that shown in the sketch at the head of Chapter VIII. A well-known example, Chanctonbury Ring, is illustrated in Plate XIX, and though the trees here were deliberately planted (in 1760), many of the conspicuous caps on the downland of Sussex, Hampshire, Wiltshire and Berkshire are self-sown.[1] The soil in which the trees are rooted is usually found to be full of flints, bleached and rotted by the weather, and many of them are partially coated with a black deposit of manganese which looks very much like tar.

The migration of soil down the slopes of hills has already been described as 'soil creep' (see page 35). In sheltered hollows, such as the coombes of the South Downs (see note on page 9), the movement of the soil may be completely checked by the growth of deep-rooted vegetation, and it may here accumulate until it is able to support trees. Thus, the coombes often contain compact little woods or 'holts' on their slopes, and these are known locally as 'hangers' (see Plate XIX, B).

The stones and clay which succeed in reaching the bottom are called 'rain-wash', but the stones may be washed out of this and carried away to form river gravels. In many foot-hill areas there seems to have been extensive flooding at the end of the Ice Age (due to melt-water), and this led to the washing out of the clay and finer grit. With the final disappearance of the water this impure clay settled down in thick layers of 'brick-earth', a name which betrays its use in brick-making. Deposits of brick-earth may be found many miles from their parent hills. At the actual foot of the hills the flints and clay are often mixed with

[1] The trees are nearly always beeches, but it is curious how many people take them for pine or fir trees. Thus Hone, writing of the Chanctonbury clump of beeches in 1841, says 'a well known height called Chankenburg Ring, crowned with fir-trees'. Pines or firs do, however, sometimes form caps on sandstone hills—*e.g.* Crooksbury Hill, south of the Hog's Back, Surrey.

angular broken chalk, forming a deposit known as 'head', or the same mixture may be lightly cemented into a more or less massive aggregate of consolidated rubble called 'coombe rock'.

To return to our tell-tale plants, there are, of course, many species which favour limy soils, and these include the wiry grass known as sheep's fescue, scabious, bee orchis, fly orchis, viper's bugloss, wild cherry, valerian, dogwood, and deadly nightshade. And there are those which delight most in clay, of which the oak is the most noteworthy. The clay flora is not, however, so useful from our point of view, for most river and lake muds will support it. Again, the water-holding properties of clay favour the occurrence of various marsh and bog plants, but these are not a safe guide to the nature of the soil. Many marshes and bogs consist of great thicknesses of peat (see page 146), and this may rest in ill-drained hollows in igneous and other massive rocks. The presence of bog-plants is therefore no more than a challenge to the rambler to look about him for more decisive evidence—such as an exposure of the actual soil in the banks of a stream. The course of a stream is often made visible from a distance by a line of willows and alders growing on its banks, and when these are present you may be sure there is some depth of clay or alluvium beneath the turf.

The change in vegetation as you pass from one type of soil to another is sometimes remarkably sudden. A change from lime or sand to clay is often very clearly marked by the sudden appearance of oaks, willows, or lush pasture, in place of dry pasture, beeches, or pines. A very instructive example is afforded by the narrow strip of farm land which crosses the bare, sandy heath covering the west of Surrey from Hindhead to the Hog's Back. (See Fig. 78.) This wild expanse of barren sand is traversed by a narrow belt of limestone on which the heather gives place abruptly to rich pasture, farm crops, and orchards.

So exactly may the nature of the rocks be deduced from the vegetation which hides them that preliminary geological surveys have sometimes been conducted by mapping the ranges of particular species of plants. In the Ekersund district of Norway the line separating two kinds of igneous rock, one only of which provided the soil (and therefore the pasture) with phosphorus, was determined by a census of cattle suffering from a disease due to phosphorus deficiency.

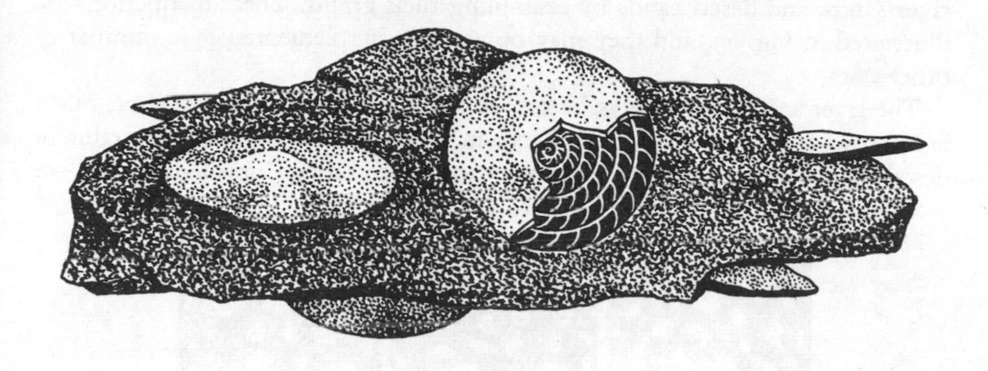

CHAPTER VI

The Living Past

A curious feature about the appreciation of landscape, as we have felt constrained to present it, is that it is almost entirely concerned with bringing past history to light. This close preoccupation with something which no longer exists is surely remarkable employment for a rambler! Yet there are only two alternatives—contemplation of the present or of the future, and, in point of fact, the rambler does consider these also. The present provides him with the data for all his deductions, and the possible future with speculation on the destiny of water-courses, the fate of coasts, or the doom of mountains.

The really remarkable thing is that for him the present affords a means, not an end. He uses the present solely for the purpose of escaping from it. The aesthetically-minded use it to escape into the world of eternal forms, the scientifically-minded to escape into the past (with an occasional peep into the future). If, then—as we might have guessed from quite other considerations—rambling is one of those forms of recreation whose chief object is to escape from the present, we shall do useful service if we can indicate a few short cuts to the attainment of this end.

Some of these we have already given. The reader will remember, for instance, that signs of glaciation where there is now no ice date back to the Ice Age, and that all limestones were once beneath the sea.[1] He has also learnt to examine rocks more closely, and knows the significance of the sizes of the crystals in igneous rocks (page 87) and how to distinguish roughly between sea sands,

[1] There are fresh-water limestones, too, but these were usually deposited in lakes so large that they would certainly be called 'inland seas'.

river sands, and desert sands by examining their grains. These distinctions are illustrated in Fig. 79, and they may be usefully supplemented by a number of other tests.

The river sands may always be recognized by their angular character, but it is not always easy to distinguish between sea and desert sands. The grains of desert sands are usually more spherical and more highly 'finished' than those

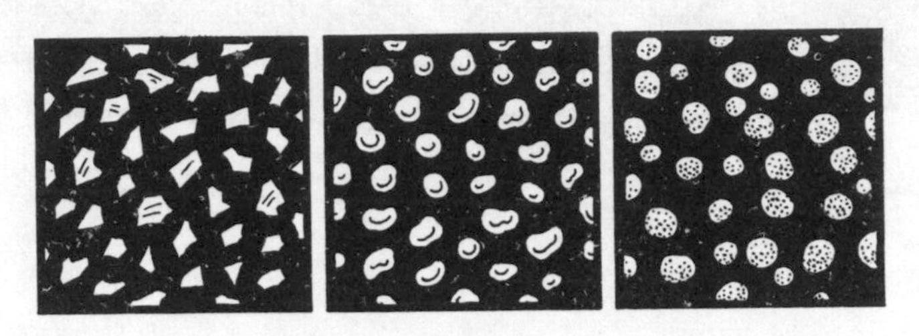

FIG. 79. Sand-grains magnified. *Left*, river sand. *Centre*, sea sand. *Right*, desert sand.

of an old sea coast, yet the sea does sometimes produce perfectly spherical grains, and those of the desert may exhibit facets like a cut gem.

The beautifully rounded sand-grains of the Farnham district of Surrey were for many years thought to be sub-aerial rather than marine, but in 1934 the author discovered fossil shells among them, and also a number of delicate fossil sponges which must have been very gently covered by sand in their living state beneath the sea. The occurrence of glauconite (and also mica) in the locality eventually provided complete confirmation of the marine origin of these sands, though they may have had a complex history. For example, they may have been subjected to wind-action for a time *before* their final deposition in the sea, and it is very likely true that they were blown into the water from a wide, dune-covered coast. A pit in these sands is illustrated in Fig. 80.

When the sand-grains are absolutely glass-clear it is usually safe to deduce a marine origin, but when they show matt or 'ground-glass' surfaces they are likely to be wind-worn grains. And if these wind-worn grains are small, perfectly spherical, and of uniform size, they are unquestionably desert sands (of the 'millet seed' type). With fine sands the size of the grains sometimes affords a clue to their origin. Perfectly rounded grains as small as one-fiftieth of an inch in diameter may occur in either sea or desert sands, but spherical grains smaller than this are formed only by winds blowing over deserts, where even the dust may become polished. Wind-worn grains as small as one-hundredth of an inch in diameter are common in deserts. Sands which contain occasional flakes of mica, however, are almost certainly water-deposited, for this soft mineral seldom survives the rigours of wind-action.

We may summarize these tests as follows. First note the colour of the sands. The green of glauconite betrays a marine origin (see page 98); other colours leave the question open. Second, examine the grains with a magnifying-glass. Angular grains indicate river sands, rounded grains marine or desert sands;

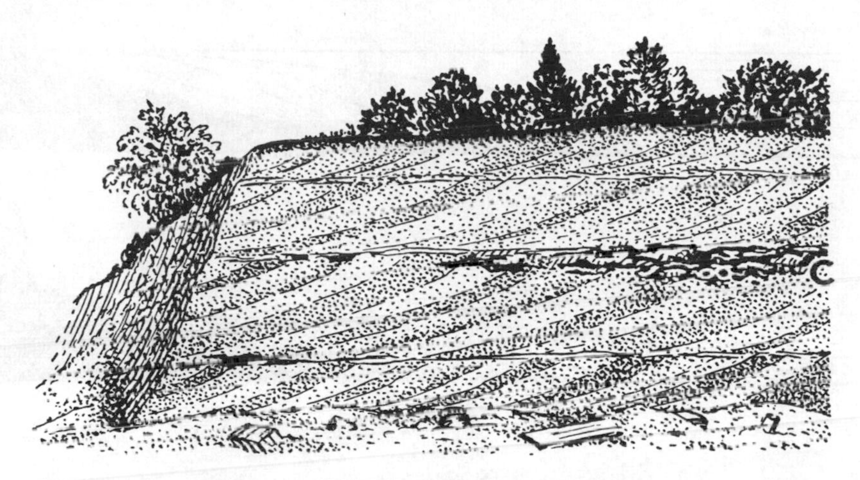

FIG. 80. A sandpit west of Farnham, Surrey, showing both true and false bedding. C, deposit of iron-pan or carstone.

glass-clear grains suggest a marine origin, dull-surfaced grains a desert origin. A sand may have had a mixed origin, but the presence of glittering flat plates of mica rules out prolonged wind-action, although the apparent *absence* of mica may mean nothing more than that you haven't found any, or simply that the sands never did contain any mica.

Sand grains may sometimes be found to be coated with other minerals (notably iron compounds) by percolating water, but though this conceals their surfaces it seldom disguises their shapes. And occasionally, small seams of perfectly round shiny grains of a black or chocolate colour, with a metallic lustre, are found. They look very much like small shot, and are clearly not *sand* grains; they are, in fact, spherical deposits of limonite (page 97) due to percolating water, and were formed long after the sands themselves. Sands containing them are called 'iron-shot' sands.

The bedding of sands is also well worth examining, for if they happen to have been deposited near a shore, or in sand dunes, their peculiar bedding is often instantly recognizable. A fleeting glance from the window of a bus or a railway train may be quite sufficient. The sand-pit shown in Fig. 80 illustrates this 'current bedding', as it is called, and the reader will have no difficulty in spotting the true bedding of these sands, which is marked by the horizontal lines (and by the seam of carstone at C). The current or 'false' bedding indicates

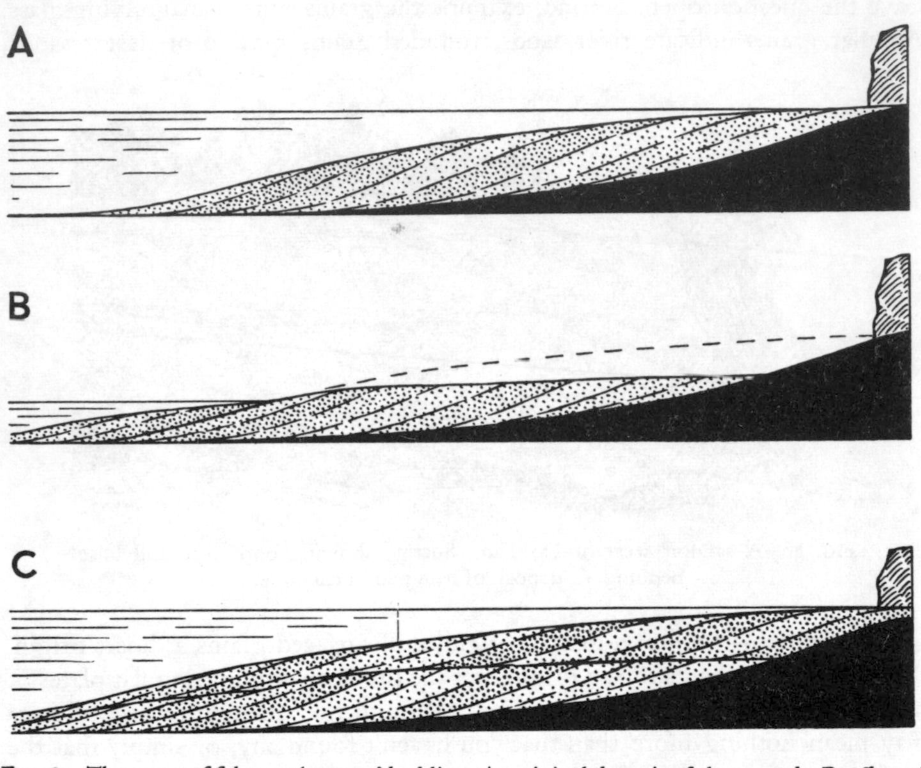

FIG. 81. The cause of false, or 'current' bedding. A, original deposit of shore sands. B, effect of temporary elevation of land. C, second deposit of shore sands following new submergence.

the shelving of a shore, or perhaps the slopes of a dune, while the true bedding indicates the sea-level of the period, and shows that the deposition was here interrupted three times, owing (probably) to temporary elevations and exposure of the sand. This is explained in Fig. 81.

Fig. 81 A shows how sand is normally deposited on a shore, and the removal of the upper layers during a temporary exposure of the surface is indicated at B. If the sand is again submerged, another deposit of a similar nature is laid on top, as at C, and it is clear that three successive repetitions of this process would result in a section of the type illustrated in Fig. 80. The same sort of formation may also result from wind-bedding, as may be seen from the manner in which the sand is deposited in sloping layers on the flanks of the dune illustrated in Fig. 43. The dune shown is idealized, and such deposition of sand by the wind is usually much less regular in form than water-bedding; it is often little short of chaotic. False bedding due to the wind may frequently be seen on the seaward face of a dune on any wide, sandy shore, and we illustrate an actual example in Fig. 82.

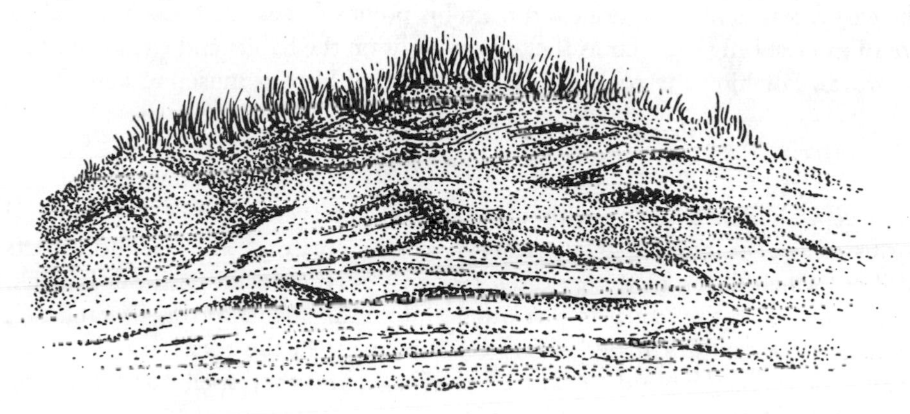

FIG. 82. False bedding due to wind-action. A sand-dune in Gower, S. Wales.

Sands which contain mica, and clays and shales, tend to settle with their grains lying flat like autumn leaves. When a fresh layer is blown or washed over them they sometimes remain in place as a buried surface—that is, they do not merge with the new deposits, but preserve their form even when the sands become consolidated into sandstone and the clays into shale. Such surfaces form planes of weakness in the rock, and it is along them that flagstones (page 91) and shales split so easily. Very often a 'fossil surface' of this kind will show the ripple-marks of ancient seas, or the impressions of rain-drops which fell in a passing shower hundreds of millions of years ago. In the same way, cracks caused by the heat of the sun in soft clays may be preserved for us in the shales they have subsequently become. See Plate XX, A.

The occurrence of fossil sea-shells in sandstones or other rocks may be taken as very good evidence of their marine origin, especially if the shells are plentiful, yet it is by no means conclusive. For example, a soft marine deposit containing shells may become exposed and weather away, leaving its harder fossils for fresh burial under land deposits; or they may get washed out of the rock by a river and carried away for ultimate preservation in much more recent freshwater sands or mud many miles distant. Such shells generally show clear signs of wear and tear, and are known as 'derived' fossils; they are often of great value to geologists seeking the origin of the material composing a rock. By far the commonest derived fossils likely to be found by the rambler are the casts of shells in flint which occur in the gravels of rivers flowing from the chalk hills.

Fossils found undisturbed in their native rock have another sort of value. In addition to throwing light on the nature of the rock, they are worthy of study for their own sakes. This is work for the biologist seeking knowledge of the earlier stages of evolution, and from his point of view the rocks themselves are of interest only in so far as they throw light on the habits and ages of extinct creatures. For him, the rocks are nature's natural history museum, and if

> From scarped cliff and quarried stone
> She cries 'A thousand types are gone,'

he accepts her statement—with etymological reservations. For the physical forms or *types* (Greek *tupos*, impress) of extinct creatures are just those parts of them which do, in fact, very often remain—graven not in flesh but in rock, and 'imposed on the stone' in due order and arrangement. In this literal sense, therefore, the types of many extinct creatures exist in the rocks exactly as the printer's type may be said to exist on this page, and they spell out something beyond the brief lament in Tennyson's lines.[1]

The rambler's interest in biological evolution is, however, limited, though his interest in fossils may be keen. We shall therefore concern ourselves here with the modes of occurrence of some typical common fossils only.

It has already been mentioned that the substance of fossil shells is altered by the process of fossilization (see page 88), and as often as not it is actually *replaced* by quite different substances deposited by percolating water. The lime of the shells may be changed to crystalline calcite (as in the scallop and 'Devil's toe-nail' in Plate XX, C, G), or it may be dissolved right away and silica, limonite, pyrites, marcasite, or some other mineral deposited in its stead. This process seems to take place very slowly, grain by grain—indeed, molecule by molecule—for even microscopic details are often faithfully repeated in the new substance.

Sometimes the shell is dissolved away without any replacement, and then there is an empty space in the rock which provides us with a 'mould', or negative cast, of the shell. A hollow left by a shell in this way may later become filled with mud or sand which hardens to form a positive cast, or replica of the original shell, and the various possibilities of this sort of preservation are illustrated in Fig. 83. You may find a fossil cockle-shell entire, as at A, and this

[1] *In Memoriam*, *LV*.

may be either an altered shell or a complete positive cast—that is, a faithful copy of it. Such a copy is sometimes called a 'hollow' cast, and in the rock from which it came there will be a hollow mould or negative cast, showing its shape and ornament in reverse, as at B. Again, you may find a preservation of the *inside* of the shell, as at C, or a complete internal mould of the shell as at D (which should fit exactly inside A if A happened to be hollow).

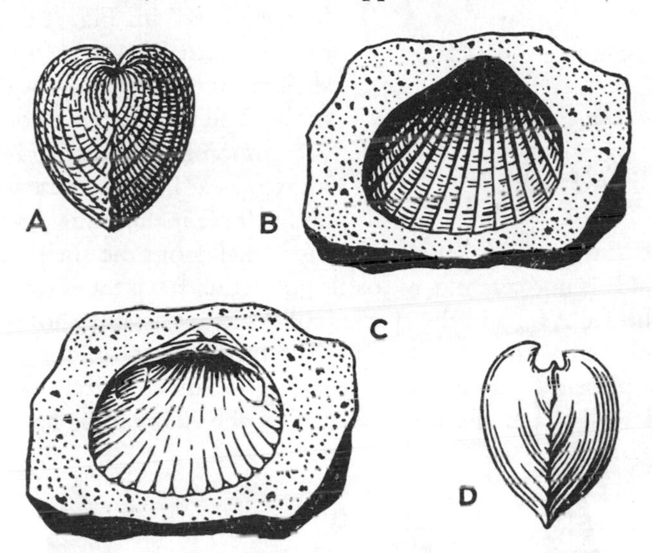

FIG. 83. Ways in which shells, or their impressions, may be preserved as fossils. A, complete cockle shell. B, mould showing ornament on outer surface in reverse. C, preservation or cast of internal details. D, internal mould.

The fossils shown in the slab of limestone in Fig. 63 are not casts, but consist simply of altered shells (and corals). The fossil in the block of sandstone in Fig. 64 is a positive cast corresponding with Fig. 83 A. The impression shown in the limestone in the same illustration is either an external negative cast (Fig. 83 B) or an internal positive one (Fig. 83 C)—it is impossible to tell which in the absence of detail. The common fossil from the Portland Stone shown in Fig. 84 is an internal negative cast precisely like that shown in Fig. 83 D. From its peculiar shape it is known to the quarrymen as a 'horse's head', and it must be admitted that it is not like anything else. It measures about two inches long.

The insides of shells, or impressions of them, often show interesting details. For example, the 'teeth' of a shell may enable a palaeontologist to determine its species, and even the inexpert may pick out the oval depressions which mark the attachments of the muscles by which the creature opened and closed its shell so many millions of years ago. It is one of these (but forming a *projection* in the negative cast) which—presumably—represents the eye of the 'horse's head' in Fig. 84. An example of an internal negative cast of a spiral shell is given in Fig. 85 at A, by the side of the shell to which it belongs. This also is common in the Portland Stone, and is known as a 'Portland screw'; it is usually about three inches long when complete.

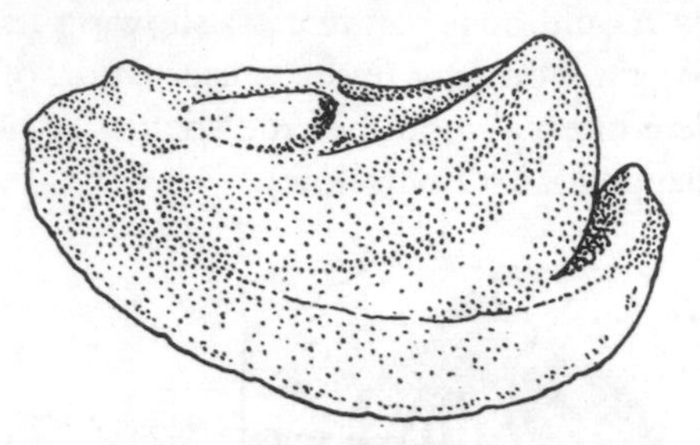

FIG. 84. A 'horse's head', the internal mould of a shell from the Portland Stone.

Fig. 85 B shows a very interesting fossil shell from the shelly sandstones of East Anglia. It is not very old, as fossils go, dating from the warm period which preceded the Ice Age, and the species still lives round our shores today under the name of 'red whelk' or 'buckie'. But this shell is unique in having two forms. The present form in Britain has a right-handed spiral (like all the common spiral shells), but the fossil shown in the illustration has a left-handed

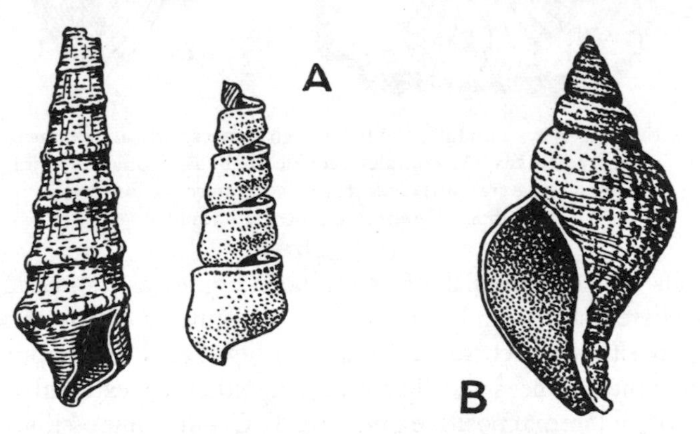

FIG. 85. A, a 'Portland screw' and the shell of which it is an internal mould or negative cast. B, a left-handed whelk dating from before the Ice Age.

spiral. Now, left-handed whelks are known today on the shores of the Mediterranean, and it has been established that they are a warm-water variety. The change in climate in Britain from almost tropical warmth to the cold of the Ice Age has been traced in the gradual replacement of left-handed by right-handed whelks, and in this respect it is evident that we are still under the lingering influence of the Ice Age.[1] It has been estimated that a drop in the average temperature of northern Europe of only ten degrees would be sufficient to cause a recurrence of glacial conditions.

These fossil whelks are scarcely altered in substance at all, though they may, perhaps, have become slightly thickened by slow mineral changes. But the

FIG. 86. A typical lamp-shell, with Roman lamp for comparison.

shells are naturally thick, and many specimens might be taken for fresh shells were they not securely embedded in the rocks. As a rule you may safely deduce from a thick fossil shell that it lived in the shallow waters of a sea-shore, for most shore shells are heavily constructed to enable them to withstand constant battering by the shingle.

Thinner shells may belong to deeper water, but very thin shells indeed, such as may sometimes be washed out of fine clays, are often fresh-water shells. This is because the lime of which the shells are made is frequently in short supply in river and lake water. We may cite as an example a small bivalve shell of paper thinness found fossilized in Hordle Cliff, on the coast of Hampshire. This species is quite extinct in this country today, but since it still flourishes in the fresh-water of the Amazon its occurrence in Hampshire suggests that the rocks there were deposited in fresh-water, and also that the climate of Britain was then very much hotter than it is today. Of course, it would be possible to hold that the creature has since changed its habits, but this is unlikely in view of the other tropical species that accompany it.

To return to our red whelk, the cottagers of the Shetlands once used its large

[1] This evidence does not, of course, stand alone, but is supported by numerous other similar changes in the distribution of warm-water and cold-water shells. The reader is asked to believe that no statements unsupported by adequate evidence have been made in this book, though it is usually quite impossible even to summarize such evidence in the space available.

shell for a lamp. They turned it upside-down and filled it with oil, resting a wick in the natural groove at the end of the opening. In prehistoric and classical Europe large shells of all kinds were commonly used for lamp-vessels, but saucer-shaped shells were preferred to whelks because it is difficult to get a wick to reach to the bottom of a spiral shell, and also to support such a shell in an upright position. The earliest earthenware lamps were simply imitation shells, with a slight modification to assist the support of the wick and a flat base to prevent accidental tipping over. On the right of Fig. 86 there is a typical Roman lamp, and the shell above it resembles it so strikingly that it is called a 'lamp-shell'. This shell is lying on its back, and the picture on the left shows its under surface.

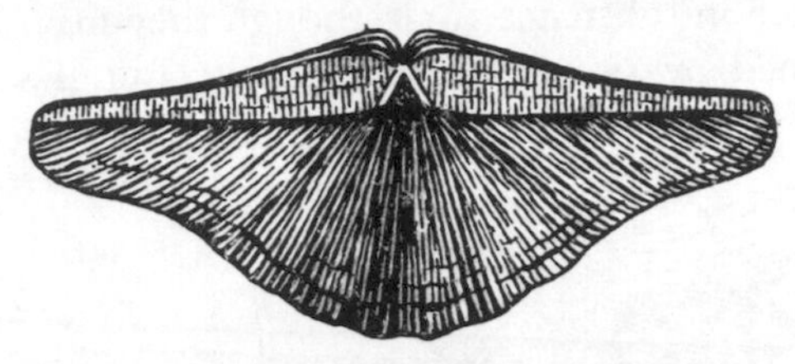

FIG. 87. A 'Delabole butterfly', a fossil lamp-shell from the Devonian slates.

The lamp-shells are very abundant as fossils, and assume a great variety of forms. A 'winged' species which is common as a fossil in the slates of Devon and Cornwall, where it is called the 'Delabole butterfly', is illustrated in Fig. 87. It has been extinct for many millions of years. Although the lamp-shells look at first sight very much like ordinary bivalves (such as the cockles, mussels, oysters and scallops), they really belong to a totally different natural order.[1] They are much more primitive than ordinary shell-fish, and though some are still found living today the majority of the known species belong to the older fossils. Like most of the shell-fish they indicate more or less shallow seas.

Other common inhabitants of shore-lines and shallow water are the crabs and lobsters, and the rambler is likely enough to come across fossil specimens in localities ranging from the Isle of Sheppey to Devonshire and Wales. Most of these will be of extinct species, and in Fig. 88 we illustrate a creature which died out some three hundred million years ago. Known to quarrymen as 'seraphim' (angels and ministers of grace, defend us!) these fossils occur in some of our older sandstones and mudstones, and are sometimes two yards in length. Another ancient fossil crustacean is the 'pod-shrimp' illustrated in Fig. 89. This occurs in Welsh shales representing muddy sea-floors of great antiquity, and measures about two inches in length.

The most remarkable inhabitants of the old sea-bottoms were the trilobites, which were not crustaceans though they belonged to a parallel class. They

[1] They belong, indeed, to a different *phylum*, and may be no more closely related to ordinary shell-fish than insects are to backboned animals.

bear a superficial resemblance to wood-lice, and some of them appear to have rolled themselves up, as wood-lice do, for protection. Their horny, segmented backs are divided into three lobes, and they had large compound eyes like those of insects; they measure anything up to three or four inches long. The trilobite illustrated in Plate XX, I, is common in a Shropshire limestone, where the quarrymen call it the 'Dudley locust'. Fragments of other trilobites may be seen in Fig. 63, and the rambler may come across specimens in many of the older rocks of the western and northern counties. All the trilobites became extinct about two hundred million years ago.

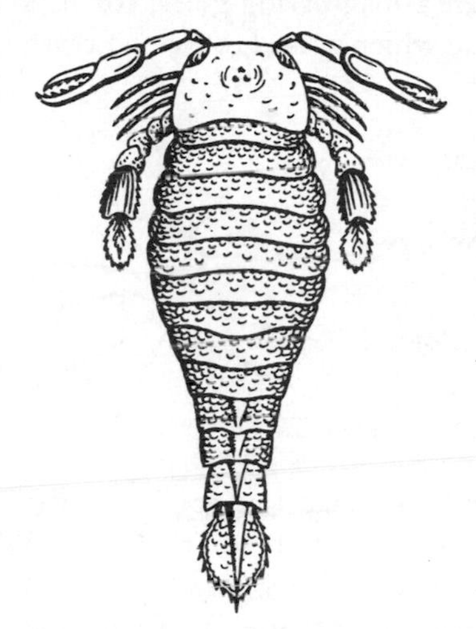

Fig. 88. One of the 'seraphim' found in ancient sandstones and mudstones.

Fossils of this kind (that is, with a horny covering instead of shells or bones) are usually found flattened between successive layers of rock. If a piece of rock contains such a fossil, a blow of the hammer on its *edge* will usually cause it to split in the plane of the fossil, which provides an area of weakness. But the devices resorted to by palaeontologists for extracting fossils are numerous, and the interested reader will find them described in works devoted to the subject. The present book is written for the rambler who chances to come across a fossil rather than for fossil *hunters*, and with one or two exceptions all the fossils we have cited are so common that they have acquired popular names. (Many of them can be obtained from quarrymen in exchange for the price of a drink.)

A type of fossil common in the older shales and slates, but which has *not* been honoured (so far as we know) by a popular name, is the graptolite (Greek *grapho* I write, *lithos* stone). These creatures belong to a primitive order not represented in modern times. They were once thought to be similar in many respects to the polyps, but it now seems more likely that they were related to a group of our own very early ancestors. Some typical specimens are illustrated in Fig. 90, where it will be seen that they resembled plants rather than animals in their habit of growth. They remained rooted to the sea-floor and developed by branching and budding.

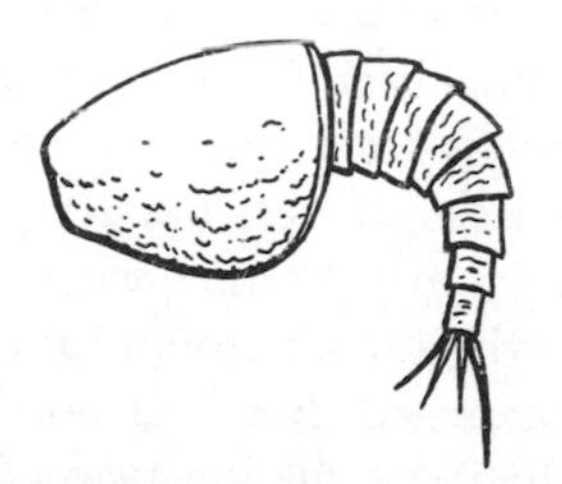

Fig. 89. A 'pod-shrimp' from the oldest fossil-bearing rocks

Graptolites appear on the split surfaces of black shales and slates as slight scratches an inch or so long. They owe their name to their resemblance to a quill pen, but it may be noted that they often look like the scratchings of a pen or pencil on the rock. All such scratchings, especially if they have a brassy glitter (due to pyrites), should be examined with a magnifying-glass, for it is surely worth while to catch a glimpse of a creature which ceased to live on earth some four hundred million years ago.

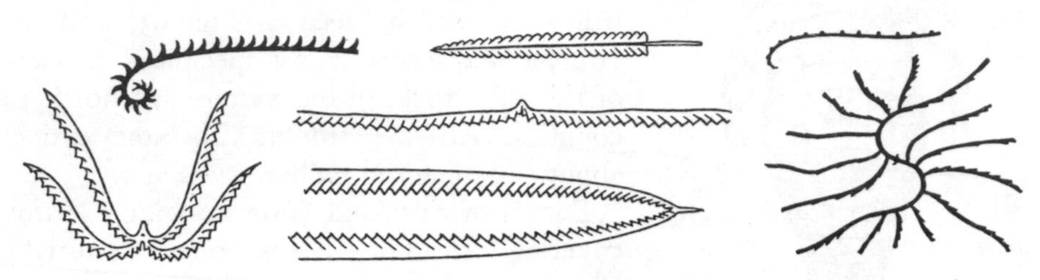

FIG. 90. Some common forms of graptolite, slightly enlarged.

Other creatures belonging to the animal kingdom which live rooted to the sea-floor include the corals and the sea-lilies, and both of these are found in many varieties as fossils. Some of the west of England limestones are so full of them that, as we saw on page 89, they are polished for use as ornamental marbles. It is difficult to describe the richness and beauty of some of the corals, but five varieties are illustrated in Fig. 91. (The 'chain' coral of Fig. 91 D may be seen again in Fig. 63.) Not the least remarkable feature of some of these fossils is their colouring. Every conceivable tint of pink, orange, purple, crimson and ivory is represented, and when the coral itself is of one colour the limestone background is often of another.

Most of these corals formed massive reefs, like those which flourish in the Pacific today, and their presence indicates shallow but clear water. This occurs round oceanic islands or far enough off a mainland to be beyond the reach of mud brought down by rivers. The particular species found fossil in the older rocks are all extinct, but some of the later ones have not yet died out. Not all corals are reef-builders; some live solitary lives attached to rocks, and these also may be met with as fossils in many limestones. They usually look like little tubular stones, often shaped like drinking-horns, and they are sometimes branched, but it is not safe to label them corals unless you see a pattern of distinct radiating *spokes* (not merely radiating *crystals*) on their larger ends. The spokes may not meet in the centre, however, for the position of the 'hub' is often occupied by a depression or hole. The outer surfaces of such corals are often ribbed longitudinally. Unornamented tubular or rod-like stones may be belemnites or straight nautiloids, ammonoids or other molluscs (see pages 128 and 129). But if irregular or sinuous in form they are probably the casts of so-called 'worm-holes',[1] especially if found associated with fossil wood.

The sea-lilies, which live in moderately deep, clear water, often grow in large colonies forming submarine 'forests', and like the reef-building corals their

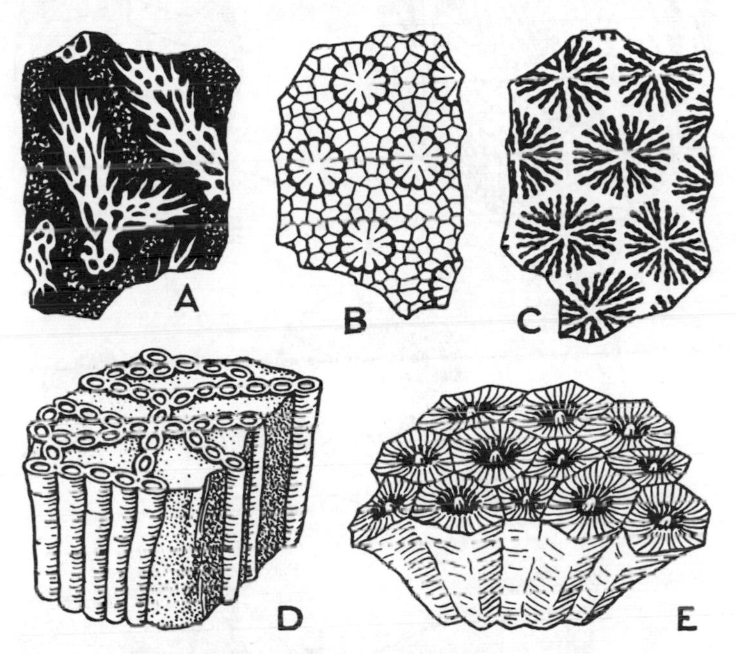

FIG. 91. Fossil Corals. A, 'stag's-horn' coral. B, 'sun-stone'. C, 'star' coral. D, 'chain' coral. E, 'flower' coral.

massed remains may constitute the bulk of a limestone. A typical sea-lily is illustrated in Fig. 92 at A, but the different parts of its anatomy vary enormously in shape in different species. They are known to zoologists as 'crinoids', and limestones consisting largely of their remains, like that shown at E, are called 'crinoidal limestones'. Since the stems and arms are most prominent in such rocks, and look somewhat like worms or snakes, crinoidal limestones are often called 'snake-stone' or 'adder-stone', and were formerly thought to provide a charm against snake-bite.

[1] Not the worm-holes produced by the furniture and death-watch beetles, but those produced by the 'ship-worm' and similar creatures, which are really molluscs with shells adapted for boring holes in stone and timber. A hole bored in a chalk pebble by the common piddock is shown in Fig. 95 A. The protective tubes secreted by true worms are also sometimes found fossilized. They often appear as small irregularly disposed tubes adhering to the surfaces of shells.

The little plates of which the columns of the stems are built up are often found fossil, and have acquired various folk-names. For example, a small

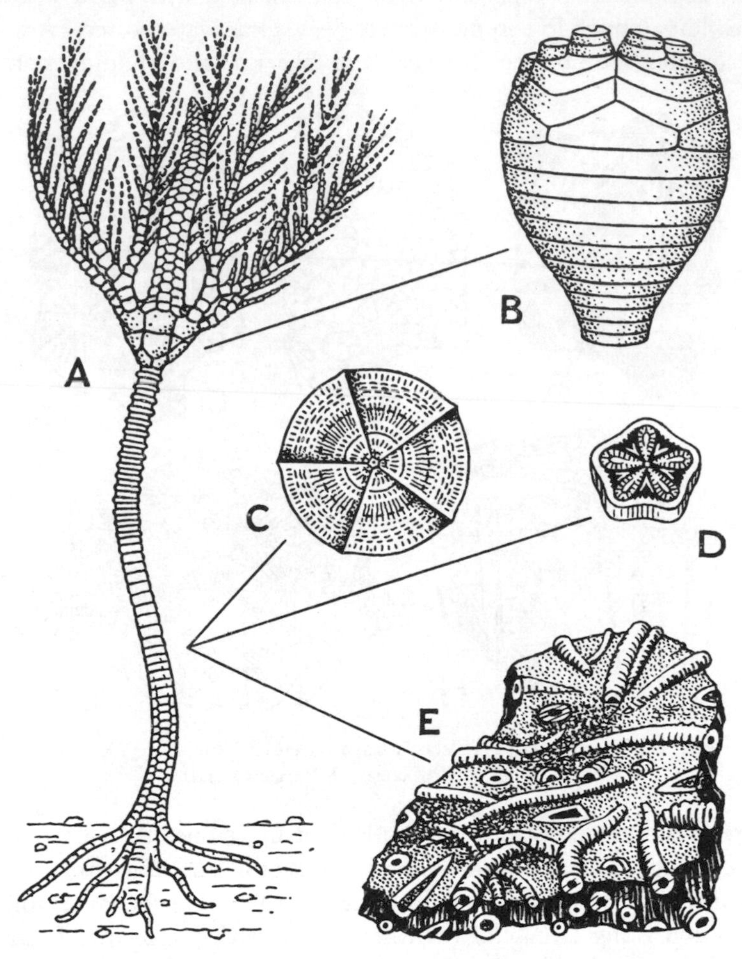

FIG. 92. Parts of different species of sea-lily, with a typical specimen (A) to show general anatomy. B, 'pear-stone' or 'peg-top'. C, 'cart-wheel'. D, 'star-stone'. E, 'snake-stone'.

species picked up on the Northumbrian beaches is known as 'St Cuthbert's beads', and Scott tells in *Marmion* how—

> Saint Cuthbert sits, and toils to frame
> The sea-born beads that bear his name.

The star-shaped kind illustrated in Fig. 92 at D is known, appropriately enough, as a 'star-stone', and this is usually about half an inch across, but the circular one shown at C may measure two inches in diameter. This is known as a 'coach-wheel' or 'cart-wheel', and it belongs to a species whose body is illustrated at B. From its shape this is sometimes called the 'pear encrinite', but it is popularly known as a 'pear-stone' or 'peg-top'.

In Dorsetshire the roots and stems of the pear encrinite are found in a bed of limestone, while their peg-top bodies occur in a layer of clay immediately above it. Now, these sea-lilies could not possibly have lived in the muddy water represented by the clay, and it is evident that they were flourishing happily in clear water over a limestone ooze when a sudden influx of mud overwhelmed and killed the entire colony. Thus may we read of a submarine tragedy which occurred on the site of Dorset one hundred and fifty million years ago!

FIG. 93. 'Cluster-stones', a group of plates forming the body of a free-swimming sea-lily.

There are a few kinds of fossil sea-lily which had no stalks at all, but swam about freely by means of their long arms. One, which is found in the Chalk, is illustrated in Fig. 93. You do not often come across a complete specimen, but groups of the plates which form its body are not uncommon, and they bear the folk-name of 'cluster-stones'. You will note that they are pentagonal in shape, and that the markings on both the 'star-stone' and the 'cart-wheel' in Fig. 92 consist of five rays or spokes. This five-fold pattern is characteristic of sea-lilies, star-fish (which are also found fossilized) and sea-urchins, all of which belong to the same natural group of creatures.

Sea-urchins of many kinds are very common as fossils, and several of them have folk-names. The one shown in Plate XX, H, is known as a 'shepherd's crown', and it may be picked up on the chalk downs (and elsewhere); similar urchins from older rocks are known in some districts as 'buttons'. The clubbed or spindle-shaped spines of sea-urchins are also common. Three other sea-urchins from the Chalk are shown in Fig. 94.

These fossils often consist of crystalline calcite covering a flint core, and if the calcite gets weathered away or chipped off, the internal flint cast remains as a very durable fossil. Many fossils from the Chalk are preserved in flint in this way, and they may survive being washed out by rain and trundled many miles along a river-bed, to end up in a bed of gravel. The flint itself is a non-crystalline form of silica, and is deposited in the fossils by percolating water.

The origin of this silica is known; it comes from the skeletons of sponges which lived and died on bottom of the sea in which the chalk was deposited.

Chalk is a porous rock, and when it was raised above sea-level the constantly percolating rain-water dissolved the silica of the sponge skeletons out of the upper layers and redeposited it as bands of flints lower down (see page 98).

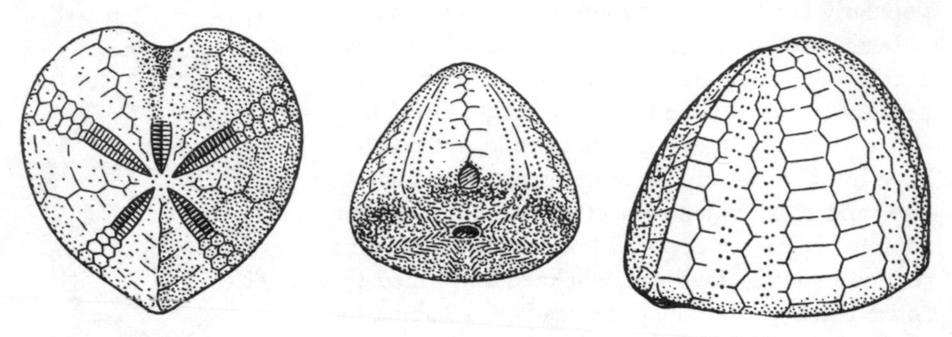

FIG. 94. Fossil sea-urchins. *Left*, 'fairy heart'. *Centre*, 'helmet'. *Right*, 'sugar-loaf'. The 'shepherd's crown' is illustrated in Plate XX, H.

The deposition seems to have occurred chiefly round existing sponge-skeletons which had escaped solution, so that we quite often find the sponges themselves preserved. A cup-shaped sponge in flint is illustrated in Plate XX, F, but this is by no means the only form of sponge to be found. Many of the grotesquely shaped flints which litter the floor of a chalk-pit are but slightly modified preservations of branching and tulip-shaped sponges, or groups of such sponges, consolidated into single masses. If you break such a flint open you will very likely find it contains a hollow, on the lining of which the sponge structure is clearly preserved. The hollow may also contain a loose core of flint which also shows sponge-structure, and small specimens in which such a core rattles when the stone is shaken are called 'rattle-stones'.[1]

Many solid flints, when split asunder, show very clearly the shape and structure of sponges, and the pattern may be accentuated by wetting or varnishing them, or—if you have the patience—by grinding and polishing a flat surface. The sponge skeletons from which the silica of flint is derived consisted originally of thousands of little rods distributed in the soft tissues of the sponge to afford it some rigidity. These rods are called 'spicules' (little spikes), for they are usually pointed like thorns. They are often branched or rayed, as may be

[1] On page 100 we described another cause of rattle-stones, and yet a third cause may be the removal by solution of a fossil shell, so that the material which filled the hollow of the shell rattles loosely in the cavity left by the shell. In Fig. 83, D should fit tightly into A, and A into B. But if A be then removed by solution, D will rattle loosely inside B.

seen in Fig. 95, and sometimes they are linked together to form a continuous network (as in the modern 'Venus' flower-basket').[1]

Odd sponge spicules frequently turn up as fossils in many kinds of clear-water rocks (besides chalk), and they occur in the beds of deposited silica known as 'chert' and 'hornstone' (Plate VIII C), which are more or less the counter-

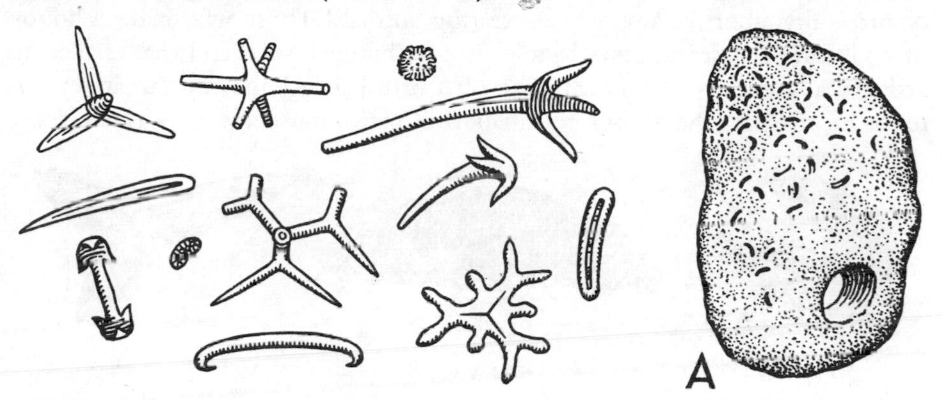

FIG. 95. *Left*, sponge spicules (magnified). A, limestone (chalk) pebble with small holes made by a boring sponge (*Cliona*). The large hole is made by a shell-fish (piddock).

parts of flint in rocks older than the Chalk. The weathered surface of some cherts looks like fossilized needle-felt, and in it the matted sponge spicules may be seen with a magnifying-glass.

Weathered flints are sometimes found to have curious parallel ridges or corrugations running round them, so that small specimens are reminiscent of the man made of motor-tyres in the old Michelin advertisements, or of some sort of amateur turnery in the piano-leg line. These are called 'banded flints', but nobody has yet succeeded in explaining them.

Flints formed round branching sponges may be perforated by one or more holes where the branches cross, and when sufficiently worn down on a beach these become 'lucky stones'. The same result is produced when a hollow flint suffers sufficient battering or weathering to open up the hollow on opposite sides, so that the stone becomes a ring. Some 'lucky stones', however, are simply pebbles which have been bored through by piddocks or similar shell-fish, and these may generally be recognized by the regular diameter of their holes, which form circular tubes. Shells, and chalk or limestone pebbles, which are plentifully punctured with small oval or comma-shaped holes (Fig. 95 A) are the victims of boring sponges (*Cliona*).

[1] Sponges of the class here described are not to be confused with the bath-sponges, which have horny skeletons—not silica ones.

The queer shapes assumed by flints often bear odd resemblances to other familiar objects. In Plate XXVII we show flints resembling a dog's head and a human leg, and there are people who have collected whole 'zoos' of animals thus mimicked in flint. Such imitations are known as 'accidental flints', and they have no scientific significance though they were once thought to represent Nature's first abortive attempts at creating animals! Those who make a hobby of collecting accidental flints have only one binding rule, and that is that no artificial alteration—such as chipping off a fifth leg or knocking out an 'eye'—must be made.[1] The visitor to small provincial museums may often come

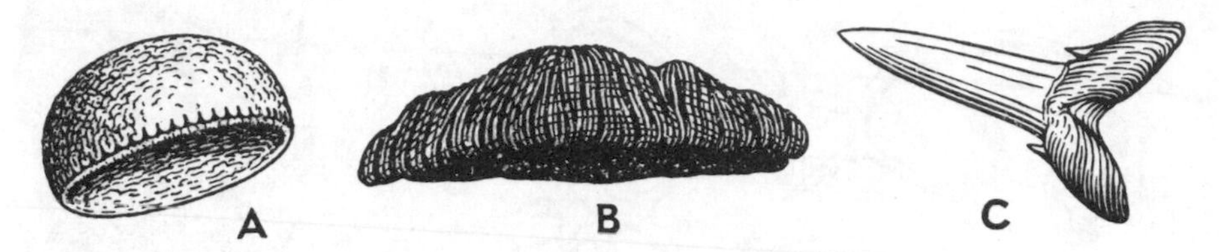

FIG. 96. Fossil fish-teeth. A, 'toad-stone'. B, 'fossil leech'. C, 'lucky tooth'.

across striking local specimens mounted on boards for exhibition, but they are not to be regarded as fossils; they are simply natural curios.

The Chalk itself was once thought to be a deep-sea ooze composed almost entirely of the crushed shells of microscopic sea-creatures. Such creatures (*Foraminifera*) live in the surface-waters of modern oceans, and there is a constant rain of their dead shells upon the sea-floor where they accumulate to form a pinkish-white ooze. They certainly make up the bulk of some limestones, but they are not as abundant in the Chalk as we should expect. It is now believed that the greater part of the Chalk was deposited in a shallow sea as a chemical precipitate of lime brought about by the action of bacteria. A thick white bacterial ooze is being formed in this way on the bed of the Caribbean Sea today.

The microscopic shells which do occur in the Chalk are most often found inside hollow flints or fossils where they have enjoyed some protection, and they are quite like their counterparts in modern seas. Such shells turn up in many other marine formations, and they belong to a primitive group of creatures distantly related to the well-known (but shell-less) *amoeba* of pond-mud. They are not all microscopic, however, and there is one group which grows large enough to obtrude itself on the rambler's notice. Shaped like a disc, a typical specimen looks very much like a fossilized farthing or halfpenny with

[1] Believe it or not, but the eye of our dog's head was found already chipped by nature (probably by the fall of the stone from the cliff-face).

a swelling in the middle. For this reason it is called a 'coin-stone' or 'nummulite' (Latin *nummus*, a coin), and some examples are shown in the drawing at the head of this chapter. It is a warm-water creature, and various species inhabit the seas and oceans of the world today.

The most obvious inhabitants of the open seas are the fishes, yet we have little to say of them here for they are not often found fossilized entire (though the rambler in the Isle of Wight may certainly come across fairly complete fossil sprats). Fish-scales, fins, vertebrae (Fig. 97, left), and sometimes detached heads

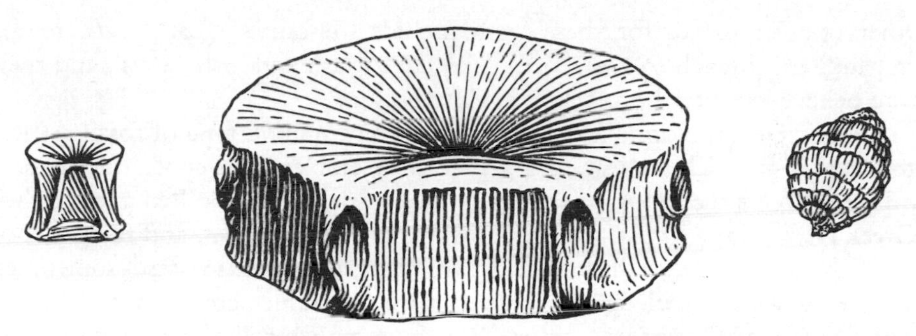

FIG. 97. *Left*, fish vertebra. *Centre*, vertebra of 'fish-lizard' (*Ichthyosaurus*). *Right*, coprolite.

or jaws, are occasionally found in the Chalk and elsewhere, but the rambler usually has to be content with the teeth. These are fairly abundant in most marine deposits from the East Coast to a line joining Bristol to Newcastle,[1] and three representative examples are illustrated in Fig. 96.

The most common fossil fishes belong to a primitive group represented today by the sharks, and their teeth are of two kinds. There is the pointed type of tooth, with roots, typified by the 'lucky tooth' illustrated on the right of Fig. 96 (which is kept as a charm by the superstitious), and there are the palatal teeth—known as 'fossil leeches'—represented in the central drawing. The palatal teeth are fairly flat, and have ribbed surfaces. They lined the roof and floor of the mouth like mosaic paving, and were used to grind food up before it was swallowed. More or less square palatal teeth may be found in the Chalk, and it is often possible to see where the ridges on these teeth have been worn down by contact with their opposite numbers.

The sharks have skeletons of cartilage which are seldom preserved, but the bony fishes have left both teeth and hard skeletal fragments in the rocks. On

[1] Geographical limits described in this manner are extremely rough approximations, but in view of our stated object (see Preface) this is of little consequence. Further, we have seldom specified the *particular* clays, shales, limestones, etc., in which the fossils referred to are found. Such information would only encumber the book with technical names and much matter irrelevant to our theme.

the left of Fig. 96 is the cup-shaped palatal tooth of an extinct fresh-water pike. This is so common in some west-of-England clays that lockets used to be made by hinging two of the teeth together, hollow sides facing. A really beautiful padlock made of these teeth was found in a churchyard at Devizes in 1838, though at that time the teeth were believed to be 'toad-stones', for—according to the legend—

> . . . the toad, ugly and venomous,
> Wears yet a precious jewel in his head.[1]

Other popular names for these teeth include 'bufonites' (Latin *bufo*, toad), 'crapaudines' (French *crapaud*, toad), 'serpent's eyes', and 'fish's eyes', and they were believed to afford protection against poison.

In Fig. 97, on the right, we illustrate a not uncommon type of fossil associated with fishes. Though at first glance it resembles a fir-cone, this nodule really represents the droppings of an extinct shark, and it is called a 'coprolite' (Greek *copros*, dung, *lithos*, stone). Many varieties are known, and their shapes —which vary from that illustrated to large corkscrew-like masses—sometimes provide us with knowledge of the soft parts of extinct creatures and betray their affinities with modern species. But the term 'coprolite' is also applied to various phosphatic nodules (occurring in sands and clays) which are now known to be of purely mineral origin.

The vertebra of an *Ichthyosaurus* (a giant fish-lizard) in the centre of Fig. 97 measures four inches across and is one and a half inches thick; it weighs a pound and a half. This is the nearest acquaintance with the giant reptiles of a hundred and fifty million years ago that the rambler is likely to make, though he may come across odd bones belonging to crocodiles and turtles, and, in Ice Age deposits, fragments of mammoth bones and teeth. Such fragmentary fossils should be referred to experts for identification, and the national museums are always ready to serve the public (free) in this respect provided full details of the locality and site of each find are given.

One very important group of sea-creatures remains to be described, and that is the branch of molluscs to which octopuses and cuttle-fish belong. The common fossils in this group are of two kinds. There are the coiled shells of the extinct 'ammonites' (named after Jupiter Ammon), and the dart-like process to the 'cuttle-bones' of the 'belemnites' (Greek *belemnon*, a dart).

The ammonites are very abundant in many clays, shales and limestones, and even in some sandstones, and the reader is probably familiar with them as 'St Hilda's serpents'. See Plate XX, E. Several species are found at Whitby,

[1] Shakespeare, *As You Like It, Act II, Sc. I.*

where St Hilda's Abbey is situated, and the arms of Whitby (Fig. 98) picture three typical ammonites to commemorate the legend of the Saint. The story tells how the Devil sent swarms of snakes to destroy St Hilda when she was building the Abbey—

> And how, of thousand snakes, each one
> Was changed into a coil of stone,
> When holy Hilda prayed.[1]

FIG. 98.
The arms of Whitby.

You may find them in the locality today, to prove it. You may also find them in the rocks over the greater part of England, and in super-abundance at Folkestone and Lyme Regis. They measure anything from half an inch in diameter upwards, and in the Portland Stone there is a giant species three or four feet across, known locally as 'conger eels'.

The nearest relative of the ammonites alive today is the pearly nautilus, and the section through a nautilus shell shown in Fig. 99 will serve to indicate the general structure of the ammonites. The coiled tube of the shell is divided into chambers by plates running across it, and when the creature is alive all the chambers are empty except the one at the opening (*C*). When the nautilus grows too large for this, it builds on another chamber and seals off the lately occupied one by another plate, leaving only a thin connecting-pipe in the centre. This pipe is used to fill the empty chambers with a gas (very much like air, but with more nitrogen), so that the old part of the shell acts as a float. Thus, this type of shell, though coiled, is quite different from a snail-shell, and the creature itself, having eight arms like an octopus, is quite different from a snail. In the fossil forms of nautilus, and in the ammonites, the chambers have often become filled with crystals of calcite, and in Victorian days the prettier ammonites were sometimes cut through and polished to show the crystals, and then mounted as brooches.

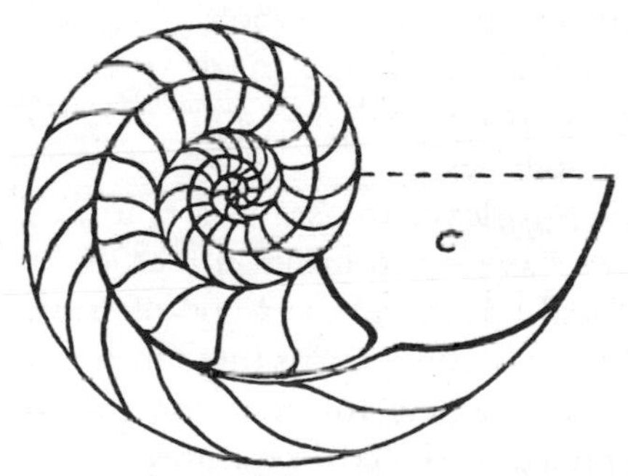

FIG. 99. Section through the shell of a Pearly Nautilus.

There are fossil forms of both nautilus and ammonite which are straight instead of being coiled, just as there are straight species of snail—of which the reader will be familiar with the 'elephant's tusk' shell common on all our

[1] Scott, *Marmion, Canto II.*

beaches (and also found fossil). A fossil nautilus or ammonite may sometimes be found in which the chambers have first been filled with crystals or other mineral matter, and then the shells themselves have been dissolved away, so that the result is a sort of coiled chain of loosely-fitting but interlocking stones known as a 'snake-chain'.

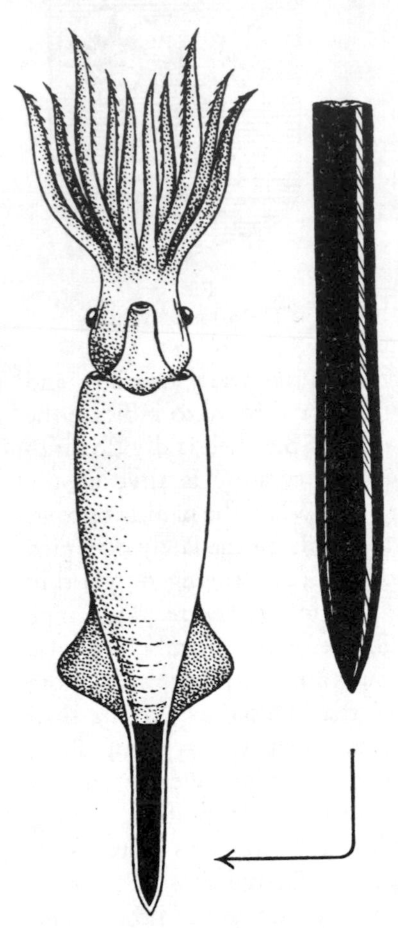

FIG. 100. Reconstruction of a belemnite. Note the hooks on the arms and the position of the guard (which is shown enlarged on the right).

The nautilus and the ammonite have external shells, but the cuttle-fish and the fossil belemnite have internal shells. That is, the hard limy substance secreted by the animal to give it rigidity takes the form of a 'cuttle-bone', and this (though not a bone) is inside the body like the bones of fishes. Most people are familiar with the soft, white, oval 'cuttle-bone' picked up on the shore; it is often given to cage-birds to peck at—presumably as a source of lime or to clean their beaks. In the belemnites this bone terminated in a hard spike or 'guard', shaped like a cigar or torpedo, as may be seen in Fig. 100, and the folk-names for it include 'fairy's finger', 'lady's finger', 'Devil's finger', 'thunder-pick', and 'thunderbolt'. Like the ammonites, they are found in all types of marine rock from shallow-water clays to deep-sea limestones.

It is time to leave the sea and return to land, for we have yet to mention the occurrence of fossil leaves and the wood of trees. The rambler may come across these in many parts of the country, for they are by no means confined to the coal measures.

In many cases the impression of a leaf in clay or shale is all that is found, but when the tissues themselves are present they are usually either black and soft, or some paler colour and hard. In black preservations they have been carbonized—that is, all the chemical constituents of the plant have been removed except the carbon. This is true of most of the plants from the coal measures illustrated in Fig. 101 and, of course, of coal itself.

In other preservations the plant tissues have been replaced, molecule by molecule, by silica, lime, or some other mineral, as we have seen is often the case with fossil shells. Replacement of this sort sometimes occurs round a small accumulation of plant-remains, and the result is a compact nodule or

FIG. 101. Fossil plants from the Coal Measures. Of the three trunks in the lower row, that on the left is a giant horse-tail; the other two are giant club-mosses.

'concretion' (see page 99). The best examples are the 'coal-balls' found in the coal-seams, and by cutting sections through such nodules it has been possible to study plant-forms of the coal period in microscopic detail. Coal-balls with a diameter exceeding four feet have been discovered, but they are generally less than a foot across.

Beds in which fossil leaves are found are most likely to have been laid down in rivers, lakes, or on swampy shores. Fossil wood, however, sometimes travels farther afield, for the branches and trunks of trees may float a long way out to sea as driftwood before becoming water-logged and sinking to the bottom. The author has a specimen of fossil wood from the Chalk, and it is occasionally found even in the limestones of moderately deep seas. A study of the distribution of fossil wood in some marine formations has given us an idea of the direction of the ocean currents of remote ages.

Most of the 'buried forests' mentioned in the guide books occur in coastal districts, and belong to a period described in the next chapter (see page 149), but much older forests have also been found petrified in their natural state. A part of a coal-forest has been uncovered at Glasgow, and in Portland there are the stumps of a forest of primitive cycads more than a hundred million years old. These stumps are hollow, and look like gigantic pudding-basins; they are known locally as 'fossil crows'-nests'. Trees of a similar kind, and of about the same age, grew also in Yorkshire, and though not true flowering plants they produced flower-like cones whose fossilized buds are known (in Yorkshire) as 'cliff-roses'.

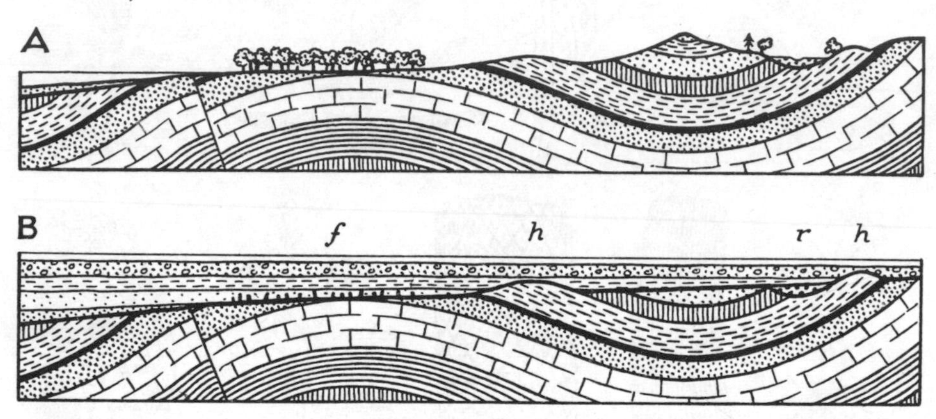

FIG. 102. A, a weathered land-surface before submergence beneath the sea. B, the land planed off by the sea and buried beneath fresh deposits. Note the preservation of old features at *f*, *h* and *r*, entitling the section to be called a 'fossil landscape'.

We close this chapter with a brief account of what Professor W. W. Watts has called 'fossil landscapes'. The word 'fossil' means 'able to be dug up' (Latin *fossilis*), and it is used of things which have first suffered natural burial. If ripple-marks, sun-cracks, or the footprints of animals can be called 'fossils' when they are preserved by burial, so also ought the larger features of a landscape. But when a landscape sinks beneath the sea to be buried under new deposits, its surface-features are usually planed off by the advancing waves in the manner described in Chapter III, and so are lost for ever. Nevertheless, hills of exceptionally hard rock may resist the wave action and stand out for a time as islands. When they are finally submerged and buried it is surely defensible to refer to them as 'fossil hills' or 'fossil islands'. See Plate XXI, A.

The process is illustrated in Fig. 102, where the landscape shown at A is slowly subsiding, the sea making its transgression from the left. There is a forest by the shore, and farther inland a river flows over its bed of gravel. The transgression is shown complete at B, and though the mountain has been planed off, at least four features of the old landscape have been preserved. They are the tree-stumps of the forest at *f*, the river-bed at *r*, and the two hills of exceptionally hard rock at *h*. At one stage of the transgression these must have been islands. In favourable places the old land-surface is probably marked by a 'dirt-bed' or fossil soil.

These fragments of the old landscape have been buried beneath several layers of new sediments, and it will be observed that the bedding of these new rocks is horizontal, and bears no relation whatever to the folds in the older strata. The junction between the two systems is called an 'unconformity', and it is because such junctions are sometimes clearly displayed in cliffs and quarries that they may come under the rambler's notice. We illustrate an actual example in Plate XIX (C), the explanation of which will be found in Fig. 103.

The rambler on the coast of Britain may also meet with one of the buried forests now being exposed for a second time by the destructive action of new seas. But the features we have been describing are not confined to coastal districts, for the greater part of Britain has been beneath the sea many times in past ages, and 'fossil' river-beds, hills, islands, deserts, and so on, must lie concealed in the rock-layers—landscape upon landscape, like the leaves of a book.

It is not often, however, that really extensive landscapes are preserved entire, yet even this may happen when the burying material is sand blown from a desert, or an inundation of river-mud due to some major catastrophe. The

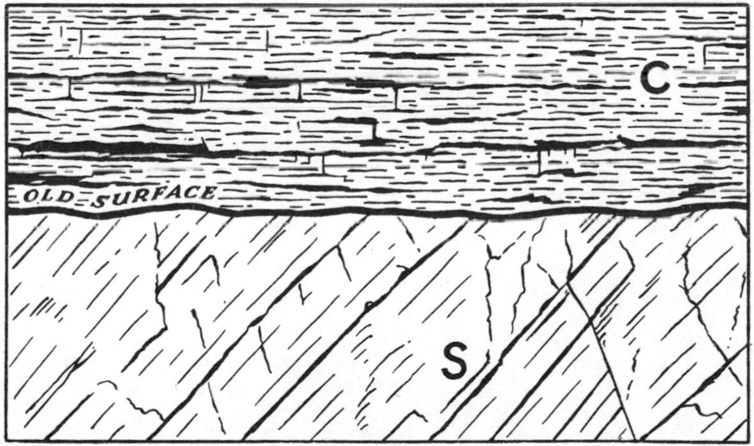

FIG. 103. Explanation of the unconformity illustrated in Plate XIX (C). The old land-surface lay over tilted flagstones (S), and was buried beneath a limestone ooze (C).

existence of such landscapes must be deduced from very fragmentary evidence, for all that is usually seen of them is an occasional detail in cliff, quarry, or road-cutting, and the unravelling of their stories is work for trained geologists. Moreover, they are seldom found in the undisturbed state of burial shown in Fig. 102 B. They must at least have been raised above sea-level again, and this has generally involved fresh folding and faulting, so that the new beds are no longer horizontal and the old folds beneath them are re-folded till they present a very pretty puzzle.

To map the rocks adequately in the first place, and then to distinguish the effects of the second folding from those of the first, and so straighten out the newer beds and reconstruct the old landscape, may require a life-time of study. The rambler will be quite content merely to note an unconformity exposed in a cliff, and draw the just conclusion that here there was once an old surface—whether of dry land or submarine plain. It is surely something to be able to recognize a fossil country when you see one, and you can afford to waive the question of whether its inhabitants were beasts or fishes.

CHAPTER VII

The Broad View

We have lingered long enough by cliff and quarry, for the clues to the past which we have gleaned from minerals, fossils, odd stones, and the bedding of the rocks, have yet to be linked up with the present forms of the landscape. It is time for us to climb once more to the hill-top and survey the landscape as a whole, for it often happens that the middle chapters of its story are more easily read by a sweeping glance round the horizon, or a broad survey of the character of the country, than by a close scrutiny of its separate features.

The alternate elevation of the land and its subsidence beneath the sea take place very slowly, but geological time is so vast that these movements have been repeated countless times. And each time the land rose, a new country was born; each time it sank beneath the waves an old country died and was buried. And whether the land was on its way up or on its way down, whenever it chanced to lie at sea-level the sea did its best to plane off a smooth, level surface, so that the old story was wiped clean off the slate before the new one was begun. We have already illustrated this in Fig. 102.

Though the successive stories are all different in detail, and sometimes in plot, the way in which they are unfolded generally conforms to a fixed pattern. This pattern begins with the elevation of the land to an appreciable height—sometimes a very great height—above sea-level. Then follows a long period of weathering, during which the land is reduced by rain, frost, wind, rivers, and gravity. And last, the time comes round for the reduced land-surface to sink beneath the sea once more. Now, that middle-period—the period of reduction by weathering—follows a regular routine called the 'cycle of erosion', and this provides the rambler with a sort of clock on which he may tell the degree of progress achieved.

The country passes through a succession of landscape types, each of which is recognizable, so that a broad view of a landscape may reveal the particular stage in the cycle of erosion to which that stretch of country has come. You cannot, however, tell the *age* of a landscape in this way; that is quite another matter. The age of a landscape is the period during which its chief physical features remain recognizable, and this varies enormously according to the

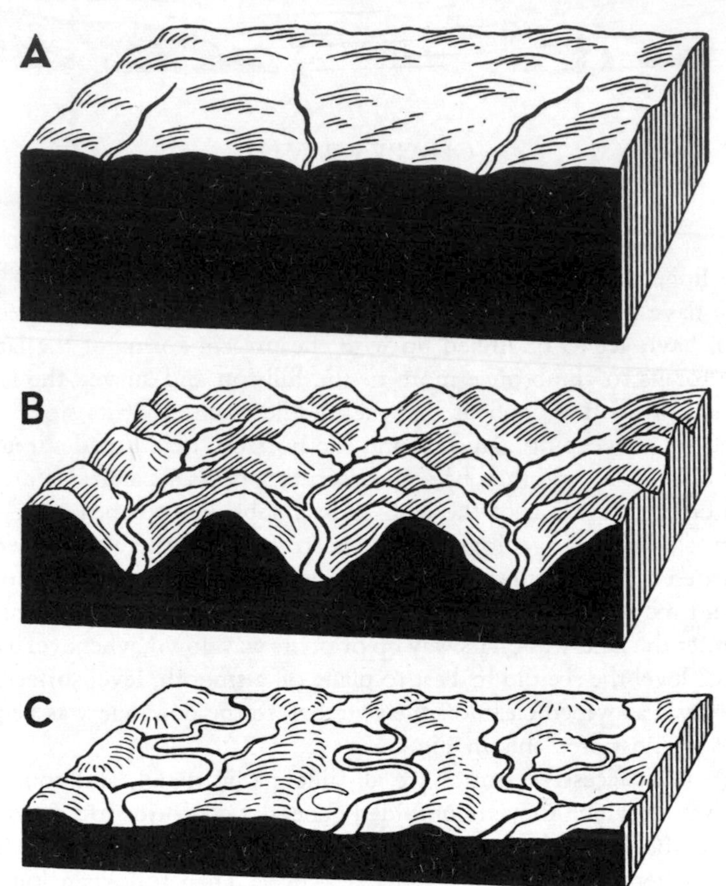

FIG. 104. The cycle of erosion. A, plateau or youthful stage. B, mature stage. C, peneplain or old-age stage.

nature of the rocks, their disposition, the elevation of the land, the climate, and many other factors. The *average* age of a landscape has been estimated at between one million and two million years.

Features characteristic of many stages in the cycle of erosion have already been described in this book, so that the following paragraphs will contain much that the reader is asked to take for useful recapitulation. The three main stages are illustrated in Fig. 104, where the attention should first be directed to the solid black faces of the blocks. These indicate by their depths the initial elevation of the land, at A, and the gradual reduction of its surface to near

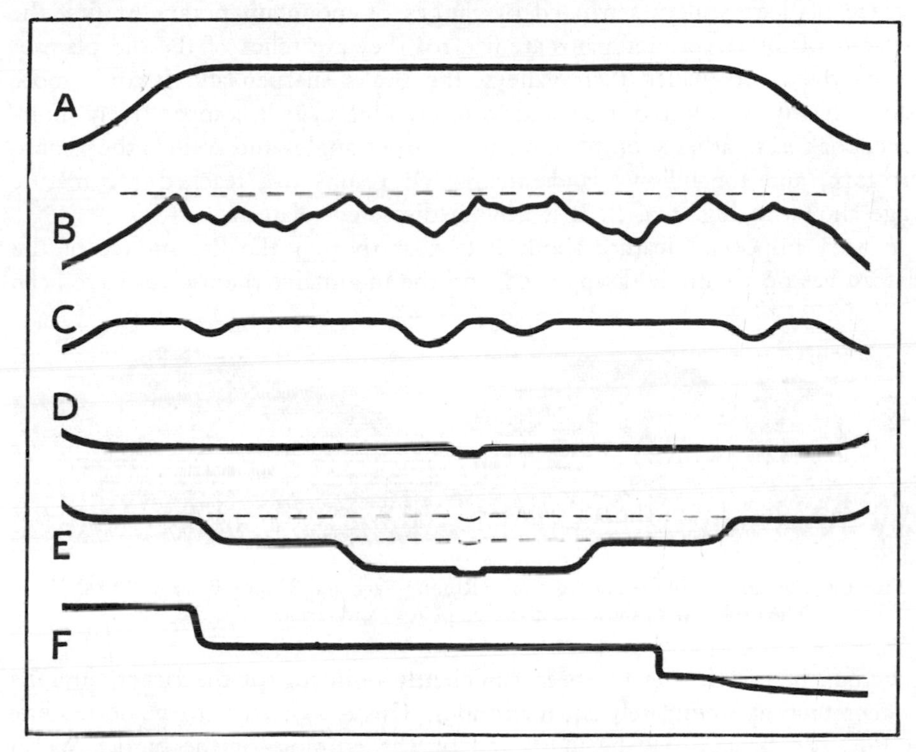

FIG. 105. Profiles of plains and plateaux. A, young plateau. B, dissected plateau. C, peneplain. D, river plain. E, river terraces. F, raised beach or coastal terrace.

sea-level, at C. The reader will recognize the development of the rivers through the stages of 'youth' and 'maturity' to 'old age' (see Chapter IV), and these terms are now to be applied to the landscape as a whole.

The youthful landscape at A is commonly termed a 'plateau'. It is characterized by its high altitude but freedom from mountain peaks, for though it is some time since it was beneath the sea it still retains the level surface with which it emerged. This surface may, however, be broken here and there by worn, isolated hills, representing ancient islands, and these are known as 'monadnocks'. We have already referred to the examples in Plate XXI, A, though these stand on a plain of marine erosion hardly high enough to be called a plateau. The typical form of a plateau (without monadnocks) is shown at A in Fig. 105, which gives idealized profiles of the broader types of land-surface.

Once established, the rivers soon begin to deepen their valleys, and the country passes through the stage of being a plateau crossed by deep valleys, to a maze of deep valleys separated by ranges of mountain peaks. At first the summits of the larger mountains are flat, for they are relics of the old plateau, but as the rivers widen their valleys, the peaks sharpen and become more vulnerable to the action of frost and weather. This stage is comparatively short-lived, for the weather soon removes the sharper angles and rounds the mountain-tops, and the billowy landscape which results has reached the mature stage shown at Fig. 104, B. It is now a 'dissected' plateau.

A very important feature about B is that though the flat surface of the plateau has now entirely disappeared, and the mountains themselves have been

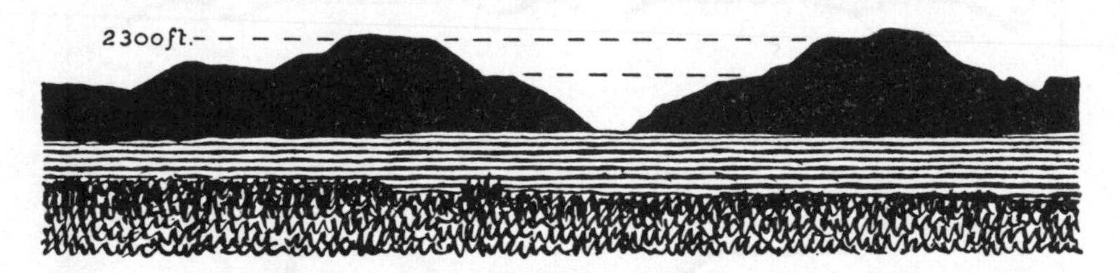

FIG. 106. Explanation of the photograph of Rhinog Fach and Rhinog Fawr in Plate XXI. The broken lines show the dissected plateau and terraces. See the text.

lowered, the weathering has been sufficiently uniform for the larger summits to keep their approximately equal altitudes. This is indicated by the dotted line in Fig. 105 B, and may be illustrated by the example of the higher Welsh mountains, many of which approximate very closely to a height of about 2,300 feet. The twin mountains, Rhinog Fach and Rhinog Fawr, in Merionethshire, are shown in Plate XXI, and in the diagram in Fig. 106 the upper dotted line shows how relics of the old plateau-surface may be traced in these mountains. The small extra elevation of the right-hand peak probably represents a monadnock on this ancient plateau.

A plateau of the kind we have been describing, which owes its level surface to planation by the sea, is sometimes called a 'plain of marine denudation', though this term strictly refers to the period of its story before it was promoted to the height of a plateau. Plains of marine denudation may occur at any height from sea-level upwards, and if the land rose unequally, as it often did, the result may be a slope to which the term 'plateau' is hardly applicable, so it is useful to have an alternative term for it.[1] The cycle of erosion pursues its normal course in such a case, but the dissection of the surface by rivers and weather will produce mountains which are of *graded* instead of equal height, as shown in Fig. 107. The same result occurs when a true plateau becomes tilted by earth-movements *after* its original elevation, and this is, in fact, the case with the mountains of Wales. These become progressively higher (on the average)

FIG. 107. Graded mountain heights indicating a dissected plateau which has become tilted.

towards the north, and the upper dotted line in Fig. 106 ought, strictly speaking, to slope very slightly downwards towards the left.

The rivers continue widening their valleys, but no longer by simple down-cutting and enlargement. They have begun to meander sideways to produce valley-flats, and to deposit some of their alluvium. Down-cutting presently ceases altogether and the deposits of alluvium form the river-plains which we described in Chapter IV as the mark of old age. While this has been going on the mountains have been slowly weathered and washed away till they have become mere stumps with flat, level tops, and the landscape has attained the state of old age illustrated in Fig. 104 C.

It will be noted from the solid black faces that the general surface of the land is now not unlike that of the original plateau at A. It is easily distinguished, however, both by the rivers it carries and its low altitude. The flat stumps of the old mountains are not quite reduced to the level of the plains, and their surface is therefore called a 'peneplain', which means 'almost a plain'. The ideal profile is illustrated in Fig. 105 at C, and it marks the completion of the cycle of erosion. The levelled top of the Chalk escarpment in Plate V, A, is part of a peneplain evident in many parts of the North and South Downs.

Our outline of the cycle of erosion requires an important qualification. The rambler's general view of the landscape should give him a good idea of its

[1] The terms are not, however, synonymous. *Any* extensive level surface at a high altitude may be called a plateau. *Any* extensive surface planed off by the sea may be called a plain of marine denudation (or erosion). Many plateaux happen to be old plains of marine denudation, but—according to a definition common in the older text-books—they are not to be called plateaux unless they stand at least a thousand feet above sea-level. By the same token, a 'hill' becomes a 'mountain' at the same height. But these old definitions have not turned out to be very useful, for so many of the traditional names of particular mountains, etc., do not conform with them.

stage of development, but he is not to jump to the conclusion that it reached that stage by uninterrupted processes, or that having reached a certain stage it must inevitably pass straight on to the next. The cycle is often held up for a time, or even temporarily reversed by renewed elevation of the land, and if, for example, an old peneplain appears to be carrying much younger rivers he will look for signs of rejuvenation (see page 79). In the case of the peneplain in Plate V he would find them in the entrenched meanders and terraces of the river Mole all the way from Dorking to Leatherhead.

In the profiles of broad land-surfaces in Fig. 105, D represents the simple plain of a large, old river. In a sense, it is the opposite number of the plateau at A. If A represents the top-floor of landscape, C is the first floor and D is the ground-level. E indicates what happens when the ground-floor is jacked up in two stages to provide a couple of 'mezzanine' floors, and has been adequately described under 'river terraces' (page 79).

The last profile, F, is the raised-beach, or—if it supports no beach—the wave-cut platform. We have already told how this sort of level arises (see Chapter III), and it is included here to show its relation to the other forms of levelled land-surfaces. It is a sea-terrace, and like the river-terraces at E it is a consequence of rejuvenation. A good example in Islay, dating from the Ice Age, is shown in Plate XVII, while the relics of a very much older one are visible half-way up the mountain-slopes of the Rhinogs in Plate XXI, B. The position of this is indicated by the lower dotted line in Fig. 106, and it was probably cut during a stationary episode in the elevation of the land.

The plain of marine denudation which first emerges when the land is raised above the sea is simply a wave-cut platform of exceptional size. It may be so vast that its bounding cliff (shown on the left of Fig. 105, F) becomes an insignificant detail—a mere ledge on the horizon—or it may be missing altogether. The extensive plain of marine denudation which now forms much of the level land in western Britain is easily seen in the picture of Reskajeage Cliffs, Cornwall, in Plate XIII and in our illustration of monadnocks in Plate XXI. It appears again very clearly in the background of the drawing at the head of Chapter IV, and yet again in the sketch at the head of the present chapter.

This sketch is of Worm's Head, in Gower, South Wales, and the vertical scale has been doubled to show more clearly how the sea has planed off the old folds in the rocks. When the folds are not so clearly visible, as may happen on a grass-covered hill inland, there is some likelihood of confusing such a formation with the type of 'mesa' illustrated in Fig. 14 C, or with the 'horst' shown in Fig. 15 D. The tests described on page 17 are of little use here, for with folded rocks it is impossible to deduce anything from specimens taken at random unless the dip of the bedding is known. Nevertheless, the prevalence in the neighbourhood of such a hill of other level land at the same altitude would make the 'horst' interpretation extremely unlikely, and the fine distinction between true-to-type mesas (in which the strata are horizontal) and other

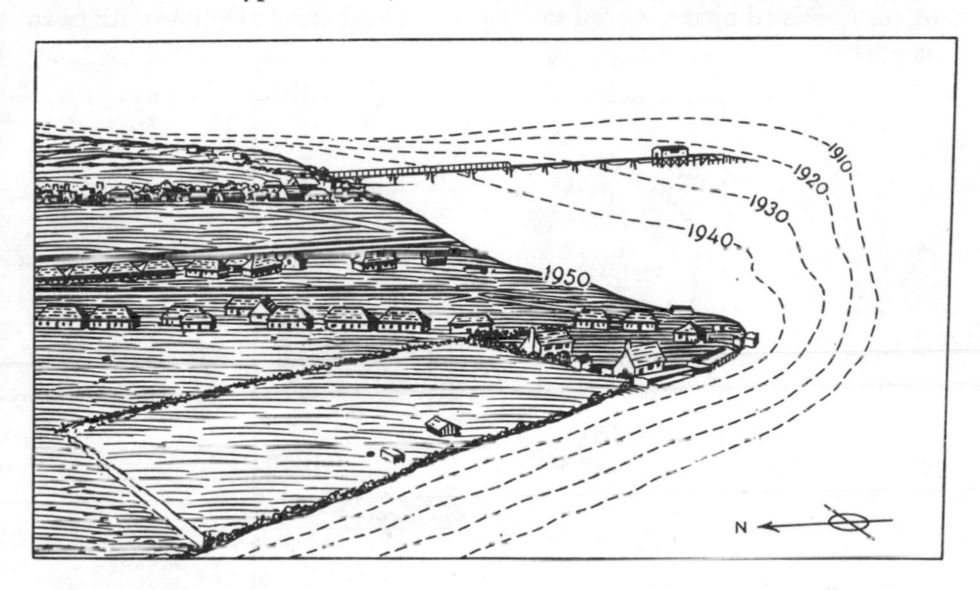

FIG. 108. Sketch from an air-photo of Selsey Bill, showing the retreat of the coastline over forty years. Extensive coast-protection was undertaken in 1953.

dissected plains of denudation is one with which the rambler will hardly bother. Mesas are level surfaces cut into flat-topped blocks by weathering or river erosion, and the surface of a mesa is as often a plain of marine denudation as not.

In our sketch of Worm's Head it will be noticed that the land has suffered considerable erosion by the sea since its elevation. The waves at the present low sea-level are constantly undermining the cliffs, and many thousands of square miles of the old elevated plain have completely vanished. The continuance of the level top of the cliff in the stacks forming the head provide a clue to its former extent. It originally reached right across the Bristol Channel, linking Wales with Devon and Cornwall, and it was, in fact, continuous with the Reskajeage Cliffs. This wholesale attack by the sea is continuing, and is a common feature of most of the British coast.

The rate at which the coastline of Britain is receding varies at different points. In a few places, as we saw in Chapter III, a reverse process is taking place, and the sea is being forced to retreat by the deposition of massive shingle banks. But on the whole the sea is encroaching on the land at an average rate of about one foot per year, the maximum destruction occurring in East Anglia and at Selsey Bill, where it formerly took five yards. In south-east England the sea is assisted by the general sinking of the land at roughly one-sixth of an inch per year.

FIG. 109. Modern coast of England superimposed on a map of Saxon England according to traditional records.

The rate at which the land was vanishing at Selsey Bill is illustrated in Fig. 108, where the lifeboat pier grew to a length of about two hundred yards. In 1920, the lifeboat house was on dry land. The old town of Selsea, with its Saxon Cathedral, was overwhelmed during the sixteenth century, and is now some two miles out to sea. Reaching much farther out, and extending right round the Bill, lies the great deer park established by the Saxon monks in the seventh century. The last records of this park appear to be the public damnation 'by bell, book, and candle' of poachers during the reign of Henry VIII.

Similar losses of townships and forests have occurred all round the coast of England and Wales, and the change in the map of the country which has occurred in historic times is quite astonishing. Its traditional outline in Saxon times, and the names of a few lost lands and towns, are given in Fig. 109. Many of the places shown were once large seaports, and there is sometimes evidence of habitation even before the keeping of proper records. For example, window-frames and pieces of doors are said to have been dredged from the sea-bottom between Land's End and the Scilly Isles, the traditional site of Lyonesse, the country of King Arthur.

The sea has arranged that such reports be taken with several grains of salt, but there is no doubt at all about the loss of many towns which flourished in the Middle Ages. For instance, Edward Balliol's 2,500 men embarked for their successful sea-attack on Scotland, in 1332, at Ravenspur, and in 1399—

> The banish'd Bolingbroke repeals himself,
> And with uplifted arms is safe arriv'd
> At Ravenspurg.[1]

Edward IV brought eighteen ships to Ravenspur in 1471 and landed 2,000 soldiers, but by then the sea had already begun its attack on the town, and by 1530 no trace of this old seaport remained.[2]

Another lost town of special note is Old Dunwich, which was once a royal demesne. By the time of Henry III it was large enough to support fifty-two churches, had its own mint and coinage, and boasted docks to hold seventy ships. Its destruction by the sea began in 1349, when four hundred houses and many shops and windmills were washed away. By 1540 less than a quarter of the old city of Dunwich remained, and in 1677 the people rose from their beds in the middle of the night to find the waves breaking over the market-place. The great storm of 1729 saw the people gathered on the walls and roofs of their houses 'loudly cursing the sea', and Old Dunwich was finally razed during the winter of 1739–40. The last of its ruins disappeared from view as late as 1920. Plate XXII, A, shows the destruction of houses by the sea on this coast during the great storm of 1936.

The rambler will find the stories of such lost towns in local and county guide-books, and these will also direct him to such remains as may be visible at low tide. We refer to them here only to illustrate the large-scale destructive advance of the sea. The detritus resulting from this destruction is deposited off-shore, and its volume can be calculated to a reasonable degree of approximation.[3] It represents a wholesale removal of the land equivalent to a reduction in the average height of the entire country of four inches every thousand years. The corresponding reduction in height due to weathering and rivers is about five

[1] Shakespeare, *Richard II, Act ii, Sc.* 2.

[2] Save a few relics like the memorial stone cross, which was preserved from destruction by removal to Kilnsea. It was later removed from Kilnsea to Burton Constable, and then again to Hedon.

[3] For the whole coast of England and Wales it works out at about 500 million cubic feet per year.

inches, so that England is being lowered nine inches every thousand years by the agents of denudation.

Now, the average height of the country is about 600 feet, so that we might expect the whole of England and Wales to be reduced to sea-level in about 800,000 years' time. However, as the height of the land is reduced the rate of denudation slows down, and there is always the likelihood of at least one renewed elevation of the land during so long a period, so that the English landscape will probably last its full million years. The effects of the work of man in coast-protection, as well as in mining and quarrying, are even more impressive, but this side of the question will be dealt with in the next chapter.

The general lowering of the surface of the land is itself the cause of many features which may puzzle the rambler. Most of the products of weathering are either carried away by rivers or are removed—swiftly or otherwise—by gravity, but on high level land the harder debris often remain in place for a surprising time. The surface supporting them continues to fall, but it carries on its slowly descending back stones and boulders which ought, by rights, to have disappeared long since. These are usually relics of formations which formerly lay on top of the present rocks, but which have now entirely vanished, and we have already given one example in the sarsens found on the chalk downs (see page 34). We now spare a paragraph or two for those mysterious high-level stony beds known as 'plateau gravels'.

In some parts of England (for instance, on the higher parts of the New Forest) there are extensive tracts of more or less angular flint pebbles which plainly do not belong to the terraces of any existing rivers. Moreover, they occur on rocks which are themselves more recent than the Chalk, so that they cannot be compared with the clay-with-flints described on page 107, for such a deposit could not form at a level higher than the top of the Chalk. Some of these plateau gravels present problems which remain unsolved, but most of them probably represent the terraces of rivers whose very basins have utterly disappeared. They provide a clue to drainage systems quite unrelated to the present form of the landscape, and though the subject is a difficult one the rambler will always find it interesting to pick up any unusual stone which chances to catch his eye, and to speculate at least where *that* could have come from. It may provide a clue to the origin of the whole gravel-bed.

It was chiefly the collection of such odd stones that first suggested the map of the ancient River Solent given in Fig. 110. This map shows the coast of Hampshire and Dorset perhaps fifty thousand years ago, and most of the named rivers are still in existence though they are now considerably shorter than they were. The so-called 'Southampton River' is a guess to account for the plateau gravels in the New Forest, for odd pebbles of Purbeck rocks have been discovered among the flints in the area marked by a cross. The nearest examples of Purbeck rocks from which these pebbles could have been derived occur in the valley of the Nadder, at the point marked by an asterisk, and it is assumed that they were carried down from this point by an ancient river. The gravels

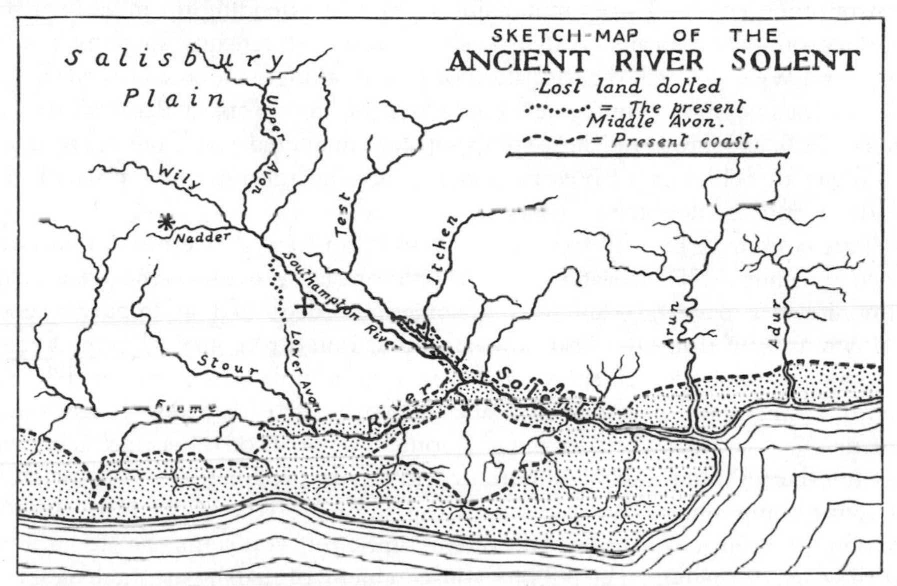

FIG. 110. Reconstruction of the drainage and coastline of southern Hampshire and Dorsetshire as it may have been about fifty thousand years ago. (*After Clement Reid.*)

are so extensive that this river must have been a large one, and it is from many such considerations that the drainage system illustrated was constructed.[1]

If this is a true story, it is evident that the Southampton River finally disappeared by being beheaded by the Lower Avon. The Avon is presumed to have begun its existence as a small stream, and to have cut back its head (see page 68) along the dotted line till it captured the headwaters of the Southampton River. This then dwindled away, its waters finally forsaking it altogether for the much stronger river Test. The present Solent, Southampton Water, and Spithead are plainly drowned river valleys, and the River Solent must have disappeared when the land subsided and the sea flowed round the Isle of Wight. But the old gravels of the Southampton River remain, and provide a good example of the importance and interest of strange pebbles occurring in plateau gravels.

[1] By Clement Reid, 1902.

Another little-understood covering of the higher lands is the mountain peat of the northern and western moors. Peat consists of the partly decomposed leaves, stems and roots of plants, in a more or less compressed state, and its occurrence in a hollow usually marks the site of an old lake or peat-bog (called a 'moss' in the north and a 'mire' in the south). But it is also found capping flat hill-tops, covering steep mountain-slopes, and extending for miles over the surface of high plateaux, and in such situations it remains something of a mystery. We can watch the formation of peat in a bog, and note how the fallen dead plants begin to support new life before they are properly decayed, so that they are finally preserved in a comparatively unaltered state, but there is no evidence that this sort of preservation and accumulation can take place on the turf covering a mountain.

Peat-bogs may be fifty feet or more deep, and are dangerous for unwary men and animals. Their water is dark brown or black, owing to the presence of limonite (see page 97), and this is sometimes deposited in impure masses known as 'bog iron-ore'. Peat-bogs are often found to contain layers of tree-stumps at various levels, showing that forests occupied their sites at different periods. The wood provides the black 'bog-oak' used for making small ornaments. A greasy product of decay which sometimes floats on the surface is known as 'bog-butter', and there is a more or less steady production of a few simple gaseous compounds. These appear at the surface of the water in occasional bubbles, but larger quantities will often come up if you stamp on the ground at the edge of the bog. The bubbles consist chiefly of marsh-gas (methane), but may contain a trace of phosphuretted hydrogen (phosphine[1]). Impure phosphuretted hydrogen, when present, catches fire spontaneously on reaching the air and ignites the marsh-gas, which then burns with the ghostly flame known variously as 'Jack-o'-lantern', 'Will-o'-the-wisp', 'corpse-candle', or (in Latin) *ignis fatuus*.

Peat is dug by crofters and other peasants for fuel, and is often cited as an example of the first stage in the conversion of vegetation into coal. It is doubtful if the peat with which we are most familiar ever becomes coal, but the process of its formation, in which all the elements in the vegetation except carbon gradually disperse, must be a similar one. The half-way stage to coal is represented by lignite, a 'brown-coal' from which all the gaseous products of decomposition have escaped. In ordinary coal (from which gas can be obtained only by roasting in coke-ovens) the carbon is mixed with about a quarter its weight of

[1] Not to be confused with *phosgene* (carbonyl chloride), a poison gas used in the First World War. Phosphine (phosphorus hydride) is also poisonous, and has a fishy or garlic-like odour. In the chemically pure state it is not spontaneously inflammable, but natural phosphine is far from virtuous and does possess this property.

complex compounds formed from the solid and liquid products of decay, and collectively known as coal-tar, but in anthracite the proportion of pure carbon may be as high as ninety per cent.

Seams of coal outcrop at the surface in many parts of Britain, and notably on the Pennines and in South Wales, and the rambler may therefore encounter it, but it is not proposed to repeat in this book the well-known story of the coal-forests. It must suffice to state that most British coals represent the remains of the primitive vegetation which flourished on great marshy river-deltas (see Fig. 117) some three hundred million years ago. The trees of the coal-forests resembled giant club-mosses, horse-tails, and tree-ferns, and were quite unlike the common trees of modern times. Some characteristic portions of them, found fossilized, have already been shown in Fig. 101.

We have, however, not quite done with the carbonaceous minerals, though the subject is leading us a little off the main subject of this chapter. Before we resume our theme we should note that where carbonization of vegetation has occurred in clayey marshes the result has been a carbonaceous shale, in which the products of decomposition have become re-arranged to form bitumen and mineral oil. Oil-shales, or bituminous shales, as they are sometimes called, have been worked in Scotland for the production of petroleum, and there are others in Dorset which contain too high a percentage of sulphur to allow satisfactory extraction and purification. Below Sussex there are carbonaceous deposits whose gaseous products have failed to escape and have accumulated in the rock-fissures. This subterranean gas was first tapped by accident in 1896, and was used until 1932 for lighting Heathfield Station.

A band of carbonaceous shale at Whitby (and elsewhere on the Yorkshire coast) supplies the beach with small lumps of a pure, clean black coal of even texture, known as 'jet'. These lumps are carried southward by longshore drifting, and may be picked up on almost any east-coast beach. They are suitable for carving into ornaments and polishing, and were once highly prized. Jet was known to the ancient Greeks, who powdered it in wine and used it as a cure for toothache, and they knew also of another curious mineral which may be picked up on our east-coast beaches—amber.

Amber is a fossil resin, and the east-coast specimens possibly came from the lignite beds of East Prussia, floating across the North Sea under the influence of tidal currents. Insects are sometimes found embalmed in it, and a piece of amber, if lightly rubbed, acquires the property of attracting light objects such as pieces of fluff or tissue-paper. This is not a unique property of amber—vulcanite, glass, sulphur, brown paper, and countless other substances possess it—but it was first discovered in amber by the ancient Greeks. The rubbing gives the amber an electric charge (as well as a pleasant scent), and it is from the Greek word for amber, *elektron*, that the word 'electricity' is derived.

Fragments of lignite and peaty clay are also found on the East Anglian beaches, but these fall from the cliffs at one or two places where a curious strip of river-clay and gravels, containing many foreign stones, is exposed. The

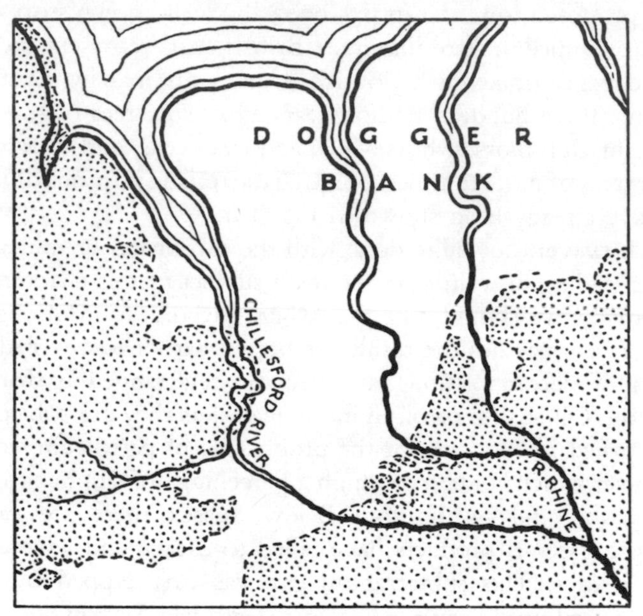

FIG. 111. Reconstruction of the old mouths of the Rhine, to account for the Chillesford River. See the text.

occurrence of lignite suggests an ancient bog or fen, but a good deal of driftwood is also present. Taken together, the evidence indicates the marshy mouth of a river, and the deposits do, in fact, lie in a narrow, sinuous belt running across East Anglia from south to north a little inside the present coastline. The foreign stones[1] and also the abundant flakes of mica in the clay, have been traced to the Ardennes and other areas in western France and Belgium, and the conclusion drawn is that they were brought into East Anglia by the river Rhine about a million years ago, when England was part of the Continent. This extension of the Rhine is known as the Chillesford River, and is shown in Fig. 111.

The map shows that in those times the North Sea reached no farther south than the Dogger Bank, now the happy hunting-ground of fishermen, and that

[1] Slate, chert, quartzites, grits, veinstones, etc.

the Rhine then possessed a vast delta of which the Chillesford River was the most westerly distributary. The Dogger Bank itself probably supported fen-plants and forests, but at the onset of the Ice Age these were replaced by an Arctic flora which was subsequently frozen out. When the ice finally melted the fen-plants reappeared and the Dogger Bank was once more clothed in vegetation, though the only trees now were birch, sallow and hazel. Relics of this vegetation, in the form of the tough, peaty masses known to the North Sea fishermen as 'moorlog', occasionally get entangled in the nets of trawlers. Apart from these plant-remains, the bones and teeth of mammoth, woolly rhinoceros, hyaena, beaver, bison and other animals have been dredged from the Dogger Bank.

Britain also became reafforested very soon after the Ice Age, and the ensuing depression which finally severed England from the Continent resulted in the submergence and burial of numerous forests round our coasts. The old tree-stumps of these, rooted in a kind of peat, are exposed at low tide in many places, and we give an example in Plate XXII, B.[1] These relics are not fossilized but rather salt-pickled, and are so plainly drowned forest-lands that they have become associated in folk-lore with the Flood, their folk-name being 'Noah's woods'. Some of them extend considerable distances inland (especially up the mouths of rivers), where they are overlain by more recent deposits of anything up to fifty feet in thickness.

We promised to return to the proper subject of this chapter, which is the 'broad view', but in our survey of the Chillesford River and the buried forests we have, perhaps, overshot the mark. But if this summarizing chapter appears to ramble a little, it will at least serve as an exercise in the appreciation of scale-relationships. One of the chief difficulties the amateur at geological observation experiences is in leaping backwards and forwards (mentally) from the very small to the very big. Yet it is often necessary to consider together the outline of some vast sea or land-mass and a few glittering specks of a mineral seen with difficulty through a microscope, and any exercise developing this sort of agility is good training. On the whole, the small-scale observations are the easier, for they are nearer the familiar scales of things human.

We have hitherto been careful to confine our attention to objects visible to the naked eye, though we have not despised the occasional use of a pocket magnifying-glass. In the other direction we have restricted our attention to

[1] The similar buried forest known as the 'Cromer Forest-bed', which is to be seen on the Norfolk foreshore, does not belong to the series of submerged forests we are now discussing. It is very much older, and dates, in fact, from *before* the Ice Age. It should be associated in the reader's mind with the Chillesford River, whose deposits it succeeded after a short interval.

objects not too vast to be seen at once in their entirety, though here again—and especially in the present chapter—we have taken a few liberties. For it is our chief purpose in these brief excursions into ancient topography to accustom the rambler to 'think big', so that he will not regard a true interpretation of his smaller finds ridiculous simply because it is monstrous. He will, in fact, generally tend to underestimate the vastness of time and space as signified in a landscape, and will find it hard to believe at one and the same time that the enormous changes to which the evidence points have really occurred, and that there have very likely been no noticeable changes at all for hundreds—or even thousands—of years. Yet he is to accustom himself to the truth voiced by the poet:[1]

The hills are shadows, and they flow
From form to form, and nothing stands;
They melt like mist, the solid lands,
Like clouds they shape themselves and go.

We have used the vague term 'millions of years' more than once, and since a period of a million years is a fair unit of time for measuring the broad changes in a landscape, it is worth a little trouble to try to realize what this period really amounts to. It is sometimes said that nobody can truly visualize so large a number as a million, but surely this is not so. We should have no great difficulty in imagining a square pile of a million bricks, for instance. Such a pile would have a hundred bricks each way, and be a hundred bricks high.

But as soon as we put 'years' instead of 'bricks', our period of a million does become a little more difficult to grasp. To experience such a period we should need to live through human history from the Pyramids to the present day about two hundred times over. Ponder that a little—try to run back into the past just that far, and you will have reached the period of the Chillesford River. Geologically speaking, it was the day before yesterday, 'yesterday' being the Ice Age, and 'today' the historical age of man—but this has hardly yet begun. On this scale of reckoning you would have to go back four months of such days to see the Chalk Sea over Britain, and ten months to see the coal forests.

And if these periods are immense, so are the thicknesses of the rocks laid down in the seas which dominated them. The Old Red Sandstone alone is nearly a mile thick, and the Carboniferous Limestone is even more massive. The *average* rate at which sediments are deposited is about sixteen inches per thousand years, and the total thickness of all the sedimentary rocks, as estimated

[1] Tennyson, *In Memoriam*, CXXII.

from a world survey, is something like two hundred miles![1] In Britain, it is less than half this, but still quite sufficient to cause the rambler to wonder what on earth—or under it—such depths can have to do with him. Yet he may often find a fossil overlain by a mile or two of sediments *all clearly visible to him from where he stands.*

In Fig. 112 we show how this commonly happens. In any region where the strata are seen (in cliff or cutting) to dip, you may walk across the outcrops till

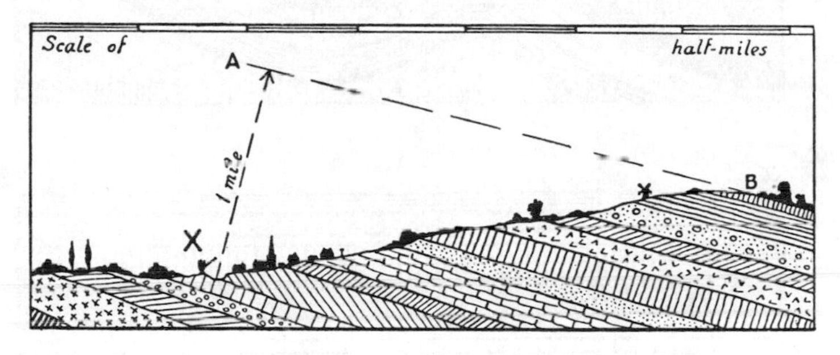

FIG. 112. Diagram to show how a fossil found on the surface at X may have to be referred to a depth of at least a mile.

you are far indeed below the original surface of the land. In the diagram the line A—B indicates the original surface before the strata were tilted, and it is plain that a fossil picked up at X must really be referred to a depth of at least a mile. At *least* a mile, because it is impossible to tell from the diagram how much more sediment may once have lain above the line A—B, and have since been removed.

Or look at Fig. 113, where A shows a tract of country over worn-down folded strata. As you walk the four miles (say) from *x* to *y* you explore the depths with an efficiency no burrowing mole could even dream about. Imagine the original strata complete and in the level state in which they were first deposited, as shown at B. You may then put your walk from *x* to *y* into its

[1] It should be explained that this does not mean that the crust of the earth is two hundred miles thick, nor that the sediments themselves approach this thickness in any one locality. A bed two miles thick may be laid down in a sea, and then be raised to form dry land. It now suffers reduction by denudation, and its waste material helps to form another bed two miles thick in an adjacent area. This second bed is subsequent to the first, so that the total thickness of sedimentation is four miles though nowhere do the actual sediments exceed two miles.

Both areas may now lie 'fallow' for a few million years, while sedimentation goes on in other parts of the world, the total increasing out of all proportion to the increase in any single locality. In spite of the great total thickness of the sedimentary rocks the crust of the earth is, in fact, only about thirty miles thick, and most of that consists of igneous rocks. The formation of sedimentary rocks consists very largely of the removal and redistribution of older sedimentary rocks, and nowhere do *continuously deposited* sediments reach a thickness of more than a few miles.

proper geological perspective, and see what it really means. You plunge underground at the outset, and have a look at the rocks two-thirds of a mile down. You then come up a third of a mile to take a second glance round at that level, but only to descend steeply again till you are a mile or more below the surface.

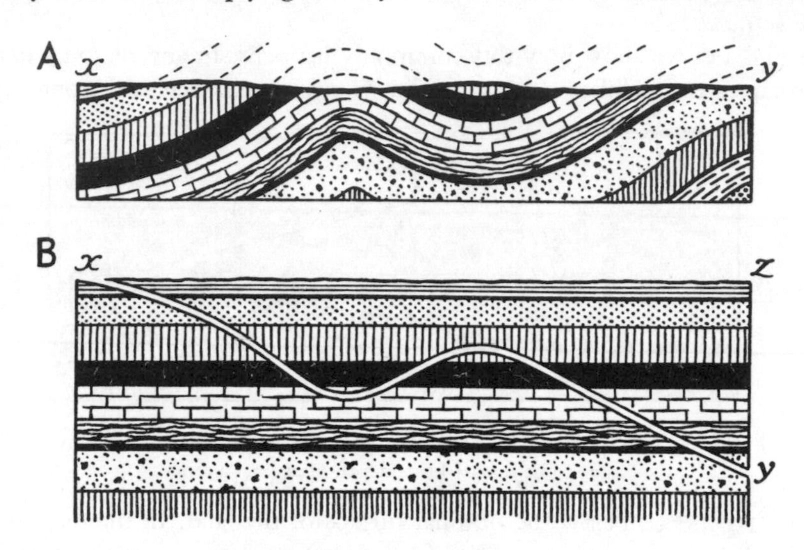

FIG. 113. Diagram to put into geological perspective the rocks outcropping at the surface *x-y* (A). The triangular block *xyz* (B) represents the material which has been removed by denudation.

Fanciful?—by no means. Imaginative, then?—certainly, and it is in such just uses of the imagination that much of the pleasure of geological observation lies. It is the imagination which, *when soundly informed*, breathes life into the dead array of gathered facts.

Such formations as we have just described are far more commonly met with than stretches of perfectly horizontal strata, and in point of fact the broad arrangement of the rocks of England as a whole is very similar to the one illustrated in Fig. 112, except that the surface should be higher on the left (west) than on the right (east). It is rather like a pile of books which has been tipped over till they have slid into a row, as shown in Fig. 114. This should be compared with Fig. 115 (top), which is a much simplified section across the northern counties from the Irish Sea to the coast of Yorkshire, the vertical scale being exaggerated to make a drawing of this size possible. Even allowing for this exaggeration, it is clear that a person standing in the Lake District (*L*) is geologically some miles lower than a person standing on Flamborough Head

(E), and on the whole, to travel westward across England is to travel (geologically) downward.

This general arrangement of the English rocks is subject to endless variation

FIG. 114. The general disposition of the strata of England illustrated by a row of books. Compare with Fig. 115.

in detail, and the second example in Fig. 115 shows a simplified section running from north-west to south-east, from Worcester (NW) through Oxford to Beachy Head (SE). In spite of its apparent complexity, there are only two major interferences with the ideal scheme, at x and y, respectively, and if the areas marked by brackets be covered by the fingers the diagram is similar to the one above it.[1] At x the reader will notice a fault (f) and an unconformity (u), and these are but well-marked examples of many such irregularities which could

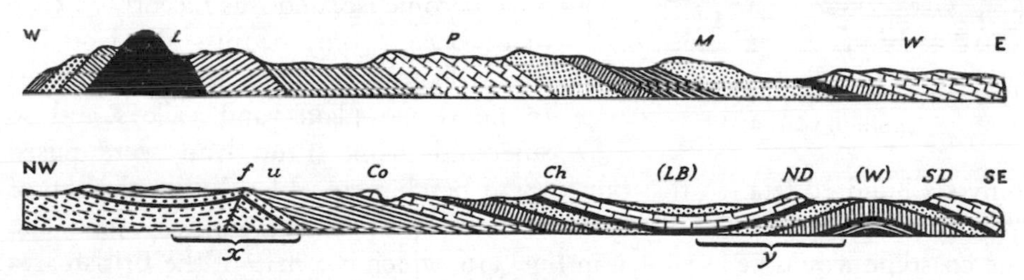

FIG. 115. *Above*, section across England from the Irish Sea to the coast of Yorkshire (*P*: Pennines; *M*: Yorkshire Moors; *W*: Wolds). *Below*, section from Worcester to Beachy Head (*Co*: Cotswold Hills). See the text.

have been included in both sections had they been drawn to a large enough scale.

[1] This is, perhaps, not quite a fair demonstration, but its weakness is itself instructive. Over-simplification necessarily involves errors, and these are usually of no fundamental significance, but in the present case there is an anomaly which calls for special comment. This is the result of the folding in the London Basin (*LB*) and the Weald (*W*), whereby the chalk which dips to the south-east at the Chiltern Hills (*Ch*) reappears and dips again to the south-east at the South Downs (*SD*). In short, when you cover the area y with your finger, the strata lying to the right of it are not new formations lying on top of those to its left, as you might suppose, but are the same set of strata staging a second appearance. Nevertheless, the general principle that the older rocks occur to the left of the diagram, and the newer to the right, holds good for the section as a whole.

It is evident, both from the massiveness of the rock formations and from their general tilt downward towards the east, that they belong to systems reaching far beyond the present boundaries of the British Isles. The British Isles are, in fact, an accident due to the temporary low level of Europe, and most of the rock formations continue unbroken beneath the shallow North Sea and English Channel, to emerge again on the Continent itself. The true western seaboard of Europe is the Continental Shelf, which is marked by the end of the shallow water some distance off the west coast of Ireland. Here, at the real edge of the Continent, the sea-bed drops steeply away from a depth of a mere hundred fathoms to more than a mile.

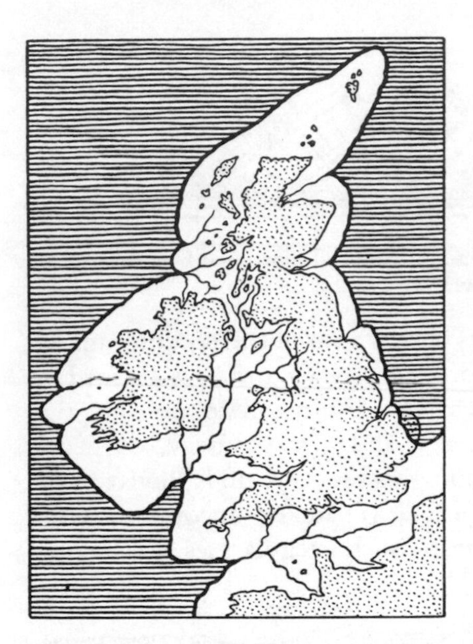

FIG. 116. Coastline of the British area a million years ago.

The present British Isles, then, must be thought of as a group of mountains on the western borders of Europe, and to have become isolated—as recently as 5000 or 6000 B.C.—only because the land has been depressed sufficiently for the sea to flood the plains and valleys and so surround them. If the land were raised only six hundred feet (so that our present beaches stood level with the top of Beachy Head), Britain would become wholly a part of the Continent again, and the coastline would be as shown in Fig. 116, which is a map of the British area at about the time of the Chillesford River. But the present form of Europe itself is, geologically speaking, a 'recent acquisition', and at no time earlier than a million years ago was there anything remotely resembling the British Isles at all.

For the greater part of geological history the British area has had a very different aspect. There has been a great continent to the north and west, over the present sites of the Arctic and N. Atlantic oceans, and the irregular south-eastern coastline of this continent, with its changing islands and peninsulas, has occupied the British area. In Fig. 117, which shows the region as it was in Coal Measure times, this continent is marked 'Laurentia'. The coal forests grew on the vast delta of a river flowing from Scandinavia and the north—a river which brought down sufficient sediments to form a bed nearly a mile thick. This bed is known as the Millstone Grit, and many of its constituent minerals are foreign to Britain but can be matched in Norway.

Whenever you have occasion to picture Britain while any but its most recent rocks were being formed, you will be far nearer the truth if you have this map

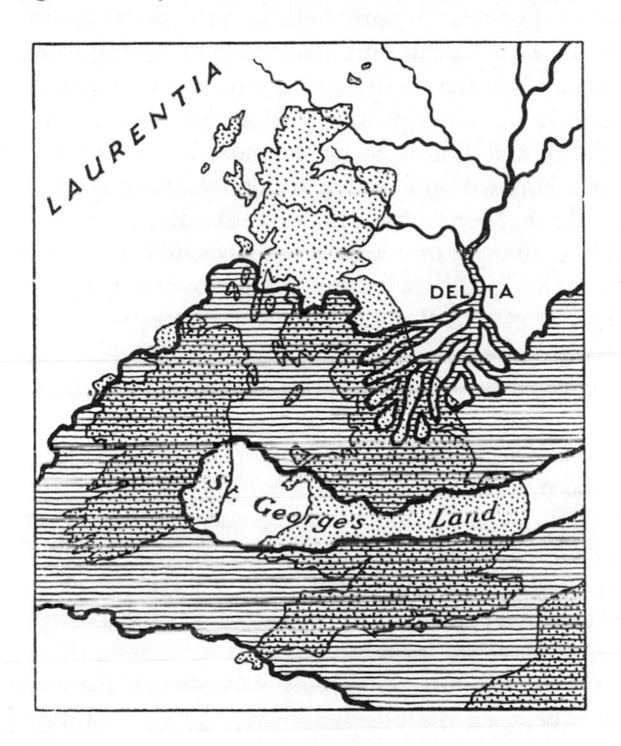

FIG. 117. Map of the British area in Coal Measures times. See the text.

in mind instead of the one in your atlas. The details, of course, have varied enormously—the river and delta were transient features, and sometimes we were utterly beneath the sea—but that great north-west continent was almost always in evidence in the background. The seas which invaded Britain from time to time flowed in chiefly from the east and south, and it is only at a late stage of our history that the continent of Laurentia disappeared. It did not, however, sink beneath the ocean like the fabled Atlantis, but broke off from the European block and drifted slowly westwards. Indeed, the bulk of it still exists—as N. America. It has taken about eighty million years to travel the two thousand miles to its present position. But there we must leave it, for its rambles have taken it far beyond the scope of ours.[1]

The rambler who is interested in the ancient geography of his country may, if he has eyes to see, perceive in the forms of landscape the ghosts of many strange and antique lands, but for this purpose he will need some knowledge of historical geology. For this we must refer him to special books on the subject, and it is for his encouragement only that we give the following examples.

We have already referred to the scenery in the Weald of Kent and Sussex, and many phases in the long geological story are here manifest. The rambler who climbs the central Forest Ridge is most likely to remember that vast ancient lake of a hundred and twenty million years ago, on whose sandy bed he now stands. At that period the land was subsiding, and as the waters of the lake widened the strange monsters which roamed its marshy shores were driven back and back, till they were finally overwhelmed by a sea which covered the greater part of Britain. This was the sea in which the Chalk was laid down (of which we have already told), and the white ooze which settled in it presently covered the old lake-bed to a depth of a thousand feet or more.

But the land rose again, and now presents the rambler with another picture. The Wealden area was humped into a huge dome of white chalk, with the ancient sands and muds of the lake as its core. The work of weather and rivers removed the chalk from the top of the dome, exposing once more the old lake-bed on which the rambler stands (see Fig. 12). On the flanks of the dome, and still visible from his view-point, the last remnants of the chalk cover remain as the two distant escarpments of the North and South Downs.

And now once more the picture changes. As the Wealden dome buckled upwards, raising its chalk cover high above sea-level, the chalk covering the London district (between the North Downs and the Chiltern Hills) buckled downwards, and became covered by a new sea whose mud we now call the London Clay. It is the scene of Tennyson's stanza:[2]

> There rolls the deep where grew the tree.
> O earth, what changes hast thou seen!
> There where the long street roars, hath been
> The stillness of the central sea.

This sea spread till it covered practically the whole of south and south-east

[1] This subject of 'Continental Drift' is still under discussion, but while the *modus operandi* remains extremely obscure, the fact of continental movement seems inescapable in the face of the evidence. Not only do the two sides of the Atlantic Ocean fit roughly into one another, like pieces of a jig-saw puzzle, but in many places the very rock-formations match. The name 'Laurentia' is derived from the river St Lawrence, though it was Labrador which probably once lay adjacent to Scotland.

[2] *In Memoriam*, CXXII.

England, as well as part of France, but the rambler on the Wealden heights is safe, for these formed a great island reaching from Hampshire to Calais. In the seas around him swam sharks and other sub-tropical fish, and he may go and find their bones and teeth in the clays and sandstones of the London and Hampshire basins.

Again, the traveller may stand upon the Malvern Hills (Plate II) and survey the plains which were desert-land two hundred million years ago, and re-create in his imagination the mysterious reptiles which sought water-holes in the sands, and there left the footprints by which alone we know them. Or he may picture the great Dead Sea which stood silent in that desert for twenty million years or more, slowly drying up to yield its salt to the mines of Cheshire. The Malvern Hills were young then, but (apart from a temporary submergence beneath the Chalk Sea) they have remained as sentinels to the present day, passive spectators of the changing landscape at their feet.

Lastly, the visitor to North Wales may try to picture the yet older story of the mountains of Snowdonia, Cader Idris, and Arenig. He must make some effort to recapture the scene as it was four hundred million years ago, and this is surely not too difficult, for this part of the country was then entirely submerged. The great north-west continent was standing by, but beyond the horizon, and a vast expanse of sea covered the whole of the British Isles north of a line drawn from South Wales to Yorkshire. On its bed were level deposits of mud, and bursting through these on the sites of Snowdon, Cader Idris, Arenig, Moel Hebog, and many other mountains of igneous rocks, were submarine volcanoes.

Masses and sheets of lava poured out beneath the sea and accumulated to form mountains which, nevertheless, did not appear above the surface until a hundred million years year later. Then they came up under the action of terrific squeezing forces (see Figs. 7 and 76), which converted the older mud of the sea-bed into the slates quarried at Penrhyn (see Plate XXVIII) and Llanberis, and they have held their heads to the weather continuously ever since.

Many such stories might be told, but we have now to leave the remote past and give our attention to some curious details of the landscape which no profundity of geological knowledge can explain. For the first time in the history of the world the landscape began, perhaps no more than a few thousand years ago, to display certain irrational features with which physical science is quite incompetent to deal. Queer-shaped hills, odd groups of boulders, puzzling terraces and other such forms, began to appear in the most unlikely situations, and without apparent cause. These excrescences were the work of the dawning intelligence of Man.

CHAPTER VIII

The Mark of Man

Man has been described as the only 'rational' animal, but since the elements of reason have been traced in apes, dogs, cats, horses, bears, and many other creatures, this is not a very good definition. Still less satisfactory is the definition of man as a 'logical' animal, for the strictest conformity to logical behaviour is found in the inanimate world, where nature faultlessly parades the very phenomena which logic is invoked to describe, and by which its conclusions are tested. The more nearly mechanical a creature is (and we may go to the ants, bees and other insects for good examples), the more simply logical is its behaviour. Man flatters himself indeed if he pretends to be the only rational or logical animal, and his pretence but serves to illustrate the real truth. He is surely the supreme example of an *irrational* and *illogical* animal.

His expression of himself in his actions very frequently contradicts his expression of his thoughts in words, and few other creatures so often do the right things for the wrong reasons, or the wrong things for the right ones. Man is said to be the only creature which drinks when it is not thirsty, but here we admit that he is matched by the sea-gulls, which will gorge themselves with grubs in a freshly-ploughed field till they are obliged to vomit—and proceed immediately to stuff themselves once more with the vomit. They are, we might say, that much human.[1] But man is the only creature known to us which builds hills where none is necessary, which up-ends huge boulders and

[1] As this is going to press a curious note concerning the gustatory habits of the Romans has come to hand quite by chance. It is to the effect that after eating prodigious quantities of oysters the Romans had a practice of tickling their gullets with a feather to cause regurgitation, when the pleasure of swallowing the oysters was enjoyed for a second time. The author cannot recollect any authority for this story, but in the present context it is sufficient that the idea has been considered credible.

leaves them in more or less precarious positions for no earthly purpose, and which carves patterns in the surface of the ground at an enormous expenditure of energy, for no better reason than the wish to carve patterns in the ground.

Much of this chapter, therefore, will be a mere description of things for which no reason can be assigned without the invocation of transcendental or irrational ideas. There will also be descriptions of highly practical works,

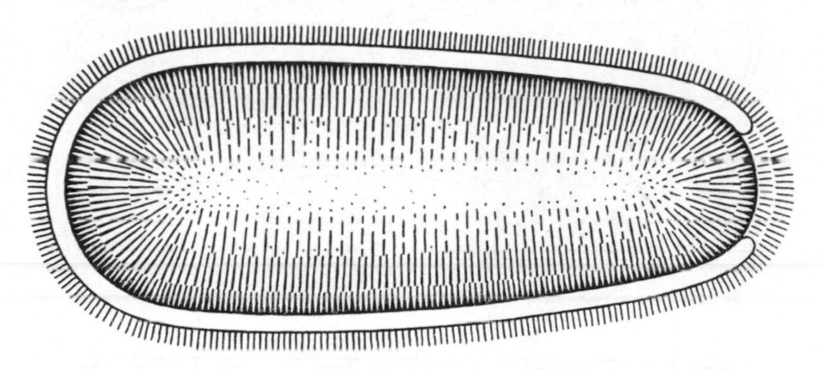

Fig. 118. Bird's-eye view of a typical long barrow. The surrounding trench has been left white.

undertaken for sound, logical reasons, for it is the crowning piece of man's irrationality that he can, without a qualm, be rational or not as his fancy dictates. Indeed, if he were not free in this respect it would hardly be rational to describe him as 'irrational'. He seems, in fact, to be at least two steps removed from all other animals: he is not only alone in his *awareness* of logic, but he also holds himself to be *above* it. He is creator as well as creature—he belongs, simultaneously, to two worlds. And this is the real clue to many of the queer modifications to the landscape for which he has been responsible.

The downs, wolds and moors of Britain have their otherwise smooth surfaces broken by occasional mounds and hillocks of artificial origin and immense antiquity. These features may, for classification among our 'elements of scenery', be divided into three groups—barrows, camps, and waste dumps. Their idealized profiles are shown in Fig. 120, and their artificial nature is usually, though not always, manifest in the geometrical regularity of their forms.

The oldest barrows are the long barrows of the neolithic period (New Stone Age), and they vary enormously in both size and shape, while some are—or were—surrounded by a low paling of upright stones. A bird's-eye view of a typical specimen is given in Fig. 118, and other forms are shown in Fig. 119;

they are usually much higher and wider at one end than at the other, but not always so. The double lines indicate the surrounding trench from which much of the material of the barrow was dug, but many long barrows are strengthened by walls of loose masonry and contain material which was probably gathered over a wide area, while some are built entirely of flat stones and slabs of rock

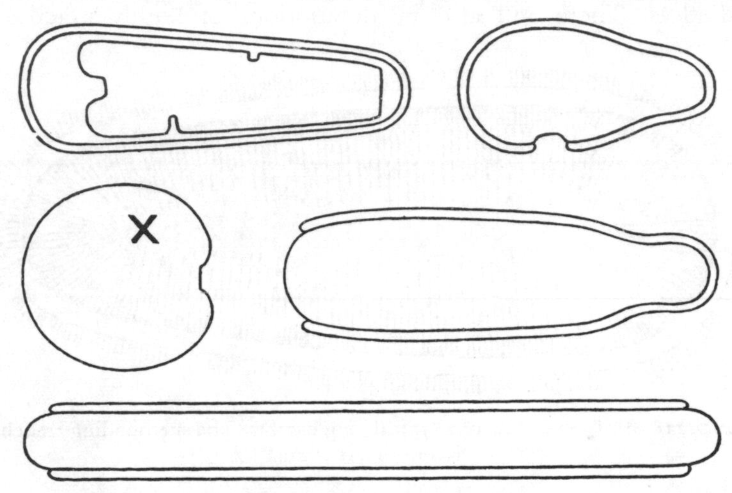

FIG. 119. Neolithic barrows, with a cairn at X. At the foot is the rare ridge barrow.

neatly piled together. A fair specimen might measure two or three hundred feet in length, fifty feet in width, and six or eight feet in height. The longest known barrow is about a third of a mile in length, and is thirty times as long as it is wide, but such proportions are exceptional. This barrow is sometimes put in a class of its own, and is called a 'ridge' barrow.

The long barrows usually contain burial chambers at their larger ends, for the earlier ones are communal graves and the later ones family vaults. We use the terms loosely, for the distinction in function is not clear. In the 'communal graves' many persons seem to have been buried simultaneously and the mound closed for ever. In the 'family vault' bodies were evidently added from generation to generation, access to the burial chamber being obtained through a passage-way. This type of barrow is sometimes called a 'passage' or 'gallery' grave. The general profile of a long barrow is typified in Fig. 120 at A. See also Plate XXIII.

Barrows built entirely of stones are known as 'cairns', and some of these are more or less circular in shape and have no surrounding trench. A plan of one is shown at X in Fig. 119, the indentation marking the entrance to the passage, and the general profile is given in Fig. 128, B. The actual burial chamber of a long barrow was often built of very large boulders, and these have sometimes survived long after the barrow itself has disappeared. We shall meet them again when we come to consider prehistoric stones.

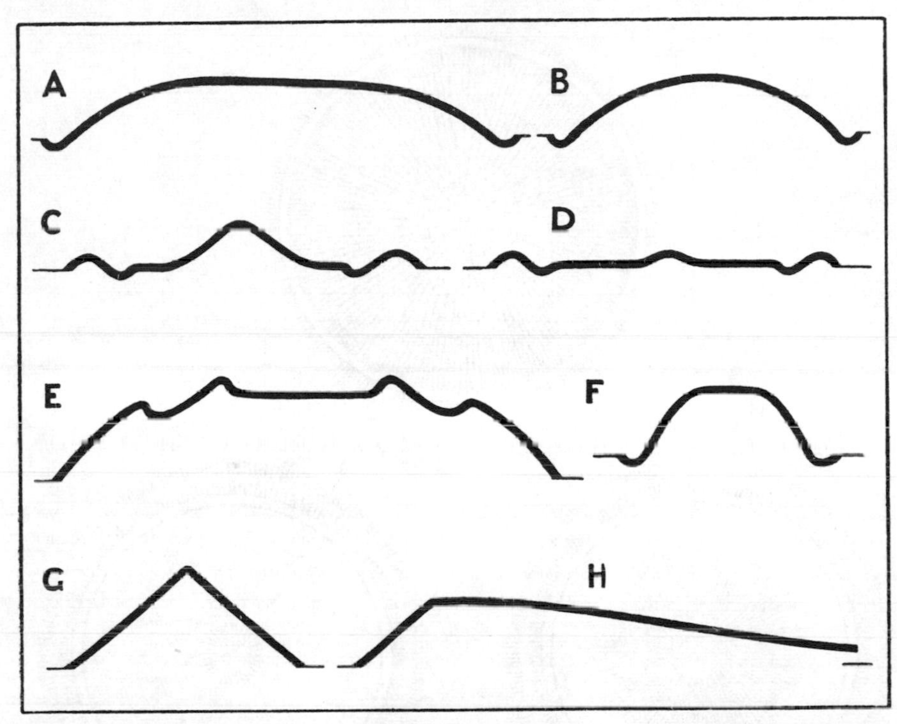

FIG. 120. Profiles of artificial mounds. A, long barrow. B, round barrow, bowl type. C, round barrow, bell type. D, round barrow, disc type. E, hill-fort or camp. F, motte. G, waste-dump. H, rubbish-tip.

The neolithic monuments so far described were built by a race of long-headed men to whom we may attach the rough date-label '3000 B.C.' They were a small, dark people who probably came to Britain from the Mediterranean *via* Spain, Portugal, and France. If this were a book on prehistoric Britain we should continue with their story here, and then pass on in chronological sequence to later races. But we are concerned primarily with the elements of scenery, and our subject at the moment being 'barrows' we pass on now to the later types of burial mound. (We shall return to neolithic times when we come to other scenic forms.)

The long-headed race was superseded by a sturdier, round-headed race who came from the Alpine countries of central Europe. The newcomers built round barrows instead of long ones, but these did not contain elaborate burial chambers; the dead were usually interred in a hole in the ground, lined with stones, beneath the centre of the barrow. Burial mounds containing no chambers

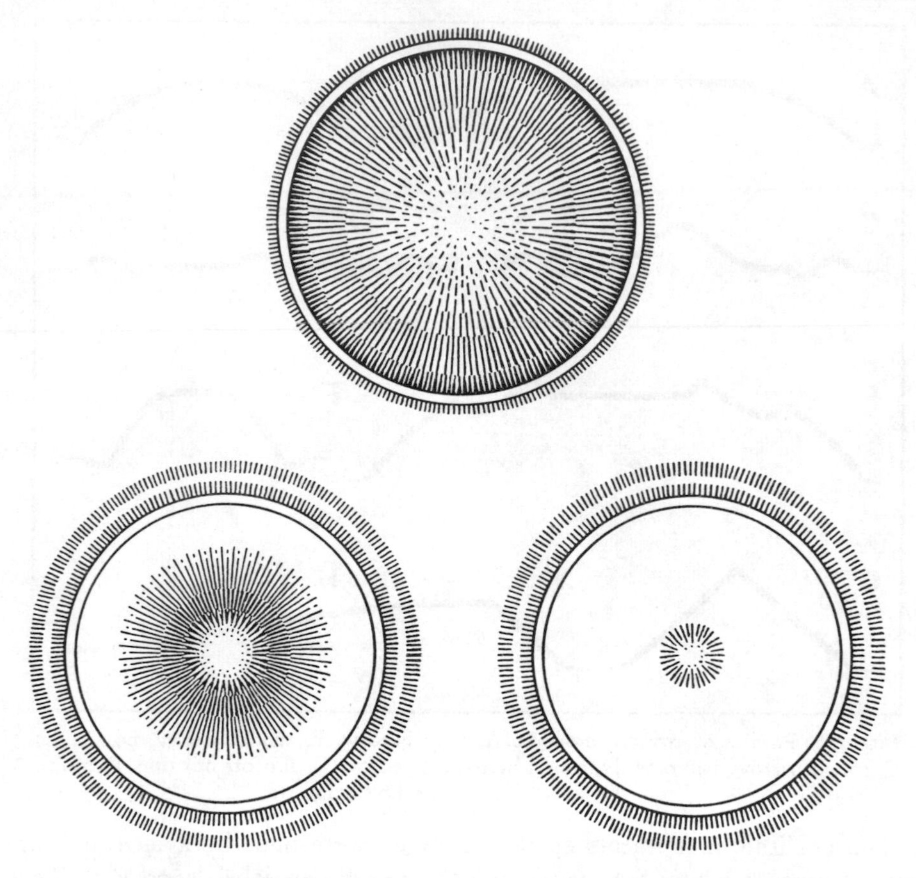

FIG. 121. Bird's-eye view of typical round barrows. *Top*, bowl type. *Left*, bell type. *Right*, disc type. Compare with Fig. 120, B, C and D, respectively.

are sometimes specifically called 'tumuli', but this is an unwarrantable limitation of the meaning of 'tumulus' (Latin *tumulus*, from *tumere* to swell), which should cover all prehistoric mounds whatsoever; it is correctly used on Ordnance Survey maps. For examples of round barrows see Plate XXIII.

There are three common types of round barrow, their profiles being given in their general historical order in Fig. 120 at B, C and D. They are known as 'bowl', 'bell', and 'disc' barrows, respectively, and bird's-eye views of them are shown in Fig. 121. The bowl type may measure from twenty to sixty or more feet in diameter, and rise to a height of about five feet. The bell type usually exceeds a hundred feet in diameter, and may reach a height of ten or

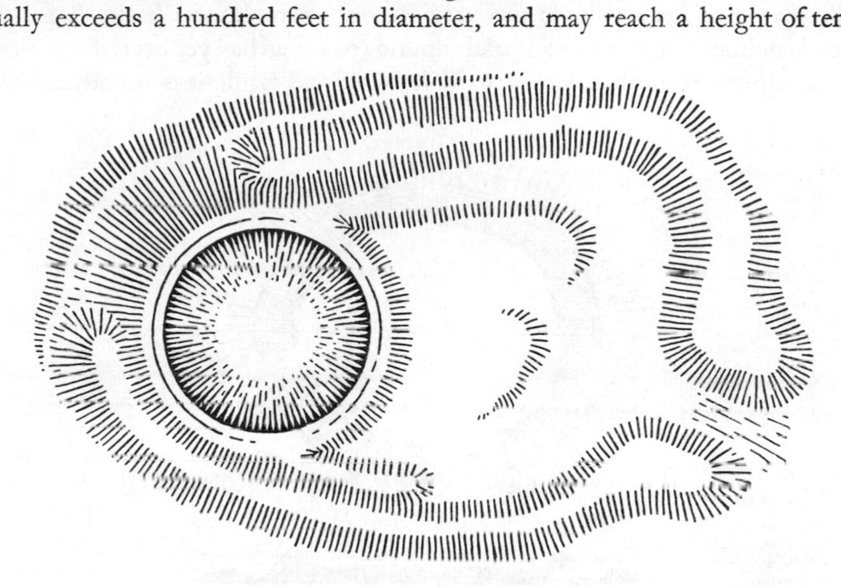

FIG. 122. Bird's-eye view of a typical motte-and-bailey, forerunner of the castle keep and courtyard.

fifteen feet. The disc barrow is about a hundred feet in diameter, and is practically flat, the tiny mound, or 'tump', in the centre being scarcely larger than a molehill. Occasionally a disc barrow may contain two or three tumps.

Because the round barrow people were in the habit of burying earthen vessels with their dead they are sometimes referred to as the Beaker Folk, and their advent marks the beginning of the Bronze Age in Britain. They also built round cairns of the type shown in Fig. 128 at B, which may be distinguished from the circular neolithic gallery grave (Fig. 119, X) by the absence of an entrance, for they contain no large chamber.

So far, the mounds we have described have all marked burial sites, but the next form, whose profile is given in Fig. 120 at F, is open to two interpretations. A small flat-topped mound of this sort, reminiscent of an inverted pudding-basin, may be a British burial mound of the time of the Roman occupation, but a larger version of the same form, possibly supporting trees, is probably a Norman 'motte'.

This was a mound built to support a wooden or stone tower, and is the ancestor of the castle keep. It usually guards a small courtyard or 'bailey' (called a 'barmkin' in Scotland), marked by an enclosing embankment and ditch. A bird's-eye view of a typical motte-and-bailey is shown in Fig. 122.

We may note here a single but very famous example of a basin-shaped hill which is neither a motte nor a burial mound (so far as has yet been discovered). This is Silbury Hill, near Avebury (Wiltshire), and while it is usually ascribed

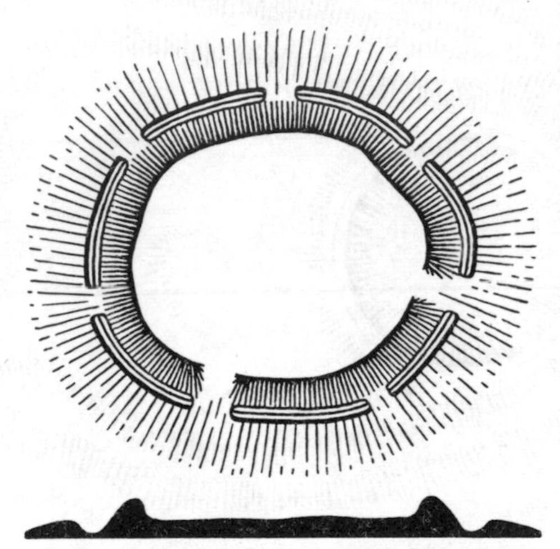

FIG. 123. Bird's-eye view and section of a simple causeway fort. This is usually surrounded by further banks and ditches of the same pattern.

to the Bronze Age its date and purpose are really unknown. It is one hundred and thirty-five feet high, and covers more than five acres; it is, in point of fact, the largest artificial mound in western Europe. (See Plate XXIV.) It is only natural that such mysterious features of the landscape should have legends associated with them, and as an example of the traditional type of 'explanation' we give the story of Silbury Hill:

Once upon a time, the town of Devizes became notable above all other towns for the goodness and holiness of its inhabitants. They were honest in all their dealings, went to church at all hours, crossed themselves repeatedly, and were rich in good works. The Devil, whose headquarters were at Avebury, felt it was high time that something were done about it, so he filled a huge sack with earth and stones and started off along the main trackway (later to become a Roman road) with the intention of burying the town of Devizes alive.

On his way he met a tramp carrying a load of fourteen pairs of old shoes on his back, and asked him how much farther it was to Devizes. But the tramp, who had been generously treated in the town and had departed with the blessing of the Bishop, guessed at once that the Devil was up to some mischief. He resolved to trick him, and so directed his attention to the worn state of his fourteen pairs of old shoes. He did not know how far it was to Devizes, he said, but in walking hither from the town he had worn out all those shoes, and the Devil could draw his conclusions. The Devil glanced at his own shoes (which were already gaping in several places) and decided he could never make the journey. So he emptied his sack then and there, and went back to Avebury. And the great mound of earth which he tipped beside the road has been known as Silbury Hill ever since.

We have now to consider another class of earthwork—that which we designated 'camps' in our threefold division of artificial mounds. The general description of a camp, in this sense, is an area of land, usually on a hill-top, enclosed and protected by encircling banks and ditches. The camps or 'hill-forts' of various ages have their own characteristics, but the general type-profile is that given in Fig. 120 at E, while their general scenic appearance is shown to the extreme right of the hill-top (Cherhill Down, Wiltshire) illustrated at the head of this chapter.

The oldest of such earthworks in Britain are the neolithic (long barrow age) camps, which are visible today as roughly circular banks and entrenchments of the general pattern shown in Fig. 123. This is simplified in that only one encircling bank, surrounded by a ditch, is shown, whereas there are often several concentric rings of banks and ditches, the total area of which far exceeds the central area which they were apparently intended to protect.

One curious feature about these neolithic camps is that the surrounding ditches were not continuous, but were broken up into sections by paths or 'causeways' which, nevertheless, do not appear to lead anywhere. This has been explained on the supposition that each section of ditch represents the excavations of a single gang of workers, and that nobody troubled to join the various sections together afterwards. It does not seem a very good explanation, and it is perhaps nearer the truth to regard the causeways as giving access to the spaces between the banks, for these spaces were often very wide. They may, indeed, have been used as cattle pens, and the ditches were certainly used for cooking for they contain the remains of many a culinary operation. Broken pottery, bones, vegetable remains, fire-cracked stones—all are to be found in the ditches. These 'causeway forts', as they are often called, may occupy an area of twelve acres or more, and are now considered to have been fortified settlements rather than military camps.

The next distinctive type of camp belongs to the Iron Age, which began in

Britain at about 1000 B.C. with the first invasion of the Celts and Teutons. The simplest kind of Iron Age fort is illustrated in Fig. 124, and its characteristic features are the incurving horns of the entrance and the level platform between the bank and the ditch. The entrance seems to have been designed to

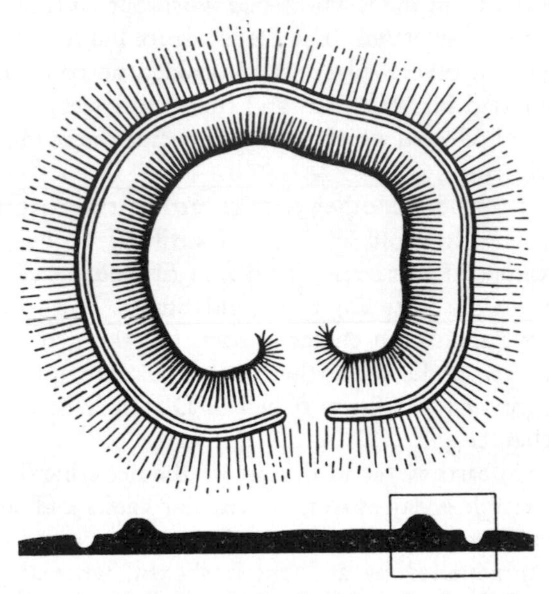

FIG. 124. Bird's-eye view and section of a simple Iron Age fort. The part enclosed by the rectangle is shown enlarged in Fig. 126.

compel an invading force to run the gauntlet in single file, and it must have been very effective. Later Iron Age entrances are set on the skew, so that an invader who carried his shield on the customary left arm would be compelled to expose his unprotected right to attack.

Some of the more elaborate Iron Age forts consist of many series of concentric banks and ditches, and have outlying strongholds or 'barbicans' to guard their outer entrances. The entrance-passage itself may be narrow, long and tortuous, and so planned that the invader exposes his right side to attack all the way. An example is given in Fig. 125, where *x* indicates the barbican.

The bank or rampart (called by the Romans *vallum*) was often reinforced by a revetment of wooden stakes, as shown in Fig. 126, which is a detailed drawing of the part of the section in Fig. 124 marked by a square. Sometimes the stake-holes are still traceable in the ground. The 'berm' (French *berme*, ledge), a narrow platform between the rampart and the ditch, was designed to afford such of the enemy as had crossed the ditch a nicely exposed place on which to be slaughtered. The ditch itself ('fosse', Latin *fossa*) afforded some shelter, but here there was none, and arrows and spears—and perhaps worse horrors—were showered on the enemy from above. The Iron Age warriors evidently thought that mere resistance to attack was not enough, and that it is better to kill an enemy than drive him off. The most elaborate Iron Age fortress in

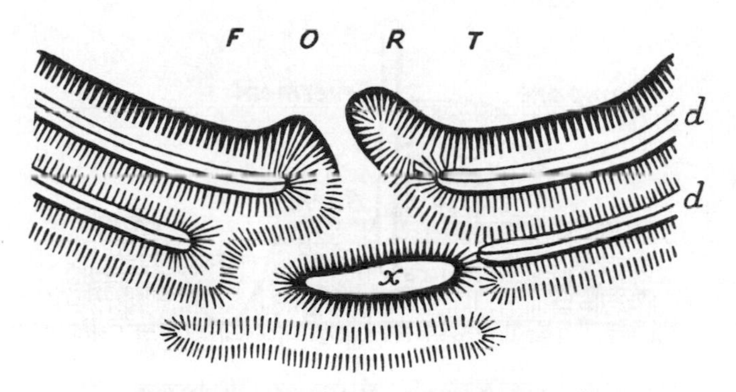

Fig. 125. Entrance to an Iron Age fort, with barbican shown at *x*.
The surrounding trenches are indicated at *d*.

Britain is Maiden Castle, in Dorset, and this is illustrated in Plate XXIV. Like many others, it was built on the site of earlier works, and was further modified in later times.

With the coming of the Romans a new type of fort appears. This usually consisted of a single ditch and bank, and it had straight sides. The Romans preferred a square shape, with an entrance at the centre of each of the four walls, as shown in Fig. 127, but pentagonal and other straight-sided shapes are common. Small forts of this type were often 'marching camps', provided at frequent intervals along the Roman roads for the use of troops on the march. The larger earthworks were probably garrisoned fortresses or 'stations', guarding settlements or strategic points. There is an unimportant one beneath the trees of Chanctonbury Ring, illustrated in Plate XIX, and here, as in many similar sites, you may pick up oyster shells thrown away by the Roman soldiers. They seem to have eaten a prodigious number of oysters.

In connection with camps and forts we should mention a different type of defensive earthwork which occurs, as a rule, along the lines of ancient territorial boundaries. This is the 'dyke' (or *dike*), and it may consist of an entrenchment, a rampart, or both. The term (O.E. *dic*) seems to have meant a wall made from material thrown out of an adjacent ditch, though some were clearly built by stacking turves. Some dykes are of immense length, and may be traced (in fragments) right across the country. They may measure, at favourable spots, a hundred feet in width and thirty in depth. Such works have been built from the Iron Age onward, but it is not possible to provide rules for distinguishing Celtic from Saxon dykes, or Roman from later ones. In particular cases the rambler should consult a local guide, for he is quite likely to come across

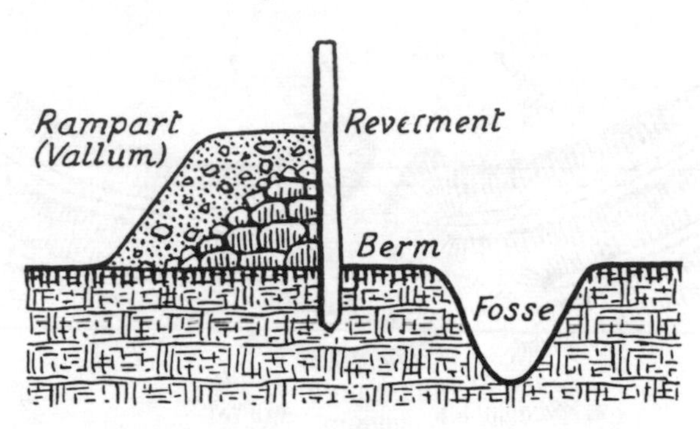

FIG. 126. A detailed enlargement of the area within the rectangle in Fig. 124.

entrenchments and banks which are no older than Oliver Cromwell—or, for that matter, the last World War.

Similar problems sometimes arise in connection with roads, and here there may be the additional complication of the modernization of a really ancient trackway. Even old railway and road embankments and cuttings are not always as easily recognized as one might think, and as an example we cite the surviving sections of the Grand Surrey Iron Railway, barely traceable between Croydon and Merstham, and the numerous grassed-over lanes which were once highways but have since been by-passed by straighter arterial roads.[1] More puzzling—and perhaps more interesting—are the 'green roads' of very ancient times, for traces of these sometimes appear along the crests of hills, or on hillsides, far from modern highways. Some run parallel with existing roads, or cross and recross them at intervals, while others have become obliterated for long stretches by their coincidence with modern routes.

The neolithic peoples made trackways along the tops of the hills, the forests below being dangerous on account of bears, wolves, wild boars and other

[1] The old Saxon Road running along the foot of the South Downs escarpment is a case in point, and the better-known Pilgrim's Way (from Salisbury Plain, through Winchester, to Canterbury and Dover) is another. The Pilgrim's Way itself, however, runs over a much older trackway—possibly of Bronze Age date—for a great deal of its length.

savage animals. When thus elevated they are called 'ridgeways', and are sometimes evident by the shortness of the grass growing over them, which is due to the hardness of the trodden soil or its virtual absence. Here and there, these are crossed by short entrenchments or 'covered ways' ('cross dykes' in some maps)

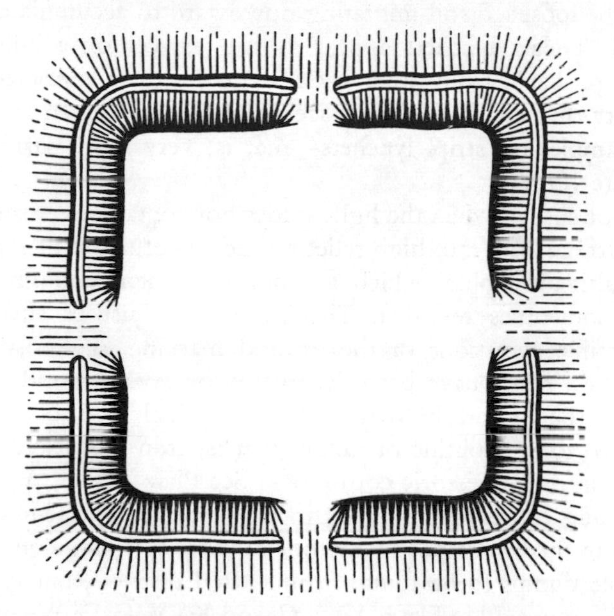

FIG. 127. Bird's-eye view of a typical Roman outpost, road-fort, or marching camp. The section is similar to that in Fig. 123.

connecting the valleys on either side of the ridge (see Plate XXIII, C). Branch tracks may run off at a steep slant down the hillsides, perhaps to visit a spring, and such tracks run down to the right of the lynchets in Plate XXV.

The later neolithic and Bronze Age people became more venturesome and made road-ledges along the hillsides at a lower level. These are called 'harrow ways', a term which may mean 'hoary' or ancient ways, or perhaps 'muddy' ways (O.E. *har*, greyish-white) owing to their being cut into the chalk or other rock. The wear and tear on these roads must have been considerable, for some of them eventually became deep gullies, and are distinguished by the name of 'hollow ways'. It is estimated that it would take a hundred years for the surface of such a road in a limestone district to be worn down two inches, so that those hollow ways which now lie ten feet below the hillside level have possibly been in continuous use for six thousand years. They are also called 'sunk(en) roads'.

To these hillside features we must add the ledges produced by plough-cultivation. These are called 'lynchets' (O.E. *hlinc*, slope), and the oldest of them are probably of Bronze or Iron Age date (say 1000 B.C.). The result of oft-repeated ploughing on the slope of a hill was to cut into the hill at the upper level, the loosened soil migrating downward to accumulate as a bank at a lower level. Today, lynchets appear as flat terraces on a hillside, and are usually distinguishable from other such forms by their restricted length and the irregularity of their levels. Their scenic profile was given in Fig. 25 at C, and some examples of 'strip' lynchets—that is, very long, narrow ones—are shown in Plate XXV.

At sunrise or sunset, when the light shines horizontally over the ground and brings every irregularity into high relief by the accentuation of shadows, traces of ancient cultivation plots which are not prominent enough to be called lynchets are sometimes revealed. They usually consist of small rectangles, barely perceptible elevations of the ground marking the position of their boundary stones. Many have been discovered on level ground, but they are best seen from the air and the rambler is hardly likely to spot them. They are usually referred to as neolithic or Celtic (that is, Iron Age) fields in the guide books, or simply as 'prehistoric corn-plots'. See Plate XXVI, A.

The remaining earthworks typified in our profiles represent more modern contributions to the landscape. We do not propose to enlarge on the numerous forms of waste dumps to be found in industrial districts, but typify these by G and H in Fig. 120, and in Plates XXI, C, and XXV, C, D. We may, however, distinguish the conical form, G (Plate XXI, C), which is produced when the material is dropped vertically from a crane, grab, or conveyor-belt, from the wedge-shaped form, H (indistinguishable in profile from Fig. 9 C, and therefore quite able to mislead the casual observer, on occasion). This is the 'rubbish-tip', its material being carried up the gentle slope in trucks, and tipped down the steep slope. Slag-heaps of this form are known as 'kimmics' in the north.

Such a dump travels across country somewhat in the manner of a sand dune (Fig. 43), and as a method of covering the ground it is used in raising the level of hollows, reclaiming mud-flats, and for other such works. Waste dumps of any sort are liable to become covered with weeds, grass, or other vegetation within a few years of abandonment, and may form very puzzling features of the landscape. The proximity of ancient mines often provides the necessary clue to their nature, especially in the case of conical mounds, but an examination of their material affords the best chance of settling the question of origin.

We are describing these 'marks of man' in roughly the same order as we have already treated the natural features of scenery, so that we now pass from the earthworks to outstanding stones and boulders. Some of these are not easy to distinguish from the types of natural boulder described in Chapter II, and it is impossible to tell whether or not some of the more striking natural examples,

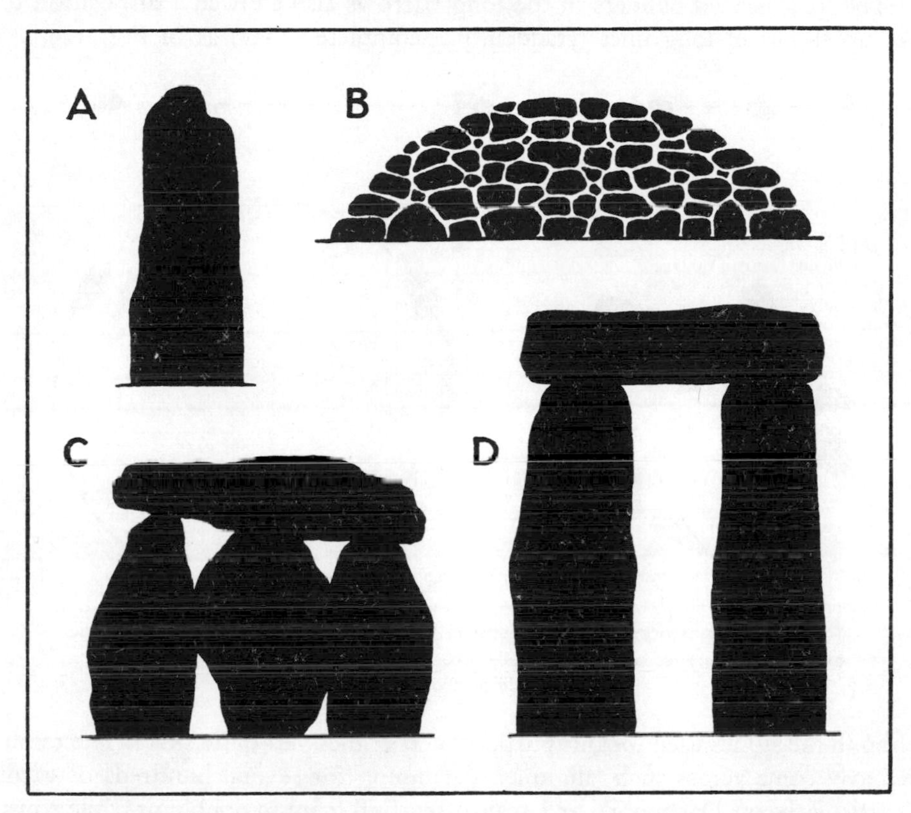

FIG. 128. Profiles of prehistoric stones. A, menhir, or standing stone. B, cairn. C, dolmen. D, trilithon.

such as the rocking-stones, were venerated by primitive man and used for religious purposes. He certainly discovered and rearranged many of the erratic blocks which nature had already distributed over the land, and utilized such residual boulders as the sarsens found on the chalk hills. These he often trimmed into roughly rectangular blocks on which his tool marks may sometimes still be seen.

The simplest of the prehistoric stones is the solitary 'standing stone' or 'menhir' (Breton *men*, stone, and *hir*, long), typified in Fig. 128 at A, and exemplified in Plate XXIII. Such stones probably mark sacred sites, and they are thought by some to be phallic symbols connected with the old 'fertility' religion. Most of them are believed to date from neolithic times, but some certainly belong to the Bronze Age.

The long-headed builders of the long barrows also showed a disposition to set up stones in long lines (frequently incomplete today) as in Fig. 129, A,

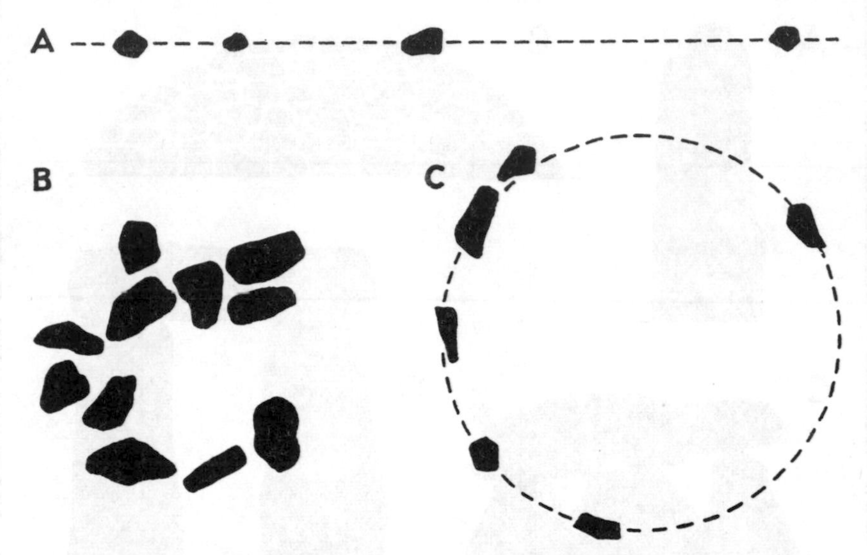

FIG. 129. Dispositions of stones artificially arranged, shown in plan. A, stone alignment. B, relics of a neolithic or Bronze Age hutment. C, relics of a stone circle or cromlech.

though the stones used for this purpose were sometimes quite small. The rambler may come across such 'alignments' running for several hundreds of yards (particularly on Dartmoor). and may often find them in double or triple rows, when they are called 'avenues'. The space between parallel rows is sometimes stopped at one end by a 'blocking-stone'. But a complete rectangle of small stones probably marks the site of a long barrow, many of which were surrounded by such 'peristaliths'.[1]

The burial chambers of the later long barrows were built of massive stone slabs, and some of these chambers, denuded of their covering mounds, remain exposed to view in many parts of the country. They are known as 'stone tables' or 'dolmens',[2] and an example is shown in Plate XXVI. The general profile is

[1] 'Peristalith'—a series of 'standing-around stones', from the Greek *peri*, around, *histanai*, to stand, and *lithos*, stone. The accent is on the second syllable.

[2] 'Dolmen'—Breton *dol*, table, *men*, stone, or perhaps Cornish *tolmen*, hole of stone.

given in Fig. 128 at C, where it will be seen that there are at least three uprights and a capstone. The capstone, and sometimes the whole dolmen, may be referred to locally (especially in Cornwall) as a 'quoit', a term which may also be used for almost any prehistoric stone attributed in legend to the Devil's habit of throwing rocks about. The very much smaller chamber of the early round barrows is known as a 'kist' (also spelt 'cist'), or 'kistvaen', from the Welsh *cist*, chest, and *maen*, stone, which sufficiently describes it.

Small groups of stones of various sizes are sometimes found heaped together on the moors, and if they show a roughly circular arrangement, as in Fig. 129, B, they are very likely all that remains of a neolithic or Bronze Age 'beehive' hut. This is especially so if the floor of the circle is depressed below the general level of the ground, and many such 'hut-circles' or 'hutments', as they are called, are known only by such depressions, their stones having been removed. The floors of some huts are paved, but others contain only a hearth-stone and a central stone or hole marking the site of the post which once supported the roof.

Similar stones disposed in a large ring may indicate a walled enclosure, or 'pound', within which many huts may once have stood, but in this book it is not intended to deal with human habitations, however old. Our business strictly ends with the recognition of human agency in the more puzzling arrangements of stones, though we confess to occasional transgressions of this rule.

The primitive cult of erecting large stones is called 'megalithic', and it extended from the New Stone Age into the Bronze Age. We have already noted the setting up of large single stones (menhirs) or 'monoliths', but in the Bronze Age these are supplemented in certain monuments by the composite 'trilithon',[1] which consists of two uprights and a lintel, as shown in Fig. 128, D. The famous examples at Stonehenge show that the stones were carefully trimmed, the two uprights being provided with dowels (projections) on their tops, which fit snugly into sockets bored in the lintel.

These round-headed people of the Bronze Age, with their round barrows, had a predilection for setting up their stones in circles. These are known variously as 'rings', 'maidens', or 'cromlechs' (Welsh *crom*, curved, *llech*, stone), but the term *cromlech* has been much abused in England and is sometimes used as a synonym for dolmen. We follow the Continental use of it here, which is in accordance with its derivation, and show a typical example in Plate XXV.

[1] It is a great aid to memory and understanding to know the derivations of special terms, and we have made a point of serving the reader in this respect throughout this book. He may work out the derivations of the terms 'neolithic', 'megalithic', 'monolith' and 'trilithon' for himself from the following Greek roots: *neos*, new; *megas*, great; *monos*, alone; *treis*, three; *lithos*, stone. Later in this chapter we shall use the terms 'palaeolithic', which contains the root *palaios*, ancient, and refers to the Old Stone Age, 'mesolithic' (*mesos*, middle), and 'microlith' (*micros*, small).

While the rambler would at once recognize so obvious an example as Stonehenge, he may sometimes come across the relics of stone circles which have almost entirely disappeared. Odd stones found on otherwise bare moors or hilltops may be natural erratic blocks, but if they lie in a fairly perfect circle, as in Fig. 129, C, they are probably relics of the Bronze Age. The rambler may feel surer still if some of the stones are standing on end, or if there is a 'clock-stone' standing or lying at the centre of the circle. He is, however, warned from jumping to conclusions when too many stones are present, for given sufficient material he will find it easy to *pick out* circles almost anywhere he pleases. The largest stone circle in Europe is at Avebury (Wiltshire), but, like all other impressive examples, this is preserved as a national monument and presents no scenic problems.

On the crest of the Downs in many counties, and often near notable summits, there are small round ponds which have been used by shepherds as far back as records go. They are called 'dew-ponds' because they are traditionally held to derive their water from the dew, but recent researches suggest that this is only partly true. Nevertheless, it is certain that no streams drain into them, that they are high indeed above the level of springs, and that a good dew-pond contains *some* water at all times of the year. During a severe drought there may be water in the dew-ponds when the springs and streams in the valleys have dried up. A view of a Sussex dew-pond in summer is shown in Plate XXVI.

Some dew-ponds are believed to be of neolithic origin, and many are certainly of great antiquity. In Stone Age times, when people lived in encampments on the hilltops, the question of water-supply was an acute one. The springs were at the foot of the hills, on the edge of the danger-zone, and dew-ponds would certainly have solved many problems. It meant going *up* the hill to fetch water, instead of down, and some authorities read a traditional record of this practice in the ancient nursery rhyme, 'Jack and Jill'. Not all dew-ponds are old, however. They have been made, and re-made, throughout the historical period, and dew-pond makers are still to be found in the villages of Sussex, Essex, Wiltshire, and elsewhere.[1]

A typical dew-pond in Sussex consists of a saucer-shaped hollow lined to a depth of nine inches with puddled chalk. The traditional method of lining the pond is to drive cattle about in it during the rainy season. This pounds the chalk up and gives it the consistency of clay, thus making the pond water-tight. A layer of chalk rubble may be added to protect the bottom from the hooves of animals. In Wiltshire, a deeper hollow is dug, and this is lined first with

[1] The price quoted for a small dew-pond by Mr Turner, of Alfriston, Sussex, in 1934, was 'about fifty pounds', the actual figure depending on the accessibility of the site.

straw and then with clay, as shown in Fig. 130, but each dew-pond maker has his own recipe, and some employ several alternate layers of straw and clay, or straw and puddled chalk. But all agree that the dew-pond, when made, will not 'work' until it has first been filled artificially with water.

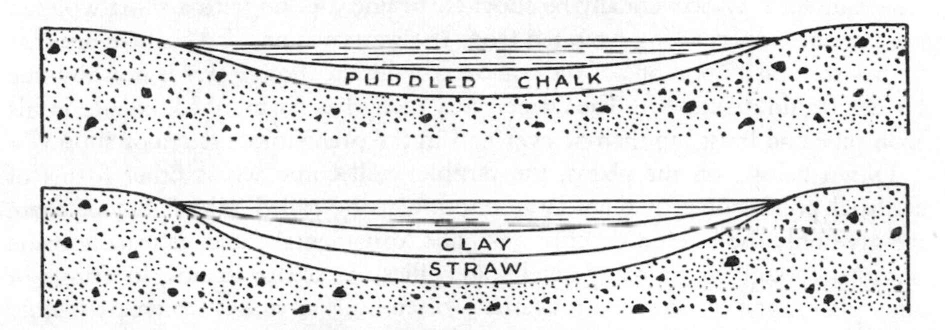

FIG. 130. Sections through typical dew-ponds. *Above*, a type common in Sussex. *Below*, a Wiltshire type.

Good dew-ponds are so reliable that attempts have been made to establish them in the United States, South Africa, and elsewhere. Experiments made on Table Mountain showed the the presence of vegetation on the margin of the pond is an important factor in the collection of water, and that mist and other forms of condensation play a substantial part, although the chief source of supply is probably rain.[1] It is worth noting that in Surrey the ponds are traditionally known as 'mist-ponds', and in Hampstead as 'fog-ponds', and that in

[1] About five inches of water were collected in an empty rain gauge from condensation of mist and dew over a period of fifty-six days, but a similar gauge containing reeds and grasses collected this quantity in four days.

The plants surrounding a pond also exhale considerable quantities of water-vapour, which condenses readily on the surface of the water already in the pond. A sunflower three feet high was found to exhale a pint of water during one summer day, and grasses and saxifrages were found to yield similarly copious supplies.

The fact that dew-ponds have to be re-puddled (by driving cattle through them) if they develop leaks is sufficient to prove that no water enters them from below, and in any case they stand high above the water-table. The layer of straw beneath the pond is believed to assist condensation by insulating the water from the heat of the earth below it.

In England, the dew-pond makers generally select a site where mist is apt to collect early on summer mornings, but experiments made in the London area on such sites indicate that no more than one and a half inches of water per year are normally deposited by condensation of mist and dew in south-east England. The proportion of this which falls during the dry season is quite inadequate to account for the water found in the dew-ponds.

Taking the year as a whole, the greater part of the water collected is undoubtedly rain-water, and it has been suggested that the real *modus operandi* has less to do with condensation than with the prevention of excessive evaporation. Yet the shape of dew-ponds is such as to encourage evaporation, and this theory fails to account for the *replenishment* of supplies during a drought, when the ponds are in constant use for watering cattle. It must be admitted that the problem remains unsolved.

some districts large boulders called 'condenser stones' are distributed round the margins of the ponds.

In recent years many dew-ponds have been lined with concrete to make them 'clean', but this has sometimes (though not always) had disastrous results. The rambler may occasionally be shocked to find a pond with a short wooden post at one side, carrying a tap fed from the water-mains. The chances are that he has stumbled upon one of the concreted failures, though this is not how the farmer would describe it. The farmer very likely has far more confidence in his iron pipe and brass tap than he ever had in the prehistoric system of supply!

Down below, on the plains, the rambler will come across other forms of artificial pond, some of them large enough to be called 'lakes', but of these we give only the briefest descriptions. The 'ornamental water' is usually made obvious enough by its many-hued water-lilies, its sedate islands, its fringe of alien plants, and its arranged rockeries—often built of stones which are plainly not of local origin. Such a lake may have been produced by building a dam across a stream, or it may be simply a cunning adaptation of a natural lake, with essentially natural islands and waterfalls. Its situation in a private or public park suggests that artificial work is likely somewhere, and it is often fun to try to discover if a cleverly-concealed dam exists.

The 'mill-pond' is much more easily detected, this time by the undisguised dam or 'weir' in the neighbourhood of the mill, or at any rate near the site on which a mill once stood. The water overflows at the weir, but a sluice-gate may allow some of it to flow swiftly through a narrow channel or 'mill-race' (often a 'flume' lined with bricks) in which the water-wheel is situated. A 'hammer-pond' is simply a mill-pond associated with the ancient iron industry of the Weald, where mills were employed to work the hammers used for breaking up the ironstone.

Most artificial ponds which have not been deliberately excavated tend to be triangular in shape, the outflow being at one of the angles. When the triangle is long, and the general shape seems to warrant it, they are frequently called 'leg-of-mutton' ponds. A perfectly circular or 'round' pond is almost certain to have been excavated. Open reservoirs often consist of a natural lake made larger by the construction of a dam. See Plate I.

Artificial rivers, or 'canals', are easily recognized by their straightness, even width, and carefully tended banks, which are usually steep (vertical) on *both* sides of the water, though there may be no perceptible current flowing. The presence of a tow-path affords contributory evidence, but this is not always provided, and in any case many natural rivers have paths running along their banks. Some canals (like the New River) are constructed simply to carry a supply of water from one place to another, and these are properly called 'aqueducts', but the majority are made to facilitate the navigation of barges, and are often marked in the maps as 'navigations'. The men employed to dig such canals came to be known as 'navvies', a name which has now entered the dictionary as a synonym for a road-maker or excavator employed in building or engineering projects.

The presence of locks is a sure indication of a canal, even if the canal extends merely for the distance covered by the locks. But there are times when the rambler mistakes carefully tended river levées (see page 77) for canal banks. The question is best settled by consulting the map, for there are no rules for distinguishing between the wholly artificial canal and the improved and straightened channel of a natural stream.

But we must return to the hills, where a number of curious features remain to be described. We have already made two references to the clump, or 'cap', of trees at Chanctonbury Ring (Plate XIX), and many such clumps are often thought to be of very ancient origin. Most of them, however, are less than two or three hundred years old, as the size of the trees themselves will testify. Some of these 'tree-rings', like the clump at Chanctonbury (where there is a Romano-Celtic camp), have been planted to mark historic sites, but others are self-sown.

Hilltops and exposed ridges may also show narrow lines or belts of trees, instead of clumps, and these are probably 'windbreaks', planted to afford shelter from high winds to both cattle and crops. (See Plate XXVI.) The trees are usually beeches in the chalk country, Scots pines in sandy or gravelly districts, or Lombardy poplars where there is much clay, but frequently many varieties of trees are mixed in order to get a dense growth at all heights above the ground.

Another feature of the hills for which man is responsible is the cutting of patterns and pictures in the turf, a practice which has persisted from the New Stone Age to the present day. The favoured districts for this work lie in the chalk country, for the snow-white chalk is easily exposed and the results are both conspicuous and enduring. Many examples will be found in the guide books, and a large proportion of them will be of 'white horses'. Some of these are truly ancient, and have been preserved only because local people have cleaned them up from time to time. Others, such as the white horse on High-and-Over, near Seaford, and the one on Cherhill Down illustrated at the head of this chapter, are of quite modern origin.[1] The purpose of the ancient figures,

[1] The white horse on High-and-Over was carved about 1860 by a farmer and his brothers. That on Cherhill Down was made by a local doctor in 1780; it is one hundred and sixty feet long.

which include the Long Man of Wilmington (Sussex), the Giant of Cerne Abbas (Dorset), and the White Horse of Uffington (Berkshire), is quite unknown, but the modern figures usually commemorate some historical event—or they were just carved for fun.

The famous Marlborough White Horse was cut by schoolboys in 1804,

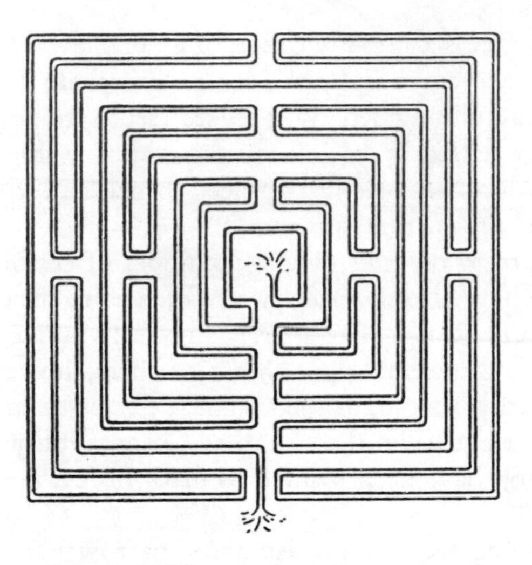

FIG. 131. Plan of the miz-maze on St Catherine's Hill, Winchester. The double line is a trench about six inches wide and four inches deep, cut in the turf.

and it is by no means the only permanent mark on the countryside left by schoolboys. On the top of St Catherine's Hill, Winchester, for instance, there is a 'maze', or 'miz-maze', which is said to have been cut in the turf by a Winchester College boy. It consists of a narrow trench in which you may walk, heel to toe, till you reach the centre, and a plan of it is shown in Fig. 131.

The practice of cutting mazes in the turf is very old, though it belongs to the Christian era. There are many of them on the downs and wolds of the country, and their origin has been traced to the mazes set in mosaics on the floors of many Continental cathedrals (for example, Chartres). In France they are called '*chemins de Jerusalem*', and to thread such a maze was once held to be a pious substitute for a genuine pilgrimage to the Holy Land. The turf mazes of the English downs seem to have lost their religious significance, however, and they are known variously as 'miz-mazes', 'Troy-towns', 'shepherd's races', and 'Julian's bowers'. Shakespeare refers to them in *A Midsummer Night's Dream* (*Act II*, *Sc.* 2):

> The nine-men's morris is fill'd up with mud;
> And the quaint mazes in the wanton green,
> For lack of tread are undistinguishable.

Many of our village mazes have now, alas! become indistinguishable for another reason—they have been ploughed over to 'grow more food'.

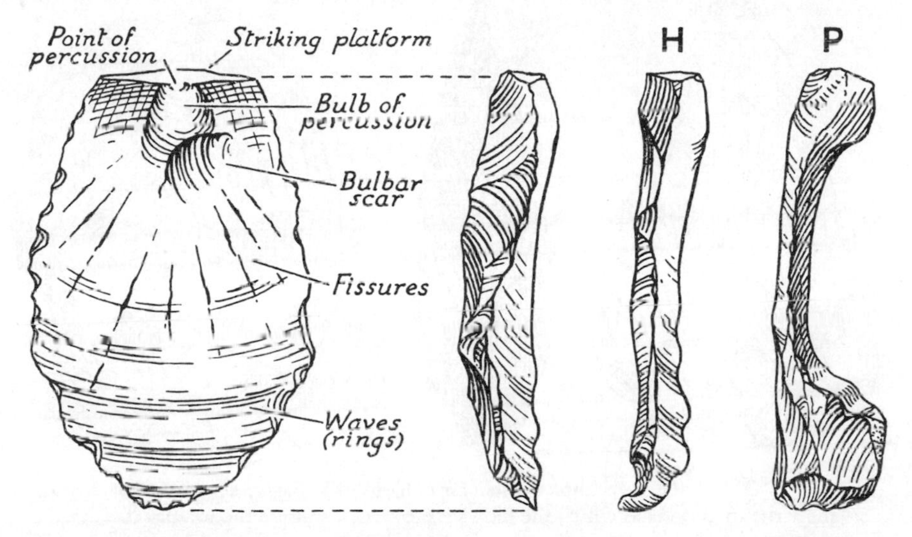

FIG. 132. Artificial fracture of flint. *Left*, the characteristics of a hand-struck flake. H, hinge fracture. P, plunging fracture.

Let no one reproach the plough, however, for a freshly-ploughed field may, when washed by a shower of rain, present the rambler with other treasures. These are the flint 'artifacts' left by our Stone and Bronze Age ancestors, and they include all manner of tools and implements, besides the chips knocked off in the fashioning of these useful things from hard, shapeless stones. The chief problem for the rambler is to know whether or not some likely-looking stone he has found is a genuine flint implement or just an accident, but though this is really expert's work we shall do our best to show how the mark of man may sometimes be recognized.

Flint fractures in a peculiar way, for it is both hard and structureless. When struck violently it fractures like glass, but when 'rotted' or fractured by the weather it behaves rather differently. A flint fashioned by man should bear the signs of violent and systematic fracturing, and familiarity with these signs is best obtained experimentally. Strike a chip or 'flake' from a fair-sized flint, using a hammer or another flint (and guarding against flying splinters), and then examine the flake carefully. You should be able to find most of the characteristics shown in Fig. 132.

The flake illustrated was struck by Stone Age man, but flint behaves in exactly the same way today. The ancient method of flaking was simple, yet it

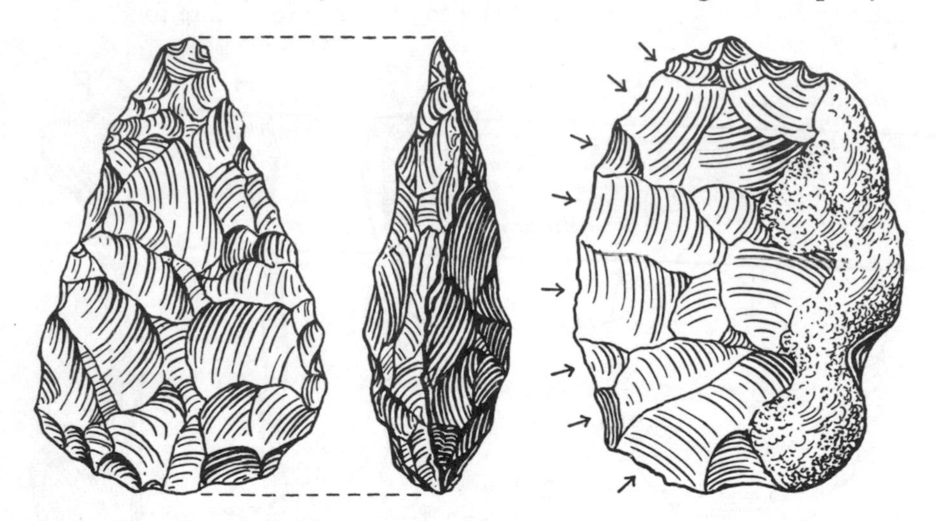

FIG. 133. Old Stone Age implements. *Left*, hand-axe. *Right*, scraper. The arrows show the directions in which the blows were struck to give the scraper its edge.

had its rules. The blow was usually delivered near the edge of a selected flat surface called the 'striking platform', but if none was present a suitable surface was made by knocking off a knob, or cracking a very large stone in half. Then the flake was struck, and the 'point of percussion' marks the spot where the blow fell. It looks like a little white bead, smaller than a pin's head, and the flint immediately below it swells outwards into a 'bulb'. The bulb bears a 'scar'—nobody knows why—and the lower part of the flake is rippled into 'waves' and crossed by 'fissures' (which are, however, not always in evidence). These are the hall-marks of a hand-struck flake, and the block the flake was struck from—the 'core'—shows them all in reverse. Occasionally, the waves are over-developed and produce the 'hinge' fracture shown at H, and occasionally they bite deeply into the core and produce the 'plunging' fracture shown at P.

So much for the violent fracture. Of course, it *could* have been produced naturally—say, by the fall of a heavy stone from a cliff-face; and it *could* have been produced by man accidentally—say, by a plough or a harrow.[1] But if the flake or core is a genuine artifact it should show signs of systematic chipping such as could not possibly have occurred by chance.

This is illustrated in the palaeolithic (Old Stone Age) hand-axe, and the 'scraper' (used, probably, for scraping skins) in Fig. 133. Both these are 'core' implements, and the reader will note from the arrangement of the waves left by the detached flakes that they were deliberately shaped. The trimming and

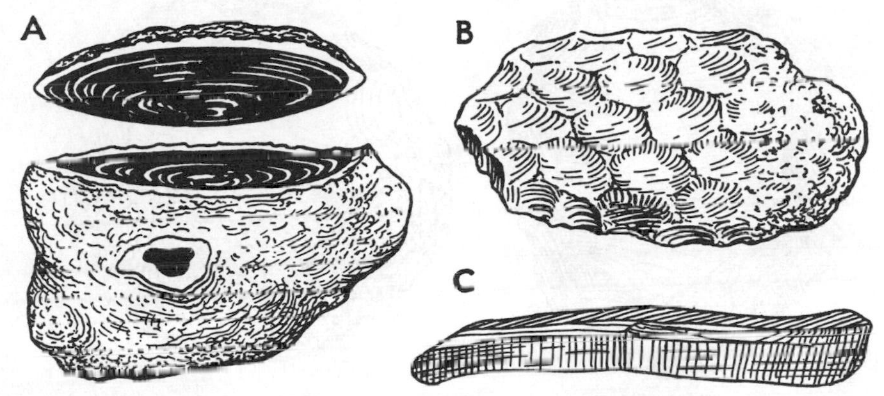

FIG. 134. Natural fracture of flint. A, pot-lid fracture. B, frost-pitting. C, starch fracture.

shaping of flint implements is done in the opposite way to the sharpening of a pencil. That is to say, the tool is applied *against* the edge (or point), not towards it, and the arrows show how the blows were struck which gave the sharp edge to the scraper. The curious form of the edge of the hand-axe, suggesting a reversed S, is particularly common in one palaeolithic culture, but many such edges are perfectly straight. Attention is drawn to the method of shaping the edges, which are generally chipped alternately on each side throughout their length. Three such implements are shown in Plate XXVII.

Finally, such very old implements as these have a characteristic, semi-polished appearance, a waxy lustre known as the 'patina' (Latin for 'dish'), which cannot be imitated. It serves to distinguish genuine specimens from fakes, for certain tramps (and others) have, from time to time, managed to produce very good copies of Stone Age implements for sale to tourists. Flint implements from gravel-pits are generally brown in colour, but they may be black, cream, or mottled in various ways.[2] Those found in ploughed

[1] The term 'spall' is used to describe a chip removed naturally or accidentally, and 'flake' for a chip removed intentionally.

[2] As in the well-known 'basket-work' patination, in which a pattern resembling rough basket-work appears in white on a bluish or blue-black ground.

fields, or on the open downs, may be black but are as often bleached white.

Now compare the appearance of the fractures illustrated in Figs. 132 and 133 with the natural fractures shown in Fig. 134. These are due chiefly to strains set up in the stones by temperature changes, but the 'pot-lid' fracture at A may be produced by great pressure. Exposure to the weather often results in the 'frost-pitting' shown at B, and the general effect may be very deceptive. Suitably

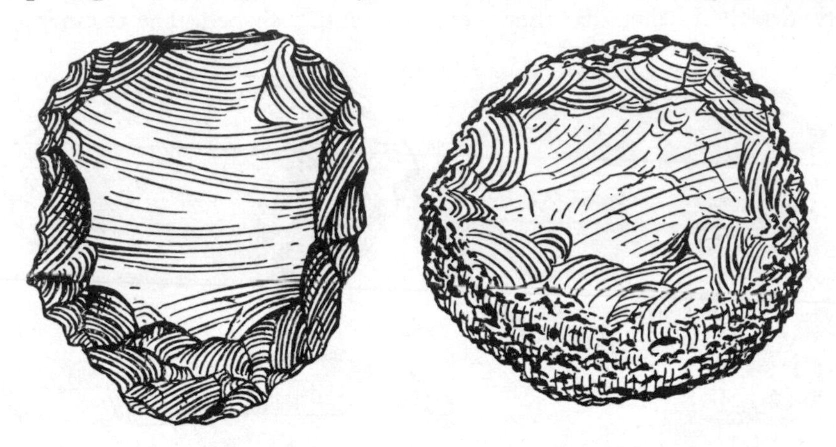

FIG. 135. Old Stone Age implements. *Left*, tortoise-core. *Right*, hammer-stone.

shaped stones which have suffered badly from frost-pitting may, at first glance, look very much like genuine implements. When frost has been at work on the white outer crust of a flint, it sometimes shatters it into curious rectangular fragments reminiscent of starch grains, but the rambler must not be misled by the geometrical regularity of such 'starch fractures', of which C is a typical example.

Old Stone Age man began fashioning his implements by striking small flakes (which he discarded) off a solid core. Later, he found that a large flake often forms a good, sharp implement in itself, needing only to be trimmed, and it could be made by a single blow. But being more or less thin it was difficult to hold for trimming into shape, and it seemed better to do the trimming first—before the flake was struck from the core. So cores were prepared from which perfectly formed flake implements, needing no further work, could be struck. One implement was produced from each core, as before, but this time it was the core that was discarded, not the flake. Such discarded cores may be picked up by the rambler, and they are known as 'tortoise-cores' from their characteristic shape. One is shown in Fig. 135, left, the view being of the flat underside of the 'tortoise', which is the surface from which the flake came away.

The chief tool employed in making the larger flint implements was the stone with which the blows were delivered, and this itself became chipped until it assumed a fairly regular form. No doubt each workman had his own favourite 'hammer-stone', and a typical example is shown in Fig. 135, right. The finer work of later periods, and much of the neolithic and Bronze Age flint-knapping,

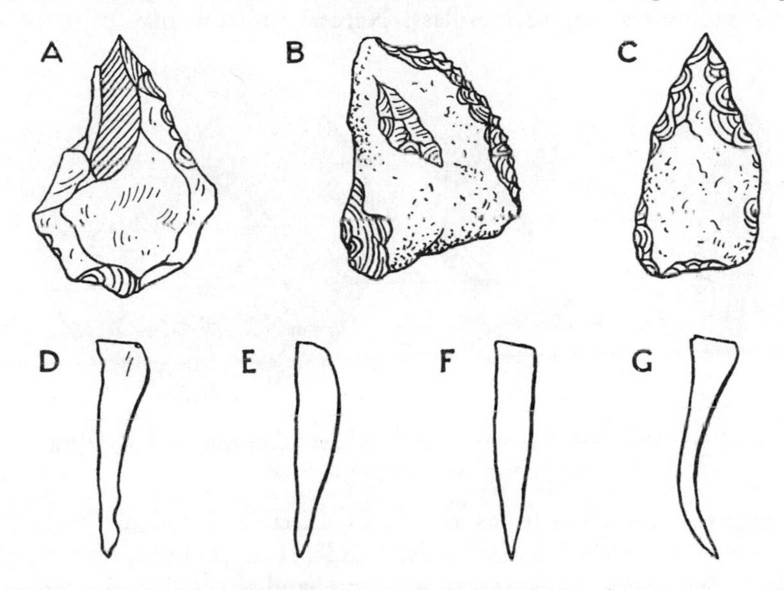

FIG. 136. Natural fracture of flint—subsoil pressure-flaking. A–C, E–G, natural stones. D, hand-struck flake for comparison. See the text.

was done by pressure instead of concussion. Edges were trimmed by pressing a small stone, called a 'fabricator', against them till minute flakes sprang off. By some such means the 'ripple' flaking of the Bronze Age arrow-head in Fig. 138, F, was done.

And here we issue a new warning to the implement collector, for flints occurring in soils are subject to natural pressure and a good deal of friction during soil-creep (page 35), and the result is the deceptive 'subsoil pressure-flaking' by which nature sometimes imitates the finer types of flint implement. For example, in Fig. 136, A and B are both natural flints the edge-chipping of which is indistinguishable from that shown in Fig. 138 at E. Fig. 136 C is a natural flint whose outline resembles an arrow-head, the deception being strengthened by the edge-chipping. The golden rule is never to rely upon either edge-trimming or overall shape alone, except in the case of *very* obviously artificial shaping like that in Fig. 138 A. Judgment must rest upon the occurrence of two or more of the flake characteristics illustrated in Fig. 132, and these may often be found on the 'back' of a flint whose 'front' carries the more striking but disputable features.

Even the flake characteristics need careful scrutiny in small specimens, however, for some of the expected features may be missing or too small to recognize without a magnifying-glass. Natural pressure may produce spalls

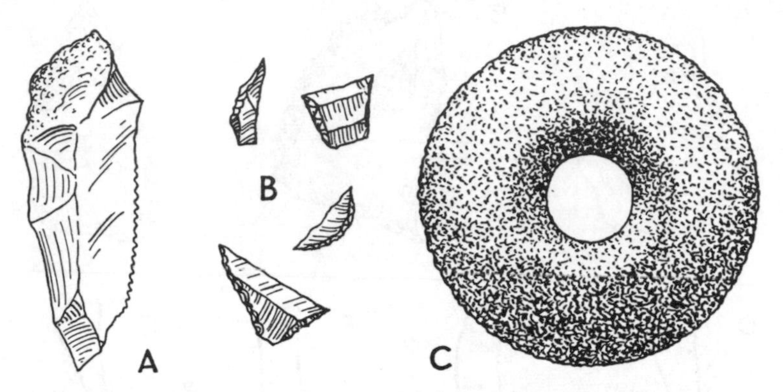

Fig. 137. Mesolithic implements. A, fine saw (teeth enlarged). B, microliths. C, quartzite mace-head.

very similar to hand-struck flakes, but distinguishable from them by an appearance of vagueness or 'slovenliness' which hand-struck specimens do not possess. Fig. 136 D repeats the edge-view of a typical hand-struck flake for comparison with the natural spalls at E, F and G. In E, the bulb is longer and lower than it should be, and carries neither ripples nor fissures. In F, the bulb is absent, though the edge looks sharp enough for a prehistoric knife and is probably 'trimmed' in a most convincing way. In G, there is a bulb, but it is too small in proportion to the curved part, which is not only devoid of ripples but is much too even in thickness for a genuine flake that is not also a freak—for, of course, freaks do occur.

Flakes quite obviously struck by man often occur in ploughed fields and near buildings, and these may be prehistoric or modern. A flake struck off by a plough or harrow, by a workman's pick, or by a flint-knapper repairing a flint wall, will bear all the important characteristics of ancient flakes save one. This is the 'patina', to which we have already referred (page 181). Familiarity with its more subtle appearances is best obtained by examining approved specimens in black flint in a museum or private collection. When characteristic, it gives the flake an appearance of having been handled by greasy fingers, and though it may be razor-sharp it has a soft, polished appearance which modern flakes never possess. A modern flake, whether sharp or not, has a matt or semi-matt surface, and its general appearance is hard and splintery. Almost all modern flakes are in black flint, and the reader need be suspicious only in areas where modern work is likely to have occurred.

Artifacts trimmed by fine pressure-work first appear in the mesolithic age, which bridges the gap between the Old and New Stone Ages, and covers the

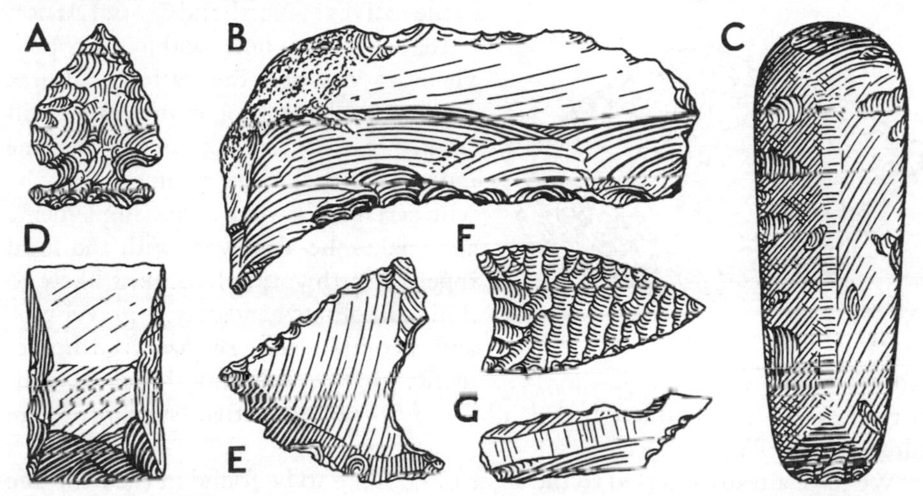

Fig. 138. Neolithic and later implements. A, arrow-head. B, borer. C, celt. D, eighteenth century gun-flint. E, curved knife or scraper. F, arrow-head with ripple-flaking. G. graver.

period when Britain was finally severed from the Continent. Apparently simple mesolithic flakes are not infrequently found to have a beautifully even row of minute saw-teeth cut in the edges. Sometimes these cannot be seen without a magnifying-glass, but may be detected by running the thumb-nail along the edge of the flake. The mesolithic peoples also made small, sharp, flint barbs for setting transversely in the shafts of their arrows (to supplement the flint arrow-head), and these, together with other very small implements, are known as 'microliths' or 'pigmy' implements. We show a few of these mesolithic types in Fig. 137, together with a 'mace-head' of the same period, ground from a pebble of sarsen (quartzite).

In Fig. 138 the work of later times is illustrated. The neolithic arrow-head at A is beautifully made, and is so thin that light may be seen through it. The implement at B is a 'borer', and was used for boring holes in wood, bone or skins. Arrow-shafts were probably straightened by means of the curved knife at E, while G is known as a 'graver', and may have been the tool with which pictures were scratched on bones and antlers. From mesolithic times onwards the surfaces of large implements were often smoothed down by rubbing them with sandstone or some other hard rock, and this practice became very common in the Iron Age. Such polished implements are called 'celts' (pronounced *selts*) and an example is given at C. At D we give a specimen of quite modern work. This is a typical eighteenth century gun-flint, of the sort used in flint-lock pistols, and at Brandon, in Suffolk, these are still being made for export to the natives of North and Central Africa.

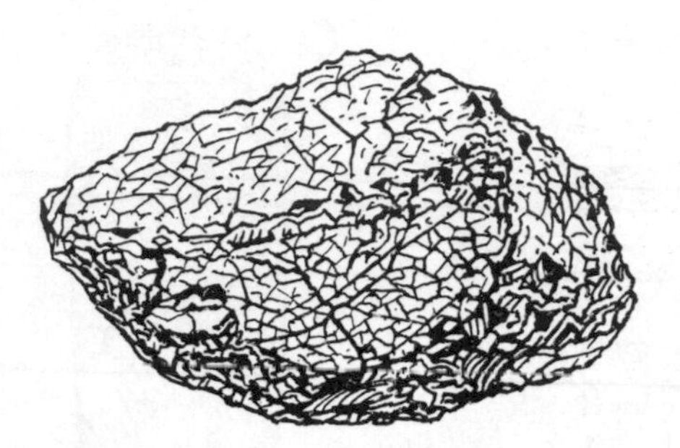

FIG. 139. A typical neolithic pot-boiler (flint).

It does not come within our province to describe the various cultures of flint implements, but the reader will rightly gather that the work became more refined as time went on, and he will certainly associate the implements and flakes he discovers with the local types of earthwork. He is most likely to find palaeolithic hand-axes in gravel-pits, and neolithic and Bronze Age implements in the neighbourhood of hill-forts, or on freshly-ploughed land. A few representative specimens are illustrated in Plate XXVII.

We have already referred to the signs of cooking to be found in the neolithic camps (page 165), and here we may also come across the 'pot-boiler' illustrated in Fig. 139. This is a white flint riddled with minute cracks, and it was used by mesolithic and neolithic man for boiling water. It was risky to place an earthen pot directly over the fire, so stones such as these were first made red-hot and then dropped into pots of cold water. Places where these signs of cooking are found are referred to by the Middle English word 'middens', or the tautologous expression 'kitchen-middens', but when oyster shells are present, as is common in Iron Age and Roman times, they are usually called 'shell-mounds'.

The rambler may also come across patches of flint chips and discarded flakes which represent the rubbish of a 'flint factory'. In the neighbourhood of such deposits there may be pits dug in the soil for the quarrying of flint, for it was discovered at a very early date that the surface stones do not make the best implements. Here and there are deeper flint mines, the general pattern of which is shown in Fig. 140 A, where galleries may be seen driven into the bands of flint.

Often such mines have been filled in again with the material dug from new shafts, and these in-filled holes may contain half-made implements, bones, crockery, and all manner of rubbish. But the rambler is warned not to mistake the naturally-formed 'pipes' which frequently appear in quarries and road-cuttings for flint mines. A typical series of pipes is shown in Fig. 140 at B,

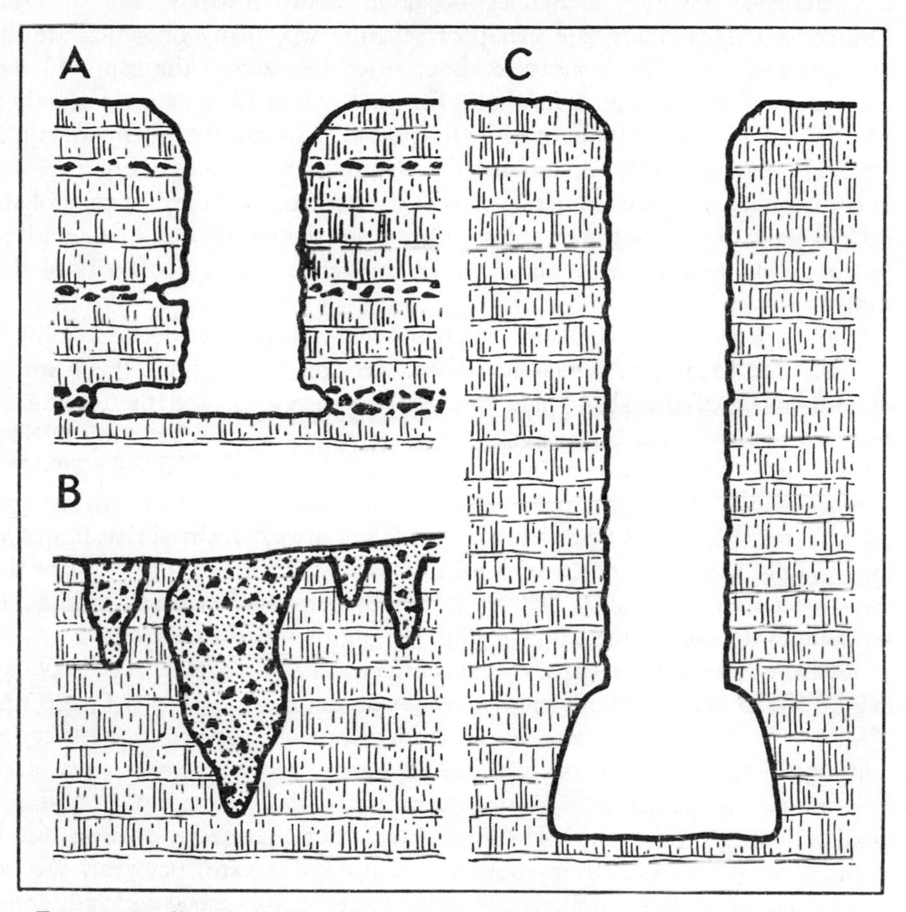

FIG. 140. Profiles of puzzling holes in the ground. A, prehistoric flint-mine, B, pipes or solution-holes. C, dene-hole. Swallow-holes are illustrated in Fig. 59.

and these are really solution-holes, similar to swallow-holes (see page 81), which have become filled with soil and clay-with-flints.

The neolithic and Bronze Age peoples knew the use of corn, and they dug more or less deep pits into the chalk for use as 'silos' or storage chambers. These are known as 'dene-holes', a term whose origin is unknown,[1] and in the

[1] Some derive the term from 'Dane' holes, on the supposition that the Saxons took refuge in them from the Danes; others see in 'dene' a corruption of the Anglo-Saxon *den*, a hole or valley.

first century they had the reputation of being the gold mines of Cymbeline. Fig. 140, C, shows a typical specimen, and the bell-shaped chamber is quite characteristic. Shallow dene-holes occur in many districts, but at Grays Thurrocks (Essex) there is a group of seventy-two, many of which are fifty or more feet deep. They measure about three feet across the top, and their walls are notched to provide footholds for those who had to descend into them. At one time they were thought to be flint mines, but many of them contain no flint. There is now little doubt that the chambers were filled with corn, and, as is the practice with Continental silos at the present day, they were probably packed tight to the roof with straw to keep out the damp. Some see evidence of the raking in and out of the straw in the remarkable smoothness of their roofs.

The mark of man on the landscape is nowhere more in evidence than in the quarries and chalk-pits which have been worked throughout the historical period. Some of the abandoned quarries are very old, and their minimum possible age can often be guessed from the size of the trees growing in them. Others, still not abandoned, have been in continuous use for centuries. The slate quarries at Penhryn, North Wales, for instance, have been worked since Elizabethan times. (See Plate XXVIII.) It is not always realized that in quarrying, mining, and other such works, man has done far more to the landscape than merely decorate it. He is, in fact, a geological agent of the first magnitude, for he changes the face of the land far more rapidly than nature herself.

We have already noted that the agents of denudation are lowering the average height of the land by about nine inches every thousand years (see page 144). If we now make a similar estimate of the work of human agents in quarrying, mining, dredging, and so on, we find that man is going to work just about five times as fast as nature. This may seem incredible, yet the figures cannot be denied. Nature's toll of the rocks by sub-aerial and marine denudation, and by chemical action, works out at about 50,000,000 cubic yards per year. We may at once set against this the 70,000,000 cubic yards of road-metal which disappear into dust every year beneath the wheels of our traffic! Thus, nature is outdone by a single minor item of human activity.

During the past hundred years of English history men have been steadily removing rock material from mines, quarries, rail and road cuttings, and harbour works, at an average rate of 180,000,000 cubic yards per year. The present rate is far in excess of this, for in 1933 the output from mining and quarrying alone amounted to 240,000,000 cubic yards. Now, the greater portion of the material thus excavated is completely destroyed as rock. In this connection, coal—by far the largest item—will at once come to mind, while at least 5,000,000 tons of stone are burnt every year for lime. Further vast quantities of rock are crushed to powder in extracting various ores, while the removal of rocks dissolved in water must also be taken into account.

The amount of 'fur' which normally collects inside a kettle in districts where the water is hard is far from negligible. Multiply it some few million times, and then add the contents of tens of thousands of boilers, and enough water-pipes to encircle the equator.[1] The answer is likely to be—considerable. But more important is the mineral matter dissolved in the water pumped from our mines, for this is at least 750,000 tons in excess of that which would have been removed by natural drainage. Again, some 2,000,000 tons of rock-salt, in the form of brine, are pumped annually from our salt mines, the total annual loss of all kinds of rocks removed in solution being equivalent in bulk to Highgate Hill.

A great deal of material is also removed, deliberately or otherwise, as mud in suspension. The geological map of Kent for 1924 shows Swanscombe Park as a hill of London Clay 300 feet high and three miles round. By 1937, this hill had become a pit, its clay having been beaten into sludge by machinery and pumped through pipes to Greenhithe, two and a half miles away, to be made into cement. The total effect of artificial rock-destruction in this country, as so far described, is equivalent to the abolition of a mountain the size of Snowdon every ten years.

On the coast, and especially in the river mouths, incredible quantities of mud and sand are dredged from the bottom and dumped far out to sea, to keep the fairways clear for shipping. The estimated total for England is 400,000,000 tons per year, but while this is hardly a direct contribution to the lowering of the *land*, it at least checks the formation of marshes and other such hindrances to the natural removal of river-mud.

In considering the long-term results of this wholesale destruction of the rocks, we soon find evidence that the pace cannot last. The coal mines and many of the ore beds will be exhausted in a few hundred years' time, and some of the former losses will be made good by the waste products of imported ores. Moreover, much of the lime removed from our hills reappears as the far more durable concrete, used, often enough, to protect the land against the ravages of nature. We illustrate this in the pictures of cliff-protection in Plate XXVIII.

The constructive activity of man is also exemplified in the long and laborious

[1] The figures quoted in these paragraphs are minimized rather than exaggerated. For example, there are enough four-foot water mains beneath London alone to reach to Cape Horn, and it is likely that the smaller pipes which regularly gather 'fur' throughout the country would encircle the equator several times. The mining and quarrying statistics are taken from pre-1939 records, and represent our twentieth-century peace-time activities.

work of draining and reclaiming the Fens, but no better single example of reclamation can be found than the construction of the new docks at Southampton. Here, the old Western Shore once formed a bay two miles long by half a mile wide, and enclosed an anchorage for numerous small boats. The Southern Railway (by arrangement with the Local Authority and approval of Parliament) decided to build a new dock-front diametrically across the bay, and reclaim the land behind it for industrial development. They began work in 1927, and the bay had been completely filled in with 22,500,000 tons of rock rubbish and other such waste by 1934.

An air view of the work is shown in Fig. 141, for comparison with the view of Selsey Bill in Fig. 108, but allowance must be made for the necessary difference in scale. Fig. 108 is an example of the maximum destructive action of the sea over a period of forty years. Fig. 141 shows how man has reclaimed about twice the same area of land in seven years. The cases are especially suitable for comparison, for not only are both coasts flat and their shores built of shingle, but the destructive work of the sea at Selsey is strictly limited to about the same length of original coast as the new dock-wall now provides at Southampton. The point of the comparison is not the equivocal one that man can set to work on occasion and shift rock and sand more quickly than nature, but that he can deliberately *cancel* the large-scale work of nature, taking not a yard for a yard—but *ten* yards for a yard.

We admit that constructive activities of this sort, though they markedly alter the coastline on even small-scale maps, bear no quantitative comparison with the destruction of rocks in mines and quarries, but there is a point of view from which even that is seen to be a contrary process to the destructive work of nature. In Chapter IV we referred to inanimate nature as the 'Arch-Leveller', and to life as a protest against her insistence on running downhill. Thus, she laid the rocks low and buried them deep; but what process is more exactly a reversal of this than mining?

We should suspect ourselves of a quibble were it not for these further differences—that the destructive activities of man are not an end but a means, and when he deliberately levels a surface he more often raises than lowers it. He performs his acts of destruction and construction in equal defiance of the law of gravity, and his work, in either case, remains a *monument* for the consideration of the discerning rambler.

It may have been observed that it is chiefly the military works of man which have endured as the most ancient signs of human activity. We do not defend military operations on these—or any other—grounds, but make melancholy note of the fact that the last memorials of vanished races are usually their battle-

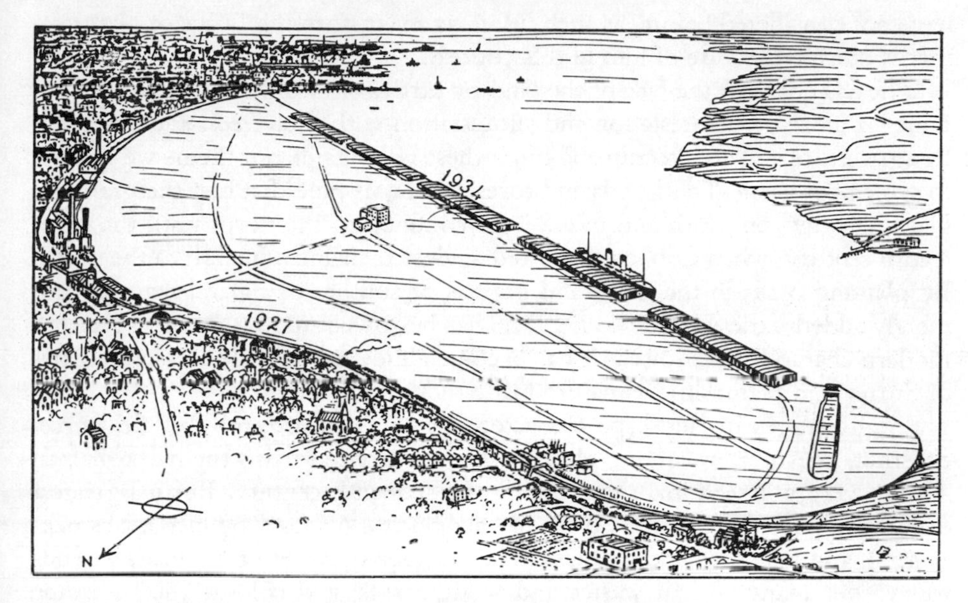

Fig. 141. Air-view showing the reclamation of the West Bay at Southampton. The position of the old Western Shore is indicated by the railway line.

scars. Yet the older sites mingle military with domestic associations; they have seen and sustained the whole gamut of human emotions for countless generations. They are, after all, works of defence—symbols of security; they do not tell primarily of

> . . . old, unhappy, far-off things,
> And battles long ago.

In the main they tell of peaceful and courageous toil, and of the first blessedness of hearth and home. The sight of a Stone Age fortress should suggest a comfortable steading well defended against marauders, not the castle of a conquering tribe, and the visitor to these ancient earthworks should come in the spirit of one who makes a pilgrimage to the home of his childhood.

They have another significance for us, too. We have considered the broad forms of the landscape as carved and moulded by the forces of nature, but here we have the earliest evidence of that other Force of Nature which Carlyle saw in the creative mind of man. These more recent disturbances on the surface of the earth are not the mere badger-scratchings and beavers' dams of a plantigrade bipedal mammal. They are the first stirrings of a new Force which perhaps we have not considered before, as such. Man, as a transforming Force of Nature—that is our final picture of him in this context.

If he has changed the face of the land by earthworks and excavations, he has done far more by deforestation and afforestation with alien trees, and more still by agriculture and architecture. Though these fall outside our theme we do well to remember them. The woods and forests of Scots pine that cast their familiar black shadows on heath and moor were confined to the north until the nineteenth century, when Cobbett protested against their introduction to the south. By planting pines in the sands and gravels of southern England man has not merely added variety to the scenery, he has bestowed upon it its most striking modern characteristic, so that it has become almost impossible to picture parts of Surrey and Hampshire as nature made them.

Local changes in landscape character due to Lombardy poplar, fir, horse-chestnut, chestnut, sycamore, plane, larch and cedar are also the mark of man—they were not seen in Britain before the sixteenth century. But his greatest decorative effects are produced by his hedgerows (created by medieval stock-raisers), and his crops and pastures. The chequered carpet of his fields extends today over many ancient wastes and wildernesses, and colours the landscape with a brighter emerald and purer gold than ever gleamed from Celtic field or native wild. He has thus painted as well as sculptured his homeland, but he has done so with restraint, labouring or refraining from labour according to his needs. It is to his everlasting credit that he has counted among his needs the preservation of large tracts of virgin land supporting native life.

For every mountain razed to feed his furnaces he has protected ten from exploitation and established them as permanent sanctuaries. For every hill levelled by his quarrying, a score have been made more rugged and precipitous, and handed back *thus* to nature—symbols not of death but of life begun anew. He has crowned their nobler summits with beechwood and pine, and here and there he has set his seal in stone upon their foreheads. And this is his greatest work, for in his architecture he has conferred a new order of beauty on the rocks of the hills.

Bibliography

Landscape:

The Scenery of England and Wales, by A. E. Trueman.
Britain's Structure and Scenery, by L. Dudley Stamp.
The Scientific Study of Scenery, by J. E. Marr.
Landscape as Developed by the Processes of Normal Erosion, by C. A. Cotton.
English Coastal Evolution, by E. M. Ward.
Physical Geology and Geography, by L. Dudley Stamp.
The Basis of Physical Geography, by S. W. Wooldridge and R. S. Morgan.
Principles of Physical Geology, by Arthur Holmes.
Geology for Beginners, by W. W. Watts. This inexpensive little book is especially recommended.
Introduction to Geology, by E. B. Bailey and J. Weir.
Outline of Geological History, by A. K. Wells.
Stanford's Geological Atlas of Great Britain and Ireland, edited by H. B. Woodward. This is a sort of geological *Baedeker*, for besides its excellent geological maps of the counties (on which descriptions of coastal rocks and places for collecting fossils are indicated), it gives geological descriptions of the scenery on all the main railway routes. It also describes the scenery of Britain county by county, and includes thirty-two plates illustrating common fossils. It is, however, a purely descriptive book; it is not explanatory.

Rocks, Minerals and Fossils:

Geology for Beginners, by W. W. Watts. (Cited above.)
Structural and Field Geology, by James Geikie.
Introduction to Geology, by E. B. Bailey and J. Weir. (Cited above.)
An Introduction to Palaeontology, by A. Morley Davies.

Human Studies:

Archaeological Remains, by J. R. Garrood.
Prehistoric Britain, by Jacquetta and Christopher Hawkes.
Prehistoric England, by Grahame Clark.
Man the Tool-Maker, by Kenneth P. Oakley. (Obtainable from the *Natural History Museum*, London, or *H.M. Stationery Office*.)
A Guide to Antiquities of the Stone Age. (Obtainable from the *British Museum* or *H.M. Stationery Office*.)
The Ancient Roads of England, by Jane Oliver.
Man's Influence on the Earth, by R. L. Sherlock.
Man as a Geological Agent, by R. L. Sherlock.

Bibliography

[illegible]

Index

Numbers in brackets are purely subject references, in which the headword in the Index is not actually quoted in the text or illustration legend. Such references are given only in cases of special usefulness or interest.

INDEX

INDEX

INDEX

INDEX

INDEX

INDEX

INDEX

INDEX

INDEX

INDEX

INDEX